SOLAR ASTRONOMY HANDBOOK

RAINER BECK • HEINZ HILBRECHT
KLAUS REINSCH • PETER VÖLKER

Published by:

Willmann-Bell, Inc.
Publishers and Booksellers Serving
Astronomers Worldwide Since 1973

P. O. Box 35025 • Richmond, Virginia 23235, USA • ☎(804) 320-7016

Published by Willmann-Bell, Inc.
P.O. Box 35025, Richmond, Virginia 23235

Copyright ©1995 by Willmann-Bell, Inc.
First English Edition

First published in German as
Handbuch für Sonnenbeobachter
Copyright ©1982 by SONNE
Mitteilungsblatt der Amateursonnenbeobachter.
Fachgruppe Sonne Vereinigung der Sternfreunde (VdS) e.V.

Printed in the United States of America

Library of Congress Cataloging-in-Publication Data.
Handbuch für Sonnenbeobachter.   English
   Solar astronomy handbook / Rainer Beck . . .[et al.].
      p.   cm.
   Includes bibliographical references and index.
   ISBN 0-943396-47-6
   1. Sun – Handbooks, manuals, etc.   I. Beck, Rainer, 1951- .
QB521.H213   1995
523.7–dc20   95-46338
                                                   CIP

99 9 8 7 6 5 4 3

For the Beginner...

"Do you own a telescope?" One day I went into the office of the nearby observatory and asked to become a member of the astronomy working group. I left as a registered member. Suddenly I stopped. What was that question a moment ago? "Do you own a telescope?" Surprised, I had said no, feeling that participating at public observation evenings, using my small planisphere and keenly studying the club's literature was more than enough. A telescope?

Three weeks later I had a longish box in front of me containing my new 60/900 mm refractor, or more descriptively a refractor with a 6 cm objective and 90 cm focal length. It had come from a mail-order company and cost only 250 DM (1973). But how was I going to bring all the individual parts I was looking at so hopefully to life? An astronomer friend came to my aid.

My refractor wobbled in the slightest gust of wind, and I could not find the N–S direction as the iron balcony railings deflected the compass. Carrying out observations kneeling on two cushions was no pleasure, and the zenith prism I had bought was not suitable for my instrument. Apart from Jupiter and its moons, Venus with its phases and a comet, I was unable to observe anything properly—although I managed perfectly well with my 8 x 25 binoculars. At about that time a neon lamp was installed near our balcony! Should I give up now? It was then that I remembered the unused solar projection screen—should I try the Sun? I had an incentive. The Sun became my field, and I became a member of the "Sonne" group. Determining the position of sunspots has become a very enjoyable activity since then.

"What happened to the wobbly telescope?" you ask. It became a very usable, and with time and study there were solutions to the other problems. I would not have been able to do all this myself but fortunately I found fellow amateur astronomers who supported me with their advice and help.

Here is a list of my problems and how I dealt with them.

1. Polar Alignment: Center the solar image on the projection screen using an eyepiece field frame at "true midday" (this expression is ex-

plained in the text accompanying planispheres). Find the declination of the Sun for that day in an astronomical almanac and adjust the polar axis, which will then point to the Pole Star.

2. The polar axis shifts during setup: When correctly adjusted, scribe reference marks to make re-alignment straightforward.

3. Finding the N–S direction: At true midday the rod carrying the counterweight must be horizontal which can be confirmed with a small spirit level.

4. The telescope is too light and shakes: Weigh down the tripod with three weights on the support plate.

5. Because of carrying the instrument about the horizontal is lost: Mount a small round spirit level in the middle of the support plate.

6. The legs of the tripod slide about: Position each leg in small permanently mounted plastic "floor protectors" or "castor cups." Mark one leg and it's matching floor protector to properly orient the mount later.

7. The right ascension setting circle moves too easily: A smooth piece of string gently pushed in between the side bearing surfaces will provide the necessary drag but will allow you to properly adjust it.

8. The original equipment rod designed to hold the projection screen is too short, the screen is too small: Mounting a longer metal rod and a larger round projection screen with a diameter of 150 mm corrected this problem.

9. The drawing template does not lay flat: Place a small tack through the center of the template and use small magnets elsewhere on the template to keep it flat.

10. Balance is lost when accessories are added to the telescope: Move the declination counterweight and apply additional weight to the front part of the tube.

11. The edge of the eyepiece field is not visible: It lies beyond the projection screen. Use a larger white card to make it visible.

12. Final tip: Do not lose heart, hang in there!

Sieglinde Hammerschmidt
Solms

Foreword

From the First German Language Edition

The aim of this book is to encourage astronomy as a hobby—a hobby which appeals to both young and old if it is pursued purposefully. Many people start to become interested in space at an early age when they begin to ask "why?", "where from?" or "where to?". This then leads on to being concerned with space, since all of us experience the Sun, the Moon and the stars and we are all part of what happens in the sky.

In some cases a heightened interest in astronomy comes about almost quite coincidently—some exceptional event in space travel makes the headlines, or the observer is overcome by the sight of the starry sky on a clear night in the mountains. The fascination of observing the skies is the basis of a hobby which can satisfy for a lifetime—astronomy.

One possible area of amateur activity is the observation of the Sun. Compared with other areas it has a number of advantages:

- Observation can be carried out during the day. No sleepless nights.

- Because of its light there is no problem in observing the Sun, even under a light polluted city sky.

- Even small telescopes will show any amount of continually changing detail. The Sun's appearance has never been and will never be exactly the same as today.

This book is not a monograph about the Sun, but a monograph about the opportunities for the amateur to observe the Sun. As can be seen by the scope of the book, these opportunities are multifarious today, thanks to excellent optical, electronic and photographic equipment. Systematic amateur observation of the Sun goes back a very long way. In Germany, amateurs have been working together in this field on a national level since 1891. And in 1976 the common considerations of regional solar observer groups in West Germany led to new forms of cooperation. The "solar group leader" of the national Association of Astronomers was replaced with a team of "specialists." In addition, the amateur solar observers' information leaflet *Sonne* was established for the purposes of information and cooperation at a national level. All "specialists" are committed to be consulting editors, whereas the authors are the individual amateurs themselves.

The idea of decentralized responsibility soon bore fruit, as everyone was able to become deeply involved in their own observation field—study of the literature, building up national observer networks to cover weather gaps, intensive correspondence with colleagues.

Soon afterwards the idea of a *Handbook of Solar Astronomy* was born. It was to be a book which reflected the current state of knowledge in amateur solar astronomy. The principle of the *Sonne* leaflet was adopted with every amateur who knew most about a particular subject writing the appropriate section, frequently in conjunction with other authors. In their contributions, all the authors are fully responsible for the content and level, style, structure and illustrations. The publishers had the task of putting the supplied material together, supervising printing and organizing distribution. All those involved worked on the book in their free time and without compensation, so that it is a true piece of work by amateur astronomers, whichever way it is looked at.

The book is divided into three major parts. The first of these, Part A, describes instruments used in solar astronomy, offers help in making decisions with regard to buying, and provides instructions for building instruments oneself. Part B deals with the many different amateur observation possibilities, while Part C gives encouragement and help in planning and carrying out expeditions to observe solar eclipses and gives details on observation. Each chapter of the book is self-contained in terms of contents and the reader can turn to those subjects which interest him most. Numerous cross-references make the reading easier and point to related sections.

What are the aims of this book?

A general amateur astronomer can easily become an amateur solar astronomer. This book offers some scientific ideas and working methods which can help the observer to be successful. Among other things the book helps him decide on and select a program. Here, both the beginner and more advanced astronomer are borne in mind.

The amateur should not try to compete with his professional colleagues. The problems dealt with by the latter have moved on from pure observation to solar physics. The amateur cannot hope to keep pace with this. Systematic amateur work can make a contribution, in that it remains with traditional observation and can take up older professional programs and continue them. The main task is statistical work: sunspots (frequency and distribution, butterfly diagrams), faculae in white and monochromatic light, and detailed investigations of sunspots (light bridges, Wilson Effect, etc.) and sunspot groups (developments, proper motion), prominences (movement diagrams) or flares (light curves). A few examples of many.

The authors have tried to put a book together which in addition to simply passing on knowledge, will show what a dedicated group of amateur astronomers can achieve through close cooperation.

English Language Edition

Following the appearance of the original German edition in 1982, which was declared the "standard work" by many book reviewers, a great deal of correspondence reached the authors from abroad requesting an English translation. From personal correspondence we have concluded that such a book in English would probably be equally well received since we have learned that nearly all amateur astronomers use the same methods of observation and the same observation programs throughout the world.

In terms of content the authors and editors endeavored as far as possible to keep to the information contained in the original edition. Where necessary, updating has taken place and errors have been corrected. Numerous passages were revised taking into account the larger, international circle of readers, and references to German-language literature have been changed, where possible, to appropriate to English-language works.

We were particularly fortunate to have Stephen J. Edberg, Bruce Hardie, Richard Hill, Patrick S. McIntosh and Donald F. Trombino, read and comment on the text just prior to publication. As active English speaking solar observers their comments were particularly helpful to us in our quest for clarity in a language not our own.

We hope that the *Solar Astronomy Handbook* will be widely distributed and that the English edition will provide advanced amateur astronomers and those newly interested in our avocation with the tools which so inspired the readers of the original edition.

By the Editors at
Berlin, Bonn, Göttingen
and Waldshut, November 1995:

Rainer Beck
Heinz Hilbrecht
Klaus Reinsch
Peter Völker

For the Contributing Authors:

Rainer Beck
Manfred Belter
Ulrich Bendel
Hans-Joachim Bruns
Michael Delfs
Jörg Dobrzewski
Ulrich Fritz
Volker Gericke
Andreas Hänel
Sieglinde Hammerschmidt
Heinz Hilbrecht
Cord-Hinrich Jahn
Jost Jahn
Elmar Junker
Hans Ulrich Keller
Wolfgang Lille
Ronald J. Livesey
Adolf Merz
Christian Monstein
Wolfgang Paech
Klaus Reinsch
Elmar Remmert
Ingo Schmidt
Walter Schmiedeck
Klaus-Peter Schröder
Andreas Seeck
Dietmar Staps
Teoman Topcubasi
Heinrich Treutner
Peter Völker
Otto Vogt
Bernhard Wedel (†)

Furthermore, the following
contributed to the success
of the American edition:

Günter Appelt
Werner Baumann
William Benesch
Lee C. Coombs
Jörg Dreyhsig
Stephen J. Edberg
Claus-Dieter Gahsche
Gordon Garcia
Ivan Glitsch
Bruce Hardie
Richard E. Hill
Robert Hilz
Johnny Horne
Kurt Huebner
Christian Kowalec
Victor J. Lopez
Patrick S. McIntosh
Robert O. Morris
Winfried Oppermann
Gayle H. Riggsbee
Andreas Saul
E. Slawik
Randy Tatum
Gregory Terrance
Donald F. Trombino
Frederik N. Veio
Jeff Young
Baader Planetarium
Celestron International
LEXUS Ltd., Glasgow, Scotland
Tele Vue

Table of Contents

The Sun and Your Safety[†]

The Sun—A Short Description

The Sun is an average star on the outskirts of an average galaxy. As the closest star to Earth, it provides us with the only opportunity for detailed observation of many stellar processes.

These stellar phenomena are often observed to be bigger, cooler, or more energetic than their counterparts on the Sun, but the underlying physical laws are the same. Thus, the Sun is our key to understanding the multitudes of stars in the night sky.

We see the Sun on every clear day, but we don't really see all of it. The interior is hidden from our senses, except when neutrino telescopes and other sophisticated observing techniques such as those of helioseismology are employed. Yet there is much to be seen, and still very much to be understood, about the phenomena visible. Even with a properly equipped amateur telescope, the features in the Sun's uppermost layers provide a forever-changing, never-the-same view that can intrigue an observer for a lifetime.

The dazzlingly bright layer that shines down on Earth's surface daily is the photosphere. Casual glances might support the view of early western philosophers that it is perfect and unblemished. But millennia ago, Chinese and other observers noted blemishes on the Sun that Galileo was the first in the West, during the Renaissance, to publicize. These sunspots are the most famous feature of the photosphere. The number of sunspots varies with a cycle approximately 11 years long. Sunspots are associated with strong magnetic fields on the Sun and are related to more energetic forms of solar activity.

The normal photosphere has a temperature of 6000°K (Kelvin is a measure of temperature starting at absolute zero with a degree the same size as on the Celsius or Centigrade scale). Even higher temperatures are observed in bright areas called faculae (singular: facula), most easily seen near the

---

[†]Written by Stephen J. Edberg, Copyright ©1995

1

limb (edge) of the Sun's disk. These are often, but not always associated with sunspots. Granules, which look like rice grains covering the photosphere, indicate the presence of convection currents that carry some of the energy away from the Sun's interior to its surface.

Immediately above the photosphere is the 10,000°K chromosphere, about 16,000 km (10,000 miles) thick. It was named for its brilliant red color, when first recognized at a total eclipse in the last century.

The most easily observed transient solar activity occurs in this layer: solar flares. Flares are short-lived brightenings in the chromosphere which release considerable energy. They occur in the bright active regions (called plages in the chromosphere) around sunspots. Flares last from a few minutes to a couple of hours and generate x-ray, ultraviolet, visual, infrared, and radio radiation, as well as streams of atomic particles. If Earth is situated in the right place, flare effects may be observed in the form of polar auroras and magnetic storms. Flares can also affect other structures on the Sun: the prominences.

Prominences (seen on the Sun's limb during solar eclipses or with coronagraphs outside of eclipses) are clouds of about 10,000°K material hanging in the 1,000,000°K lower corona. They are called filaments when viewed projected onto the disk of the Sun. How they maintain their relatively cool temperatures in the hot corona is a mystery. In addition, the processes that enable a flare to disrupt and "blow" a prominence away are also unknown. And to add to the mysteries, prominences will sometimes disrupt (and may even re-form) for no apparent reason.

The corona extends from the top of the chromosphere to well beyond the Earth's orbit. Although it is extremely hot, it has a very low density and little heat content. The large structures seen in it are due to magnetic fields that connect the active regions on the Sun. The mechanism that heats it is still debated. The shape, structure, and brightness of the corona varies with the sunspot cycle.

Transients, known as coronal mass ejections, are bubbles of plasma (electrically charged [ionized] gas) ejected by the Sun. They can be seen as frequently as once a day when observed from space, but they are not easily seen from the ground. The chances of seeing one during a total solar eclipse are low, though observers at some recent eclipses were fortunate to see mass ejections in "stop-action," since position changes during totality as viewed from any one site were small. Coronal holes are regions where the corona is absent, and appear to be a source of the solar wind, an outflow of plasma from the Sun moving at speeds of about 200 to 1000 km/s.

The Sun's outermost layers, the chromosphere and corona, can be observed at appropriate observation sites with the proper instrumentation, such as occulting disks, coronagraphs, and narrow bandpass filters. But even the best instruments at the best sites are limited in the range of their "vision." Total solar eclipses provide the best ground-based opportunity for studying these outer layers.

Whether you count sunspots, study prominence structure, or chase eclipses, the Sun offers unending variation for the observer.

Safely Observing the Sun

As intriguing as the Sun is, it is also the most dangerous celestial object to observe. An unprotected eye can be damaged by it in a fraction of a second. Both ultraviolet and infrared rays reaching the eye do damage, affecting the retina or the aqueous fluids that fill the eye.

Yet, safe observing procedures are easy to follow and an observer does not need to fear the Sun. Proper filtration will reduce the intensity of light in visual wavelengths to comfortable viewing levels, and ultraviolet and infrared are reduced to negligible amounts.

Safe solar filters reduce the amount of light reaching the eye by a factor of 100,000 (10^5) or more. Optics specialists call this an optical density (O.D.) of 5 (or more). Such filters are available commercially (see the list of suppliers in Appendix A). O.D. 5 filters should not be confused with neutral density (N.D.) 5 filters that may be available from camera stores. N.D. 5 filters only reduce light by a factor of 32 (2^5), nowhere near enough for safe observing. Safe solar filters are made with a metal coating on glass or plastic (typically Mylar). Also safe, and inexpensive but poor optically for anything but naked eye use, is Welder's Glass no. 14.

Metal coatings on glass are often inconel or chromium, which can give the Sun a tone ranging from neutral to a strong orange coloring. Aluminum evaporated on Mylar yields a cool, light blue coloring. The choice of filter can be based on aesthetics and budget, with glass filters costing considerably more than the same size aluminized Mylar filter.

Because the Mylar base is very thin, filters using this base affect the optical system minimally. Glass filter bases should be optically ground and polished to flatness and parallelism for good quality imaging.

It is advisable to check your filter (a metal coating on glass/plastic, a no. 14 Welder's Glass) first on at least a 40 watt high intensity, bare filament tungsten light. It is true for any solar filter that if the filament, or the Sun, looks uncomfortably bright, **the filter is not safe!**

Other unsafe filters include crossed photographic polarizers, smoked glass, and gelatin neutral density filters (which can have high optical density). All of these filters transmit damaging infrared radiation and should not be used for visual observations. Gelatin N.D. filters, which may be stacked to reach a desired O.D., are suitable for photography but the photographer is left with the problem of aiming and focusing the camera without exposing the eyes to transmitted IR radiation. Aiming and focusing the camera is also a problem with O.D. 4 metallic solar filters intended for short-exposure, high-resolution photography.

More insidious among the unsafe filters is the ubiquitous sun filter supplied with department store telescopes. These use a material like Welder's Glass to protect the observer's eye. Unfortunately, the filter is intended to be placed near the focus of the telescope, where it must absorb virtually all the heat and light collected and concentrated by the objective lens or mirror. This intense radiation can cause the filter to shatter, without warning, in an instant. The observer's eye is then instantaneously exposed to the concentrated sunlight coming through the telescope, faster than the observer's reaction time that will remove it from harm.

Pinholes in solar filters are common. They reduce contrast in the image and can be quite irritating, and sometimes downright dangerous. Block pinholes with a dab of black paint. This will have little effect on overall image quality. One advantage of Mylar filters is that while they, too, have pinholes, they typically are made as two layers, whose pinholes usually don't line up. The individual layers block each other's pinholes.

Commercial solar filters are usually offered as full-aperture or off-axis, sub-aperture units. Full aperture filters allow the observer to take advantage of the resolution possible with the telescope if atmospheric conditions permit. Off-axis filters are less costly but will not permit the finest detail to be seen on the best of days.

Observers at solar eclipses should use full aperture filters. When the filter is removed for totality, the telescope will be in focus. When sub-aperture filters are used, the higher focal ratio of the instrument+filter yields greater depth of focus, which means that the telescope may be out of focus when the filter is removed, demanding precious seconds of totality for refocusing.

Solar observing is always an intriguing, and sometimes an exciting pastime. Enjoy studying the nearest star, but

PROTECT YOUR PRECIOUS EYESIGHT

Part A

Instrumentation

Chapter A.1

Choosing a Telescope for Solar Observing[†]

A.1.1 Telescopes for White Light Observations

What kind of telescope should I buy? This is the question which faces everybody wanting to carry out astronomical observations. In this section we will approach this question as it relates to observation of the sun,[1] limiting our discussion to small reflectors (mirror telescopes), refractors (lens telescopes), Maksutov and Schmidt Cassegrainians (compound lens/mirror telescopes) like those found in department stores or available through mail order. There are four principal ways to observe the sun with a telescope:

1. Projection

2. Objective filters (glass or Mylar (polyester) film)

3. Eyepiece filters

4. Special solar eyepieces (see Section A.3.4)

A.1.2 Observation of the Sun in Projection

With the projection method, unfiltered light from the sun is gathered by the telescope and projected onto a screen (see Fig. A.1.1 and Section A.2.1). The main problem with this method is the heating of the objective lens or mirror and eyepiece and the air in the path between the objective and eyepiece. Refractors are usually preferred over reflectors unless the reflector is specially constructed for solar observations (Mackintosh 1986). Two examples of these special purpose telescopes are shown in Figs. A.1.2, A.1.3, and A.1.4.

[†]Written by Wolfgang Paech
[1]A general introduction to instruments can be found in Roth (1975, 1994).

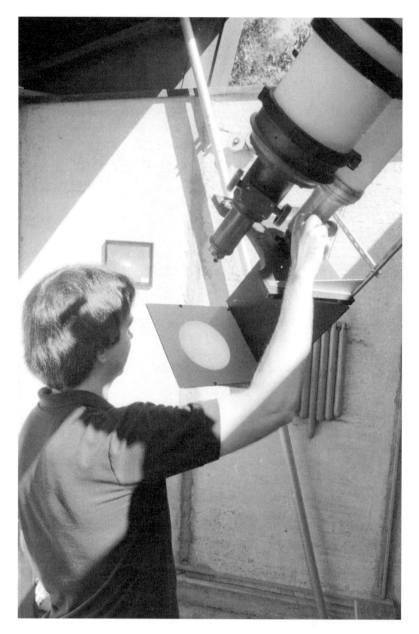

Fig. A.1.1. *Randy Tatum projecting an image of the sun using a 3-inch refractor mounted on the 7-inch Mogey refractor at the Richmond Astronomical Society's Ragland Observatory. Photo courtesy Perry W. Remaklus.*

Fig. A.1.2. *Steve Sands' Newtonian telescope with a partially aluminized window set at 45° to the incoming light. The primary is unaluminized and reflects light back towards the window which acts as a diagonal directing the greatly attenuated light out of the tube to the eyepiece. Photo courtesy Perry W. Remaklus.*

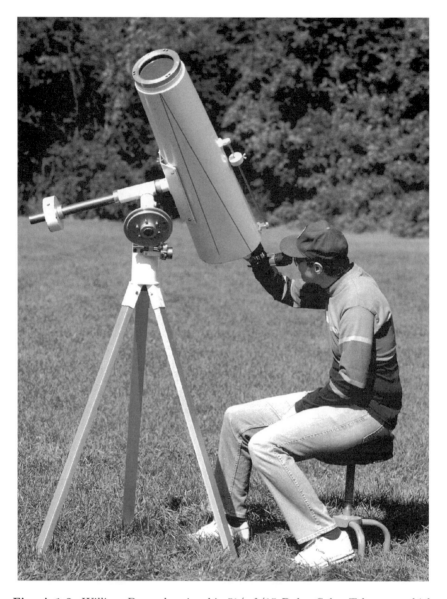

Fig. A.1.3. *William Benesch using his 5¼ f/15 Daley Solar Telescope which he built from a description in Advanced Telescope Making Techniques, Vol. 1, p. 213. In this telescope light passes through a partially silvered (½% transmission) window to an uncoated concave primary mirror which reflects the light back to the window which is tilted so as to reflect the light back down the tube to the eyepiece. Photo courtesy William Benesch.*

Fig. A.1.4. *Gayle H. Riggsbee built this horizontal refractor for viewing the sun. Light from the sun is directed through the objective down the tube by a clock driven flat mirror. Images produced by this telescope are extremely stable and the observing position is quite comfortable. Photo courtesy Johnny Horne.*

The refractor's tube is closed by the objective lens at one end and the eyepiece at the other end. Although the column of air in the tube heats up during the course of observation, there is little chance of turbulent thermal exchange with the air outside. A Newtonian reflector is usually a different matter, as the tube is normally open both at the top and bottom and the warmed column of air rapidly undergoes an exchange of heat with the outside air unless uncoated mirror systems are used (Hückel 1978). Also, the secondary mirror lies in the vicinity of the focal point and can become very hot. This heat causes changes in the optical shape of the mirror which in turn leads to a deterioration of the image. In both a reflector and refractor the eyepiece is located in the vicinity of the focal point and thus becomes very hot. Therefore, *under no circumstances* should cemented eyepieces (i.e., an eyepiece consisting of 2 or more lenses with 2 or more surfaces held in contact with optical cement) be used when the sun is being observed in projection. Reflectors generally have a higher focal ratio than refractors (reflectors approximately 1:4 to 1:8, refractors 1:10 to 1:15); therefore, the intensity of illumination and, consequently, heating at the focal point is, on the whole, greater in reflectors than in refractors. In other (commercially available) reflector systems (Cassegrain, Schmidt-

Fig. A.1.5. *Refractors because of their closed tubes can, with the proper accessories, make excellent solar telescopes. Photo courtesy Celestron.*

Cassegrain, and Maksutov), there are often plastic components located in the path of the rays which can easily melt if unfiltered observation is carried out. Therefore, the use of such telescopes to project an unfiltered image of the sun is not recommended.

A.1.3   Observing the Sun with Objective Filters (see also Section A.3.3)

If one observes the sun using an attenuating glass or Mylar objective filter, which transmits only 0.1% to 0.01% of the sun's light, thermal problems are eliminated. In a refractor this attenuator is located *in front of* and covers the objective; in a reflector it is covers the entrance aperture. In

Fig. A.1.6. *Inexpensive overcoated Mylar filters like those shown above can adapt practically any telescope for casual solar observation. Off-axis aperture masks are a practical way to reduce heat build up in large instruments. Photo courtesy Celestron.*

both types of telescope, the column of air and the optical components are barely heated. Objective filters can be either plane-parallel glass plates, which are often coated with a thin layer of chrome, Inconel (a form of stainless steel) or aluminum coated Mylar. The quality of the glass filters lies in their accurate surfaces ($\lambda/10$), and since large surfaces are more difficult to accurately fabricate, the price disproportionately increases with increasing size, making them quite expensive. Since reflectors tend to be on average larger than refractors, a "full aperture" glass filter for a reflector can be still more costly. Of course, if the entrance aperture is reduced to save money, the resolution also is reduced. A rule of thumb states that the diameter of a mirror should be about twice that of the object lens in a refractor to obtain equally good images. This guideline is principally based on the fact that in most reflecting systems the secondary mirror and its mounting lie in the path of the rays and thus cause image deterioration—primarily through diffraction.

A.1.4   Observing the Sun with Eyepiece Filters

Eyepiece filters are usually supplied as accessories to inexpensive "department store" instruments. Their use, however, is not recommended as these filters are fitted very close to the focal point in both refractors and reflectors and therefore become very hot. The heat can cause them to suddenly fail without warning and allow the intense sunlight to burn your eye resulting in serious damage or even loss of sight. If eyepiece filters are to be used to observe the sun, then the diameter of the objective or mirror must be *no greater than* 60 mm (under $2^1/_2$ inches)—remember, solar observation without safe filtering is very dangerous and eyepiece filters are *not* inherently safe.

A.1.5   Conclusion

Practically any telescope can be used for solar observing provided proper procedures are taken to reduce the incoming sunlight to safe levels. Ideally, the optimum solar telescope is a 8 to 12 cm refractor. Although the initial cost of such ar refractor will be greater than a comparable reflector and despite the fact that it may exhibit chromatic aberration and prevent violet photography (see A.5.5) refractors are generally preferred by many dedicated solar observers. Finally, mention must be made of the size of telescope for solar observation. The smallest objects the amateur can observe have a diameter of about 1 to 2 arc seconds (granulation); the largest, about 10 to 300 arc seconds (sunspots). Simple formulae for calculating the angular resolution of a telescope are as follows:

Refractor resolution (arc seconds) = 120/objective diameter (mm)

and

Reflector resolution (arc seconds) = 240/mirror diameter (mm)

Atmospheric turbulence, which causes distortion (see Section B.1.2), generally permits the observation of objects of 1 to 2 arc seconds (granulation) during the daytime. However, as the beginner will not initially be observing granulation, a refractor with an objective diameter of 8 to 10 cm or a reflector with a mirror diameter of 15 to 20 cm is quite adequate. Only in very few cases will it be worthwhile even for the more advanced observer to exceed the limits of a 10 to 15 cm refractor or a 20 to 30 cm mirror. Aperture envy is not a common characteristic of solar observers!

Chapter A.2

Telescope Accessories for Sun Viewing

A.2.1 Solar Projection Screen[†]

A solar projection screen enables the observers to see sunspots and faculae (see A.1 and Fig. A.1.1) in absolute safety. It is also the simplest method of observation. Heat can build up in a telescope that projects the sun and therefore cemented eyepieces should *never* be used—use only Huygens, Mittenzwey, or Ramsden eyepieces. The owner of a telescope having a cemented objective mounted in a black cell should cover the black areas with reflecting aluminum coated Mylar to dissipate the heat. Even with these precautions prolonged observations of the sun can cause the cement between lens elements to melt, thereby damaging the objective.

The projection screen and its mounting should be as stable as possible (or as stable as the telescope mounting allows) because the screen is not only to be used for observation, but the shapes of the sunspots and their positions are also to be marked on a paper overlay. Apart from photography, using an overlay is the simplest method for the amateur to determine positions (see Chapter B.3). Commercially manufactured telescopes are usually supplied with projection screens which are optically and mechanically appropriate to these instruments. The observer who has built his own telescope should have no problems with the mechanical adaptation if he decides to purchase a screen.

A home-made example is shown in Fig. A.2.1. The complete screen is attached to the telescope tube with pipe clamps. If the drawings are to be accurate, the distance between the screen and the eyepiece should

---

[†]Written by Wolfgang Paech

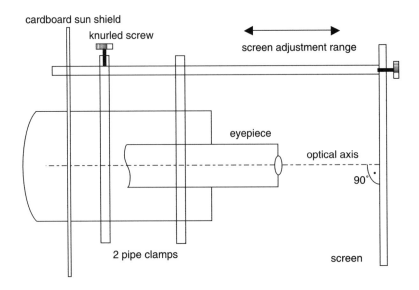

Fig. A.2.1. *Solar projection screen*

be adjustable since during the year the earth's elliptical orbit changes the apparent size of the sun. To compensate for this change, a set of two smooth fitting telescoping tubes are adjusted to the proper length, then firmly connected with a clamp and set screw. The screen itself, preferably of light weight aluminum, can be either circular or square. It is important that the screen is at a right angle to the optical axis of the telescope— otherwise the projected image becomes distorted. To prevent interference from stray light, a light weight screen can be attached around the telescope tube. The drawing paper overlay is attached to the aluminum plate with clothes pins so that it can be easily positioned in an east-west direction. The following projected diameters are recommended: 11 cm for a 2 to 4-inch telescope and 15 cm for telescopes 5 inches and larger.[1]

Finally, here is a simple formula for a solar projection screen. It only applies, however, if the focal length of the eyepiece is substantially less than the distance between the eyepiece and the projection screen! The projected solar diameter is B_1; the distance between the screen and the eyepiece is A. In addition the diameter of the solar images B_o at the focal point of the objective is required (rule of thumb: $1/100$ of the focal length). The focal length of the eyepiece is f_{ok}.

$$B_1 = B_o \frac{A}{f_{ok}} \qquad (A.2.1.1)$$

---

[1]Fifteen centimeters is a standard size used by professionals.

For example, if the focal length of the telescope is 1000 mm, then $B_o = 10$ mm, and B_1 should be 110 mm; f_{ok} is 20 mm.

$$A = \frac{B_1 \times f_{ok}}{B_o} = \frac{110 \times 20}{10} = 220 \text{ mm.} \qquad \text{(A.2.1.2)}$$

A.2.2 Spectroscope[†]

All spectroscopes are similar in construction. A spectroscope consists of an entrance slit (S), a collimator (K), a prism (P) or grating (G) and an optical system for recording the image (the eye or a camera) (see Fig. A.2.2).

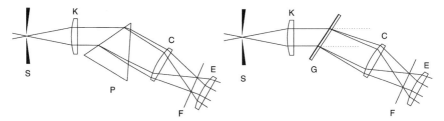

Fig. A.2.2. *Schematic diagram of a spectroscope. Entrance slit S, collimator K, prism P, or grating G. C is a camera or reimaging lens on focal plane F. Film for photography of the spectrum may be placed at F or an eyepiece, E, may be used for viewing the spectrum.*

If purely monochromatic light falls on the entrance slit only the image of the slit in this light will be seen in the focal plane. If, however, white light falls onto the slit, images of the slit corresponding to the various colors of the rainbow appear as a continuous spectrum.

If the sun had no atmosphere, a continuous spectrum would be apparent; however, the sun's glowing atmosphere produces a spectrum of discrete lines corresponding to all the gaseous atoms and ions contained therein, each of these having a characteristic "pattern" of lines. From the continuous spectrum of an emitter like the solar photosphere, a gas ("solar atmosphere") absorbs precisely those frequencies which it normally emits. The result of this phenomenon is dark lines, or absorption lines, in the solar spectrum. Fraunhofer, who was the first to catalogue these lines (and after whom they are named), did not realize their significance. Kirchhoff and Bunsen discovered the significance of the Fraunhofer lines which were the key to the chemical analysis of the sun and other stellar atmospheres.

[†]Written by Walter Schmiedeck

Prisms deviate the light in only one direction. The degree of deviation and dispersion, and consequently the intensity of color splitting, depend on the material. For this reason flint or barite prisms are used as they have a high level of dispersion. Unfortunately they are very expensive, but with these materials the light yield is at a maximum which can otherwise be achieved only with blaze-gratings. To prevent deviation in the optical path, an Amici direct vision prism, which consists of three prisms cemented together, is inserted within the light path. Hand-held spectroscopes of this type are very small and easy to use, but they have the disadvantage of low dispersion. For a long time such a device provided this author his only means for observing the solar spectrum. With photography I obtained a spectrum of almost a meter in length. The resolution in the violet region was about 2Å (Schmiedeck 1978, 1979) (see Fig. A.2.3).

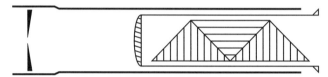

Fig. A.2.3. *Direct vision Amici prism.*

An optical grating is a glass plate onto which typically 1000–1500 grooves per millimeter have been scribed or photographically reproduced. Such a grating can diffract light (how much diffraction occurs with a particular grating depends to a greater or lesser extent on the wavelength of the light) so that the light is split into its component colors. In contrast to the prism, a grating disperses the light into several "orders" of decreasing intensity. The more lines per millimeter, the higher the dispersion and the lower the intensity of the individual orders (see Fig. A.2.4).

What can the amateur do with spectroscopy? First, one may take photographs of a large spectral range. For this purpose only high resolution film such as Agfaortho 25 and Kodak Technical Pan 2415 should be used. It is impossible to lay down guidelines with regard to exposure times as the number of variables involved necessitates some experimentation. To identify as many absorption lines as possible, a scale against which the wavelength of a Fraunhofer line can be read off is required. In some spectroscopes such a scale is projected into the spectrum. If this is not the case, a dispersion curve will have to be produced using the photos, taking as a starting point distinct hydrogen and calcium lines. With the help of the resulting curves or straight lines (with a grating), the wavelength of an unknown line can be determined (see Fig. A.2.5). To do this a table is required that shows the chemical element which produces the lines. Such tables are given in Landolt-Börnstein (1955) and Rowland (1928).

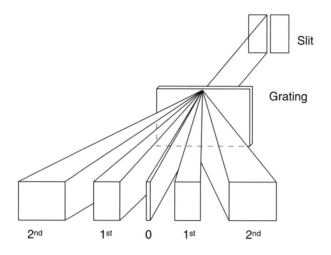

Fig. A.2.4. *Diffraction at the grating.*

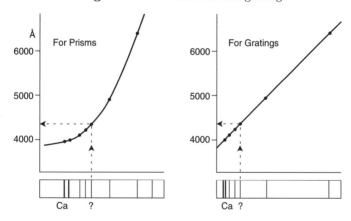

Fig. A.2.5. *Determining the dispersion curve.*

A diffraction grating can be used with a telescope. The spectrum of a (large) sunspot should differ somewhat from that of the clear solar surface with regard to line intensity as the latter is around 2000°K hotter than the umbra. By projecting a sunspot onto the spectrograph slit both spectra can be shown simultaneously (see Fig. A.2.6). A tantalizing application of the spectroscope for observation of prominences and flares, the field of spectroheliography, is described in a special section of this book (A.4.1; see also Baxter 1973). (The section on solar eclipses dedicates a chapter to the observation of the flash spectrum [see C.2.1]).

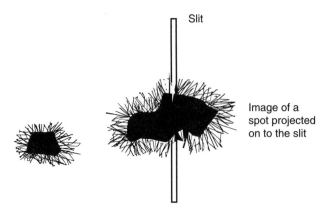

Fig. A.2.6. *Image of a sunspot projected onto a slit.*

Today, not much room is left for maneuvering in amateur spectroscopy beyond observation of the phenomena. Nevertheless, the theory and practice of spectroscopy, which have only been touched on in this chapter, have played an essential part in developing our understanding of important astrophysical phenomena.

A.2.3   Micrometers[†]

Of the many types of astronomical micrometers, the amateur solar observer is generally going to use either a graticule eyepiece or a micrometer lamella which includes a scale. Information regarding the use of home-made micrometer eyepieces for position measuring purposes is given in Section B.3.2.

A.2.3.1   Graticule Eyepiece

A short focal length eyepiece incorporating a graticule will enable calculation of the extent of a group of sunspots or the apparent diameter of the sun, which changes due to the earth's elliptical orbit. To perform this calculation, a stopwatch, accurate to at least $1/10$ second, and an equatorially mounted telescope are required. A clock drive is unnecessary as the observation is carried out with a fixed instrument.

Once the telescope has been pointed at the sun, one of the lines forming the graticule is oriented in a north–south direction so that a sunspot will remain exactly on the line and perpendicular to it when the instrument is

---

[†]Written by Ulrich Bendel

moved along the polar axis. With a fixed telescope a stopwatch is started as soon as the forward edge of the sunspot touches the north–south line and is stopped when the entire sunspot has passed the line. This process is repeated several times and the results averaged to improve overall accuracy. Groups which are very close to the limb should not be measured. This method should be used only for larger sunspot groups where it is most accurate. As the time required by the transit depends on the declination of the sun, the following relationship exists between extent a in arc seconds, measured time t, and declination of the sun δ:

$$a = 15t \cos \delta. \tag{A.2.3.1}$$

If, however, a is to be determined not only in arc seconds but also on a linear scale (e.g., km), the following conversion has to be carried out where R is the actual radius of the sun (696,000 km), and r the angular radius of the sun at the moment of observation.

$$A(\text{km}) = \frac{R(\text{km}) a('')}{r('')} \tag{A.2.3.2}$$

$$A(\text{km}) = \frac{696,000}{r} 15t \cos \delta. \tag{A.2.3.3}$$

Strictly speaking, transit time t should be measured in sidereal time. However, stopwatches measure mean solar time. With short time intervals this difference is of no great significance, but with longer intervals the seconds are multiplied by $k = 1.00274$. If the sunspots being measured are not in the immediate vicinity of the center of the solar disc, the perspective foreshortening towards the limb must be taken into account. The value calculated on the basis of Eq. (A.2.3.3) then has to be divided by $\cos \theta$, if θ is the angle between the two radii running from the center of the solar sphere to the center of the sunspot and to the point on the sun's surface corresponding to the apparent center of the sun (θ = the heliocentric angle, see Fig. B.4.11). If the projected image of the sun has a radius b (mm) and if the measured sunspot is c (mm) from the apparent center of the sun, then

$$\sin \theta = \frac{c}{b} \tag{A.2.3.4}$$

and

$$\cos \theta = \left(1 - \left(\frac{c}{b}\right)^2\right)^{1/2}. \tag{A.2.3.5}$$

Using this method, however, the length of the sunspot group has not necessarily been measured as in fact only its east-west extent in kilometers has been determined. This situation may necessitate taking into account the position angle of the solar axis and/or the obliquity of axes of the sunspot group with regard to the sun's equator, but this process is time-consuming and gives rise to problems which are not encountered if a micrometer lamella is used.

A.2.3.2   Micrometer Lamella

A glass lamella with scratched or engraved divisions can be built into a microscope eyepiece. The scale on such a micrometer lamella has, for example, 100 divisions per 1 cm—i.e., one division on the scale s is equal to 0.1 mm on a linear scale. Of course, lamellae can also be built into an astronomical eyepiece. They are attached by careful gluing to the eyepiece diaphragm. The diaphragm may have to be moved slightly if the scale and the image of the sun do not appear equally sharp. To make this modification worthwhile, however, an equatorially mounted telescope with a drive system should be used. The minimum interval w between divisions in arc seconds is calculated using the formula

$$\tan w = \frac{s}{F}, \tag{A.2.3.6}$$

where F is the focal length of the object lens. The focal length of the eyepiece does not affect the dimensions of the image—it really affects only the diameter of the field of view and the enlargement. (The eyepiece magnifies the image created at the focal plane by the object lens; however, eyepieces with a short focal length enable more accurate measurements to be made as the intervals on the scale seem larger to the eye.) If a Barlow lens is used, however, the focal length of the optical system is increased and therefore, according to Eq. (A.2.3.6), the minimum interval between divisions is correspondingly reduced on the scale. For example, for $F = 900$ mm and $s = 0.1$ mm: $\tan w = 0.0001$ and $w = 22\farcs9$, a Barlow lens ($\times 2$) produces an effective focal length of 1800 mm which results in $w = 11\farcs45$.

As a check, the scale value should always be determined empirically, as in the Huygens and Mittenzwey eyepieces, the arc distance w is generally larger than that which the formula (A.2.3.6) produces (depending on the focal length and type of the eyepiece). For the micrometer test the scale is oriented parallel to the apparent direction of celestial movement (east–west orientation). With a fixed telescope the sunspot's transit time is measured using a $1/10$-second stopwatch. If the transit time is t seconds,

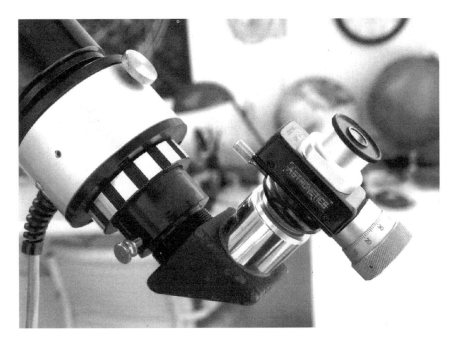

Fig. A.2.7. *A bi-filar micrometer used with a DayStar TS-II 0.6Å Hα filter permits the observer to determine the length and height of solar prominences, and to calculate the size of sunspots, flares, filaments and other features in the sun's photosphere and chromosphere. Note the small tuning knob at the top of the Hα filter. It is used to "fine tune" the Hα filter pack (etalon). Turning it slightly will shift the filter off of the Hα center line for Doppler shift observations. When tilted sufficiently the filter will reveal "continuum" (photospheric) features such as sunspots. Photo courtesy Donald Trombino.*

then the relevant scale length is λ (a multiple of s) in arc seconds:

$$\lambda('') = 15t \cos \delta. \qquad (A.2.3.7)$$

Here, too, the measured time can be multiplied by the factor $k = 1.00274$ if necessary. With a known interval between markings in the degree scale, the width and length of sunspot groups can be directly measured in arc seconds ($\lambda_{\mathrm{B}}, \lambda_{\mathrm{L}}$).

If the values are also required on a linear scale and are to be corrected because of perspective foreshortening, information relating to positioning has to be used. A good approximation of the linear values for the length (La) and breadth (Ba) in kilometers is obtained if the following formulae are used:

$$La(\text{km}) = \left(\frac{696,000}{r}\right)\frac{\lambda_L}{\cos\theta} \qquad\qquad (\text{A.2.3.8})$$

$$Ba(\text{km}) = \frac{(696,000/r)\lambda_B}{(1-\cos(B-B_o))\sin l + \cos(B-B_o)} \qquad (\text{A.2.3.9})$$

where

$\theta =$ heliocentric angle

$B =$ heliographic latitude

$B_o =$ heliographic latitude of the center of the solar disc

$l =$ central meridian distance (further details in Section B.3.2).

If a micrometer lamella with very narrow spaces between each division is used (e.g., $s = 0.02$ mm), relatively small sunspots can be measured, or detailed investigations of larger sunspot groups (umbra size, Wilson effect) can be carried out. The movement of the limb can also be measured directly in arc seconds to determine the "quietness" according to the Kiepenheuer scale (see Section B.1.2.3).

To subdue light and heat, the use of an objective filter or solar prism is recommended for all micrometer measurements, as achromatic eyepieces, micrometer components and most importantly your eyes are likely to suffer damage.

Appendix A lists sources of supply for micrometer lamellae.

Chapter A.3

Filters

A.3.1 Introduction[†]

As has been explained earlier, when the sun is observed directly through a telescope, the effects of light and heat must be reduced to safe levels by suitable filters. The sun must *never* be observed without filters—instant blindness would be the result! Smoked glass or overexposed film *are not suitable* as filters since they have little effect on the rays that damage eyesight. Specially manufactured filters in the form of eyepiece and objective solar filters are available that do reduce the light and heat to safe levels.

A.3.2 Eyepiece Filters

Eyepiece filters, which are relatively inexpensive, are used within the telescope; in other words, the light has already been collected through the objective and now has to be filtered to a harmless intensity. As the amount of heat produced increases with the square of the objective diameter, filters should be used only in the path of the rays in telescopes with an aperture of no more than 60 mm. Above this they are likely to shatter in use. Although some 4″–5″ telescopes are delivered with eyepiece solar filters **do not** use these filters as your sole means of light reduction. If necessary to reduce heat, the aperture should be reduced with a mask. As a rule the filter is fitted at the eyepiece, preferably before the field lens—i.e., it is screwed into that part of the draw tube directed towards the objective. On no account should the filter be fitted at the telescope's focal point as it will almost certainly rapidly overheat and shatter without warning. Another point where heating may occur is the eye lens. Cemented eyepieces can

---

[†]Written by Volker Gericke and Wolfgang Paech

also be damaged by heating. Finally, the filter must be made of glass as plastic materials would melt in the heat.

Filters provided as accessories to ordinary "department store" telescopes are mostly of good quality. Fitted in the eyepiece tube, they give the sun a green appearance and an image rich in contrast—even a very small sunspot can easily be recognized. A number of companies market metal-coated filters which reflect the heat and part of the light. They are, therefore, suitable for telescopes with a somewhat larger aperture. However, these filters do not provide a final solution to the heat problem as they too can shatter without warning. For different atmospheric transparencies, filters of different strengths should be used so that they can be combined with each other depending on the atmospheric conditions.

A.3.3   Objective Filters

Objective filters provide the best solution for subduing light. Fitted *in front of* the object lens, they prevent heat and light from ever entering the telescope and provide a reliable way of protecting the eye as they cannot suddenly shatter because of an excessively high temperature. Terms used in measuring the light transmitting capacity of such filters are "transmission," "optical density," and "absorption in astronomical magnitudes." Transmission is the proportion of transmitted to incoming light and is usually expressed as a percentage.

Transmission T and optical density ρ_{opt} are related as follows:

$$\rho_{opt} = \log_{10} \frac{100}{T(\%)}. \qquad (A.3.3.1)$$

Absorption in astronomical magnitudes is calculated as

$$m = 2.5\rho_{opt}. \qquad (A.3.3.2)$$

For amateur purposes the following filters can be considered:

ρ_{opt}	T (%)	Δm	
3	0.1	7.5	
3.5	0.03	8.75	} Photographic
4	0.01	10	
4.5	0.03	11.25	} Visual
5	0.001	12.5	

Eyepiece filters are used if the image is too bright. An image which is too dark, however, cannot be made brighter.

Fig. A.3.1. *Gordon Garcia with Astro-Physics 130 mm Starfire EDT refractor on Astro-Physics 800 German Equatorial mount. Baader Planetarium full aperture glass solar filter (white light). Photo courtesy Gordon Garcia.*

Objective filters are manufactured with either a glass or polyester film supporting surface. The actual filter consists of a partially transparent mirror coating on the glass or polyester (usually Mylar$^{\text{T.M.}}$) film. Glass is usually coated with chromium or Inconel (stainless steel) while polyester film is usually covered with aluminum. Glass objective filters which work solely on the principle of absorption are less common. On the whole, glass filters present few problems, but since they are several millimeters thick, they have to be ground plane parallel and polished very precisely to avoid distortion. For this reason, glass filters are relatively expensive. Figures 3.2 a/b show interferograms of two different objective filters. On the left is a cheap float-glass filter (several waves from flat); on the

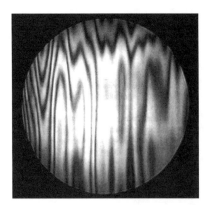 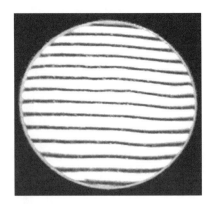

Fig. A.3.2 a/b. *Interferograms showing (left) a cheap float-glass which is not plane parallel over it's entire surface and (right) a high precision filter which is plane parallel within a quarter wave at the test light (source) wavelength. Photo courtesy Baader Planetarium.*

right, a high precision filter ($1/4$ wave). They produce an orange-colored image of the sun. Less expensive are the filters made of polyester film, which are marketed by Tuthill in the USA, under the name "Solar Skreen." This type of filter consists of two thin Mylar sheets, both of which are coated with aluminum on one side. The polyester film is so thin that no refraction and internal reflection can take place. The two sheets have different transmissions and when combined have a neutral density of five.

In practice, however, there are great variations between polyester film filters, resulting in widely diverging opinions on the value of a solar screen. Some observers find the image too dark while others find it too bright. Some complain about poor contrast between faculae and the photosphere and penumbra and umbra, while others praise the good contrast produced by the filter's characteristic blue image. There is general agreement, however, that when it is windy the polyester film tends to flap and interfere with observation. The author uses only one section of the polyester film in front of the objective and an eyepiece filter on a 60 mm refractor.

The "space blanket" polyester film used for insulating injured mountaineers and skiers against the cold can also be used as an objective filter. It is obtainable in two different forms, but in both cases polyester is the supporting material. One type is coated with aluminum on both sides; the other is aluminum-coated on one side and is colored gold on the other. As the coating is not even, an appropriate piece must be selected from a larger sheet. This film is generally unsuitable for visual purposes but produces satisfactory photographs. The blanket is approximately 220×140 cm^2 in area and is very reasonably priced. The "gold" polyester film is slightly more expensive than the polyester film coated with aluminum on both sides.

Compared to glass, polyester film is very fragile; it is next to impossible, for instance, to clean the Mylar filters with a lens cloth. It is best to obtain glass filters complete with mounting, but if a polyester film filter is used, it can be mounted with a homemade cardboard ring. However the filter must be firmly mounted to the telescope so that the wind cannot blow it away and allow the unfiltered rays to reach the observer's eye.

In summary, the use of small filters somewhere along the light path (but not at the focus) is practical with small telescopes, but larger telescopes require objective filters to reduce heat build-up in the instrument and to prevent injury to the eye. Because glass is more durable, glass filters are recommended if price is not a consideration. Those with less money to spend can try a Mylar filter. A filter made from a "space blanket" is sufficient for the casual observer.

Sometimes group purchases of glass objective filters can significantly lower the individual price. Finding other interested amateurs is possible through the Association of Lunar and Planetary Observers (ALPO) or the classified ad section found in some astronomy magazines. Appendix A lists some sources of supply for eyepiece and objective filters.

A.3.4 Helioscopes[†]

Solar eyepieces, also known as "helioscopes," reduce the light and heat through reflection, refraction or variable polarization, or through a combination of these three phenomena. As the heat at the eyepiece is low, cemented eyepieces and accessories along with auxiliary devices such as micrometers may be used. All these devices have different optical thicknesses, however, due to the longer optical path, reflection or refraction in the prisms and require variable focusing. Without a Barlow lens this fine adjustment cannot be achieved with all telescopes. The less expensive solar eyepieces produce an inverted image. To obtain an astronomically correct image an even number of reflections is always necessary.

The diagram shown in Fig. A.3.3 is intended to help in finding a suitable helioscope for an existing telescope. The dimensions, assessments, and prices shown are only guides and relate to 1990 price levels. In this section only very general information on the types and purposes of the helioscopes will be given. The best helioscopes are capable of variably attenuating (by refraction and polarization) the solar image without distortion; even the weakest glass filters discolor the image to some extent. Unfortunately, the

---

[†]Written by Hans-Joachim Bruns and Wolfgang Paech

cost of such a helioscope is at the top end of the highest price category.

The following diagrams and charts provide information to help choose an appropriate helioscope.

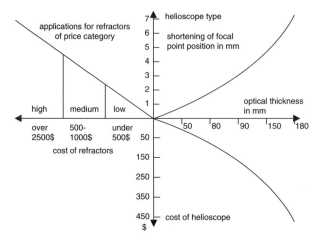

Fig. A.3.3. *Factors to consider in selecting a helioscope.*

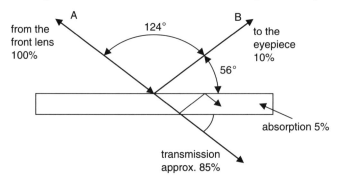

Fig. A.3.4. *Type 1, Brandt Polarizing Helioscope*

Type 1 Characteristics

Method of reducing light and heat	Reflection
Light reduction	$\approx 90\%$
Heating of auxiliary devices	High
Proportion of infra-red	High
Optical thickness	≈ 50 mm
Additional subduing glass required	Yes. Transmission approximately 0.01%
Undesirable side-effects	Ghosting possible
Cost of acquisition	Reasonable

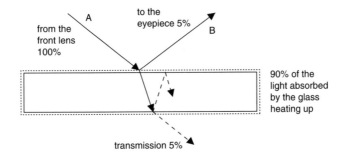

Fig. A.3.5. *Type 2, Reflection Helioscope with Reflection Mirror (dashed lines).*

Type 2 Characteristics

Method of reducing light and heat	Reflection
Type of image	Reverted
Light reduction	≈ 95%
Heating of auxiliary devices	High (heating up)
Proportion of infra-red	High
Optical thickness	≈ 80 mm
Additional subduing glass necessary	Yes. Transmission approximately 0.2%
Undesirable side effects	Ghosting
Cost of acquisition	Reasonable

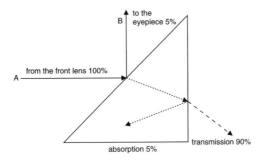

Fig. A.3.6. *Type 3, Helioscope with Right-angled Glass Prism*

Type 3 Characteristics

Method of reducing light and heat	Reflection
Type of image	Reverted
Light reduction	≈ 95%
Heating of auxiliary devices	Medium
Proportion of infra-red	Medium
Optical thickness	≈ 80–100 mm
Additional subduing glass necessary	Yes. Transmission approximately 0.7%
Undesirable side effects	None known
Cost of acquisition	Middle upper price range

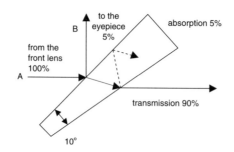

Fig. A.3.7. *Type 4, Helioscope with Herschel Optical Wedge*

Type 4 Characteristics

Method of reducing light and heat	Reflection
Type of image	Reverted
Reduction in light	$\approx 95\%$
Heating of auxiliary devices	Medium
Proportion of infra-red	Medium
Optical thickness	$\approx 80–100$ mm
Additional subduing glass necessary	Yes. Transmission approximately 2.2%
Undesirable side effects	None known
Cost of acquisition	Middle bottom price range

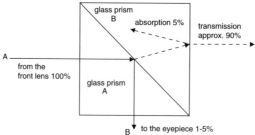

Fig. A.3.8. *Type 5, Helioscope with Double Right-angled Glass Prism light reduction by selection of glass types and dividing layer. Glass prism B can be produced as a hollow prism filled with oil.*

Type 5 Characteristics

Method of reducing light and heat	Diffraction and reflection
Type of image	Reverted
Reduction of light	$\approx 95–99\%$
Heating of auxiliary devices	Low
Proportion of infra-red	Medium
Optical thickness	≈ 100 mm
Additional subduing glass necessary	Yes. Transmission approximately 7%
Undesirable side effects	None known
Cost of acquisition	Top lower price range

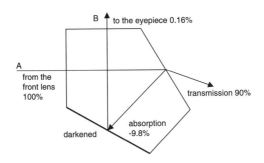

Fig. A.3.9. *Type 6, Helioscope with Penta Prism*
Type 6 Characteristics

Method of reducing light and heat	Diffraction and reflection
Type of image	Astronomically correct
Light reduction	$\approx 99.8\%$
Heating of auxiliary devices	Low
Proportion of infra-red	Low
Optical thickness	140–150 mm
Additional subduing glass necessary	Yes. Transmission approximately 22%
Undesirable side effects	None known
Cost of acquisition	Upper middle price range

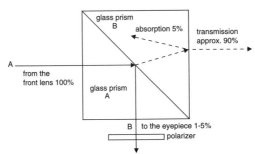

Fig. A.3.10. *Type 7, Helioscope with Double Right-angled Glass Prism and Additional Polarization Device Diagram as in Type 5 with additional polarization device between the glass prism and the eyepiece.*
Type 7 Characteristics

Method of reducing light and heat	Diffraction, reflection and polarization
Type of image	Reverted
Reduction in light	$\approx 100\%$
Heating of auxiliary devices	Low
Proportion of infra-red	Low
Optical thickness	≈ 130 mm
Additional subduing glass necessary	No
Undesirable side effects	None known
Cost of acquisition	Top upper price range

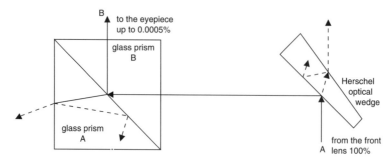

Fig. A.3.11. *Type 8, Helioscope with Herschel Optical Wedge, Double Right-angled Glass Prisms, and Additional Polarization Devices. This type was also produced by Carl Zeiss (Jena) with the addition of a Barlow lens.*

Type 8 Characteristics

Method of reducing light and heat	Diffraction, reflection and polarization
Type of image	Astronomically correct
Reduction in light	$\approx 100\%$
Heating of auxiliary devices	Low
Proportion of infra-red	Low
Optical thickness	≈ 150–200 mm
Additional subduing glass necessary	No
Undesirable side effects	None known
Cost of acquisition	Highest price range

A.3.5 Summary

For visual observations practically any filter or helioscope with transmission between 0.1 and 0.001 can be used. If the image is too bright it can be reduced with neutral density or polarization eyepiece filters

For photography of the whole solar disc (focal photography) an objective filter with a transmission of about 0.1 to 0.3 should be used.

For high resolution images with large focal ratios (eyepiece projection photography) a 0.1–0.3 transmission objective filter will attenuate the light too much. Therefore, a helioscope using a penta prism or a Herschel wedge should be used. Figures A.3.12–A.3.15 are examples of how various filters perform.

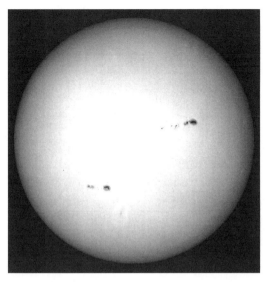

Fig. A.3.12. *The sun in white light on 1991-10-09 taken with a 6″ Starfire refractor and a Baader Mylar objective filter (t = 0.03) on Kodak TP 2415. By E. Slawik, Eggstätt, Germany.*

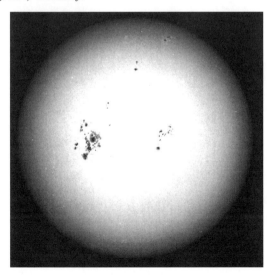

Fig. A.3.13. *The sun in white light on 1991-10-26 taken with an 8 inch refractor with 3300 mm focal length and a λ/10 objective filter (t = 0.1) on Agfa Ortho 25. By W. Paech, Hannover, Germany.*

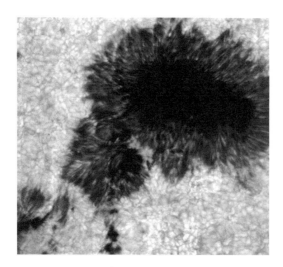

Fig. A.3.14. *The sun in white light on 1991-05-22 taken with a special 12 inch solar telescope and a Herschel wedge at a focal length of 45 meters on Kodak TP 2415. By W. Lille, Stade, Germany.*

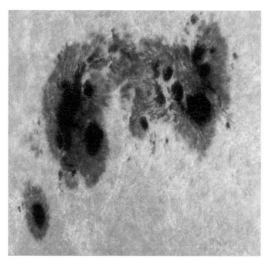

Fig. A.3.15. *The sun in white light on 1984-04-24 taken with an 8 inch refractor and a solar penta prism with a focal length of about 35 meters on Kodak TP 2415. By W. Paech, Hannover, Germany.*

A.3.6 Sun Viewer[†]

A sun viewer (Glitsch 1980) enables observation of the sun with both eyes and without a telescope. The intensity of the sun's light is reduced by multiple partial reflection on the surface of the glass and by absorption at the rear of the glass, which is painted black. By varying the angle of incidence of the light, the number of reflections can be increased or reduced, resulting in the image of the sun being variably darkened or brightened (see Fig. A.3.16).

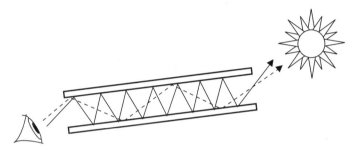

Fig. A.3.16. *Path of light rays in a sun viewer at various angles of incidence.*

A.3.6.1 Assembly Instructions

The viewer consists of two glass plates, which are painted black on one side, and two pieces of wood to hold the glass. The following materials are required:

- 2 glass plates (90 mm by 130 mm, 4 mm thick), possibly welding glass
- 2 pieces of wood (10 mm wide, 20 mm high. See Fig. A.3.17)
- Epoxy adhesive
- Black paint

The wood is painted matte black except for the hatched surfaces shown in Fig. A.3.18. One side of each glass plate is also painted matte black and after it is fully dried a protective covering of lacquer is applied over the matte black. The other side of these two glass plates must not be painted or scratched. Once they are dry, epoxy adhesive (in which two components are mixed together prior to application) is applied to the paint-free surfaces of the wood, and the glass plates are attached with their unpainted surfaces facing each other (see Fig. A.3.19).

[†]Written by Ingo Schmidt

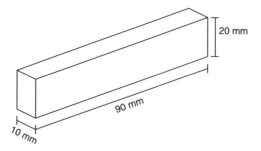

Fig. A.3.17. *Dimensions, in mm, for the sun viewer's 2 wooden components.*

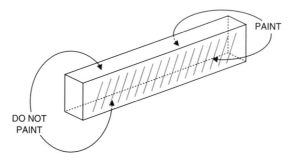

Fig. A.3.18. *Hatched lines showing the unpainted surfaces of the sun viewer.*

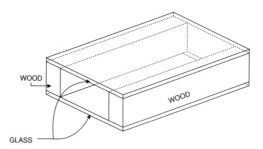

Fig. A.3.19. *How the sun viewer is assembled.*

The advantage of this glass filter over "space blanket" polyester film filters (see Section A.3.3) is better optical quality and variable reduction of the light. One disadvantage is the double image which occurs because of a secondary reflection from the rear of the glass plate (see Fig. A.3.20). Welding glass can replace the clear glass plates in this system to sharply reduce the intensity of this secondary image.

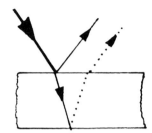

Fig. A.3.20. *How the double image in the sun viewer is formed.*

A.3.6.2 Applications

The sun viewer, though simple, enables a person to view the sun with both eyes. It is of particular value during an eclipse. Since the light intensity can be adjusted to compensate for the changing brightness of the sun, even children can easily use it. Using this instrument for "casual" visual observation frees up more capable instruments for other purposes, for example, photographing the eclipse. Large sunspot groups (Waldmeier type F) can also be picked out. Finally, the viewer is useful to monitor for clouds which are very close to the sun and which could prevent a successful photograph.

Chapter A.4

Special Instruments

A.4.1 Spectrohelioscope[†]

A.4.1.1 Introduction

The introduction of spectrography into solar research required an image of the sun that would contain only the narrowest possible bandwidth. Ideally, a single spectral line would be selected to show particular levels of the solar atmosphere (solar spectral lines are produced at particular excitation temperatures and therefore altitudes).

A.4.1.2 Spectroheliograph

After the introduction of the spectroscope (section A.2.2), astrophysicists attempted to observe prominences by slowly moving the entrance slit over the solar limb. Recording this movement on film allowed the entire surface of the sun to be shown monochromatically, i.e., in the light of a precisely determined spectral line. With spectroscopic apparatus a spectrum was created and projected onto a surface containing a narrow slit through which a single spectral line could fall onto a photographic plate located behind it. This photographic plate was mounted so that it could be moved perpendicularly to the slit. With the telescope guide system switched off, the sun moved slowly across the entrance slit in step with the earth's rotation. By moving the photographic plate at the same speed, the sun was recorded monochromatically. The complete solar image was thus obtained as if the observer had photographed a series of solar spectra, removed a particular spectral line, and placed these adjacent to one another. This method, which was invented by Wilson, required long exposure times (i.e.,

---

[†]Written by Heinz Hilbrecht

precisely the time taken by the sun to move across the entrance slit) resulting in restrictions on resolution because of atmospheric turbulence (see
Section B.1.2). The speed of producing an image, therefore, had to be
substantially increased.

A.4.1.3   Spectrohelioscope

The solution to this problem lay in moving the entrance slit across
the sun rather than moving the sun across the entrance slit. Mechanical
and optical devices were required, but these were difficult for the amateur
to produce until a committed American amateur astronomer, F.N. Veio,
described a disc containing 24 slits. His disc rotates once per second and
thus produces 24 images per second. As with motion pictures, the eye
no longer perceives the received information as a succession of individual
images but sees a "stationary" picture. Although for photographic purposes
exposure times of more than $1/24$ second are still required before the slit
is moved across the entire sun, significant progress has nevertheless been
made. Very good pictures can, of course, be obtained with birefringent
filters (see Section A.4.4), but these are between five and a hundred times
more expensive than a home-made spectrohelioscope.

A.4.1.4   Operation of the Veio Spectrohelioscope

Figure A.4.1 shows the essentials of the spectroscopic section of the
apparatus. The image of the sun is projected via a telescope onto a slit on
the rotating disc and passes through a positive meniscus lens onto a grating.
Here the sunlight is split into its spectral components and reflected back
through the positive meniscus lens to the exit slit located on the side of
the disc opposite to the entrance slit. Light of any wavelength can be
projected onto the slit by moving the grating with the result that the sun's
image appears in, for example, the hydrogen line. Similarly, observation
can be carried out in all other wavelengths. Photographically, even the
near ultraviolet (e.g., the calcium II H and K lines) and the near infra-red
ranges, which cannot be perceived by the human eye, can be covered.

According to Veio's description, the optical system preceding the spectroscopic section can consist of a heliostat which reflects the sun's light into
a 50 mm front lens with a focal length of 1250 mm. The movable heliostat
mirror allows the entire apparatus to be rigidly mounted. Of course, even
minor tube distortions substantially impair operation and image quality,
and the weight of the spectrohelioscope would require a large (and expensive) mounting. As an alternative, a coudé system can be used.

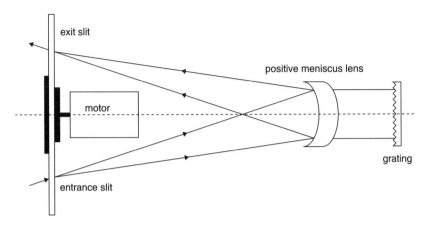

Fig. A.4.1. *The spectroscopic section of F.N. Veio's spectrohelioscope. (Note that the light is made parallel by the positive meniscus lens.)*

By using a Barlow lens the focal length of the objective is doubled, and the overall length of the instrument reduced. From a semi-translucent deviation mirror, the light passes through the entrance slit onto a second deviation mirror and then onto the grating. From the second deviation mirror, the spectrum is projected onto the exit slit, from which the selected single spectral line passes through the semi-translucent mirror and into an eyepiece through which the monochromatic solar image can be observed.

A.4.1.5 A Scanning Spectrohelioscope by Young

Figures A.4.2–A.4.4 show layout and system descriptions of a spectrohelioscope built by Jeff Young (Campbell, California, photograph of the instrument in Fig. A.4.5) in 1981. This system applies a scanner sweeping up and down at an angle of ±1.8° to generate the synthesized image of the sun. Jeff Young encourages the telescope maker and questions some of the myths related to spectrohelioscopes. In August 1993 he wrote:

> Spectrohelioscopes *can be* relatively simple and forgiving optical instruments to design, assemble, align, or use. They do not need to have complex slit or prism scanners, fancy solar tracking mechanisms, or precision machining. The only required precision is a good diffraction grating which can be bought "off the shelf" at the same cost as a good eyepiece. The rest is basic Newtonian telescope 'nuts and bolts' technology. My spectrohelioscope is a kluge; its parts were primarily from junk bins and salvage yards, and machining was minimal. It amazes me what a properly integrated pile of junk can produce!

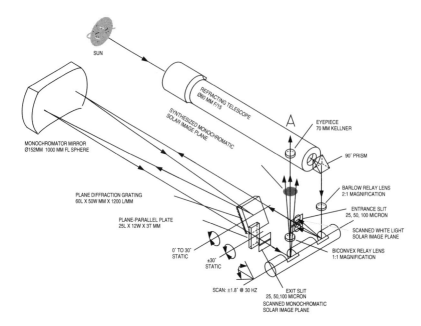

Fig. A.4.2. *Spectrohelioscope optical layout by Jeff Young, 104 Victor Ave.,
Campbell, California 95008, U.S.A.*

A.4.1.6   Spectrohelioscope Resolution

We define resolution of an optical system as the two smallest detectable
adjacent points in the image which do not touch each other. In a spectrohelioscope the resolution depends on the diameter in millimeters (D_E) of
the solar image at the entrance slit and the width (S) of the entrance and
exit slits (also in millimeters).

$$\text{Resolution}('') = \frac{S}{D_E} \times 2000''. \tag{A.4.1.1}$$

Two thousand arc seconds is the mean apparent diameter of the sun in
the sky. With a slit width of 0.15 mm and an image diameter of 25 mm
(270 cm focal length), the resolution is $12''$. Resolution, however, is the
result not only of the focal length and width of the entrance slit, but also
of the contrast between the object being observed and its surroundings. In
practice the following resolution is obtained for various features: faint flares
and faculae, $12''$; bright faculae and flares, $6''$; faint filaments 12–60″, dark
filaments, 6–30″ and prominences $6''$. The half-width value of attainable
spectral resolution is 0.6Å.

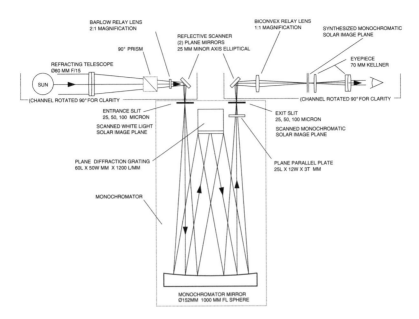

Fig. A.4.3. *Spectrohelioscope optical layout details by Jeff Young.*

Spectrohelioscope system description (see Fig. A.4.3 directly above):

- White light solar image is focused on entrance slit by telescope. The light path is folded twice by the 90° prism and entrance channel scanner mirror. Relay lens increases magnification to give desired image size and provides focus adjustment.

- Ebert Monochromator disperses the white light slit image received through the entrance slit and transmits a monochromatic slit image through the exit slit. Desired observing wavelength obtained by grating tip adjustment. Plane-parallel plate is used to fine tune the transmitted wavelength.

- The monochromatic slit image transmitted at the exit slit is observed by a low power eyepiece. Exit channel scanner mirror folds the light path. Relay lens provides optical access to the exit slit image plane.

- Reflective scanner constructs a coherent, monochromatic solar image "slit image-by-slit image." Synthesis method: synchronized mirror tip ± 1.8° at 30 Hz.

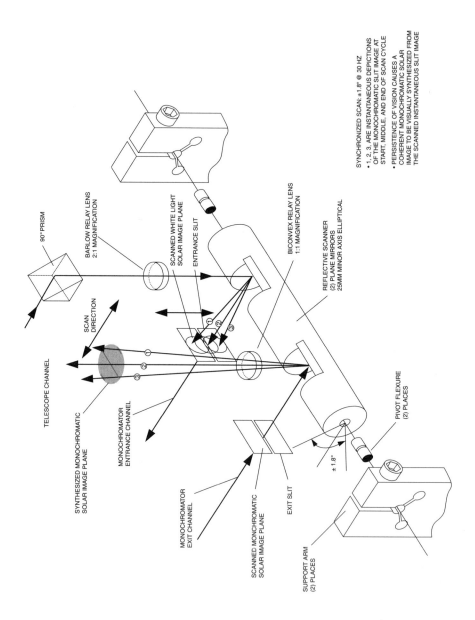

Fig. A.4.4. *Reflective scanner operation and design details by Jeff Young.*

Fig. A.4.5. *The spectrohelioscope built by Jeff Young. For system layout, see Figs. A.4.2–A.4.4. Courtesy Jeff Young.*

A.4.1.7 Variants of the Spectrohelioscope

The simplest variation consists in fitting a third deviation mirror before the exit slit, which deflects the spectrum laterally. When the disc is stationary, the spectrum can thus be observed or photographed to identify deformations and shifts in the spectral lines and to measure these if they occur. The polarities of a magnetic field (for instance, in a sunspot) can also be easily determined. In a magnetic field, light is forced to adopt either a clockwise or counterclockwise plane of oscillation according to the polarity of the field. A $\lambda/4$ plate fitted in front of the entrance slit turns this circularly polarized light into "normal" light polarized in one plane. The apparatus is completed by fitting a polarizing filter behind the slit. The $\lambda/4$ plate alters right- and left-handed circularly polarized light so that the corresponding wave fronts oscillate perpendicularly to each other. Only waves which have been polarized in a particular plane can pass through the polarizing filter; thus turning the $\lambda/4$ plate or the polarizing filter by 90° permits only light originating from the north or south pole of a magnetic field to enter the spectroscopic section of the spectrohelioscope. Examples of application in solar observation are given in Section B.8.

Simultaneous use of two spectrohelioscopes is required to observe Moreton waves (B.9.5.4) and the shifting of the hydrogen alpha line in the presence of an increasing magnetic field, as occurs during the formation of an active region. The Doppler shift phenomenon is used here to determine the direction of movement. If there is movement directed towards the observer and the spectral lines are coming from the source, a shift occurs towards the blue end of the spectrum. If there is movement away from the observer, a red shift occurs. If the sun is being observed through two spectrohelioscopes, one of which is set to the blue and the other to the red sections of a spectral line (e.g., 0.5Å from the line center), the use of two screens allows the light to reach the eyepiece alternately. Areas where there is different field polarities will then flash intermittently.

A.4.1.8 Concluding Remarks

To the amateur, the spectrohelioscope is a valuable instrument for observing the sun. Although it is not commercially available and tests the skill of an instrument maker if it is constructed at home, the possibility of observing the entire visible spectrum in monochromatic light is of such value that the widespread use of the spectrohelioscope is highly desirable. As an individual cannot totally exploit the capabilities of this instrument, either scientifically or aesthetically, building and operating a spectrohelioscope with others in a group is recommended. Veio (1991) gives very precise assembly instructions. For this reason, no attempt has been made to give details regarding construction, especially as assemblers throughout the world have shown a willingness to share their experiences.

A.4.2 Prominence Attachment[†]

Refractors, with their straight through optical path make excellent instruments for solar limb prominence observations when teamed up with a cone stop at the focal point to cover the solar disk (B.9.4). Deviation mirrors in a folded refractor cause a deterioration in the image contrast (scattered light caused by aluminum layers on the mirrors). With a simple 80–100Å hydrogen alpha filter nothing at all can be seen. The quality of viewing obtained from narrow (5–10Å FWHM) filters is equivalent only to that of elongated instruments with simple filters. Three types of prominence telescopes are used.

1. The principal object lens (cemented achromate or Fraunhofer achromatic type, 50–100 cm focal length) is in the front part of a tube with the optics and mechanisms for making prominences visible located towards the rear. This tube, which is 1 to 2 meters in length, can only be used for observing prominences. In addition, it is awkward to change the cone stops and adjust them to the correct sharpness. Much has been published about the "classic" prominence telescope which will not be repeated here (sources in the bibliography of B.9).

2. In an arrangement derived from the above, light is deflected through 180° behind the secondary lens (with the conical screen mounting) using two prisms. (As the prisms are not coated with aluminum, no additional scattered light is produced.) The new eyepiece is thus close to the principal object lens. Although the telescope is scarcely any longer than the focal length of the primary optic, the two prisms have to be high quality. The price of the complete prominence telescope can therefore double. Some telescope makers also insert a flat mirror into the path of rays just before the focal point to be able to use the telescope for night observation.

3. The most flexible devices, however, seem to be prominence attachments, for which assembly instructions are given in this section.

A prominence attachment is only 25 to 30 cm long and weighs around 500 g. It can be made without too much machining and with parts obtainable from a camera shop.

The attachment consists of three principal parts.

1. The first element consists of an annular dovetail mounting for aligning the prominence attachment on the eyepiece support. A 42 mm photographic adapter ring is used as a mounting (without inner release). Then follow two adapter rings between which a secondary lens is located (40 mm diameter and f = 80 mm with a 3 to 4 mm hole bored through the center). The lens does not require a separate mounting as it is held in place by the adapter rings between two rubber "O" rings.

[†]Written by Wolfgang Lille

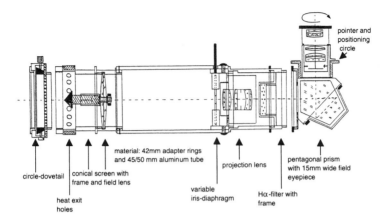

Fig. A.4.6. *Schematic drawing of Lille's prominence attachment.*

The conical screen mounting, which can accept various sizes of conical screen for aphelion to perihelion (brass, back blackened, conical
surface rhodanized), is then screwed onto the lens. At the top of the
cone there is a heat outlet which can be closed off with a covering
ring.

2. The second (middle) section consists of an aluminum tube approximately 80 mm in length (40/50 mm). The two ends are provided
   with 42 mm threads; an adapter ring is cut and the thread sections
   are used for the tube. An iris diaphragm is built into the rear section
   such that it can be adjusted from the outside. The field lens re-
   images the objective on this diaphragm, which holds back scattered
   light produced at the edge of its mounting.

3. The rear section consists of a large adapter ring or a short aluminum
   tube with a thread as described above. This section is where the
   projection objective is built in. Slide projection objectives with a
   focal length of 85 to 100 mm are very suitable, but even better are the
   lighter and thinner photographic enlarger lenses with a focal length
   of 60 to 75 mm.

   Ready-made threaded ring nuts, which can easily be fitted into a
   42 mm photographic adapter ring, are available. However, the focal length of an ordinary 50 mm object lens is usually too short.
   For a 20 mm solar image, I use an objective with a focal length
   of 75 mm. Using an eccentric and a 2× teleconverter in front of
   the camera achieves an equivalent focal length of 4 m, with which I

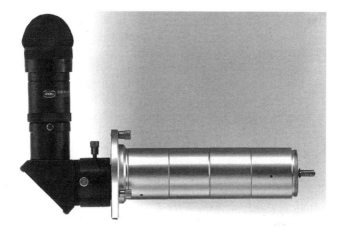

Fig. A.4.7. *The Baader prominence coronagraph. This is a commercial version of Lille's coronagraph.*

have obtained my best photographs. For photographs showing the entire solar limb, I use an $f = 60$ mm projection objective and so achieve a solar diameter of 11 mm. This size also fits comfortably into the field of view of an ordinary eyepiece. The gap between the projection objective and focal point is bridged with a penta prism with a preceding Hα filter mounting. This method produces images which are laterally correct and *the right way up* (the projection objective being a system which inverts images). Pointers in the field of view of the eyepiece together with a graduation plate enable the viewer to determine the positions of the prominences.

I use my attachment on an 80/1300 mm chromatic and a 125/1300 mm achromatic lens. To photograph prominences the penta prism is removed and the dovetail ring fitting and microfine adjusting ring (from a photography store) are inserted between the projection objective and the camera. With this adjustment mechanism, I can focus on the conical diaphragm. Using the telescope's focuser I bring the conical diaphragm, including the prominence attachment, into coincidence with the focal plane of the primary objective. Once the diaphragm has been set to the most favorable contrast, exposure time can be $1/15$–$1/500$ second (depending on the size of the image and transmission of the Hα filter) onto Kodak TP2415. The half-width values of the Hα filters should, if possible, be under 100Å. Best of all are filters with a half-width value of 1.5–10Å. Although they are expensive, narrow filters produce a darker background and are not as sensitive to atmospheric scattered light.

The best cameras for our purposes are those with interchangeable viewfinders and focusing screens. Focusing is accomplished with a 5 to 15× magnifier focused on a clear focusing screen with a graticule. As the individual components of the prominence attachment are screwed together, almost an endless series of options exist for the amateur willing to experiment. In addition to various projection objectives, a 20 mm projection eyepiece mounted on an eccentric which can be rotated into position can provide focal lengths of 5–10 m (only worthwhile in still air). Also, a flat or prism, which can be turned from outside, can be installed so as to direct the solar limb into the small format of a converted super-8 film or video camera. Ordinary binoculars and telescope accessories such as a 40 mm zenith prism with large field eyepieces or a smaller eccentric mount with a series of short focal length eyepieces for greater magnification, can also be used to increase the range of observational opportunities.

Following are the most important data relating to a prominence attachment (with various secondary lens and projection objective focal lengths):

	mm	mm	mm
diameter of O_1 (primary objective)	125	125	125
f of O_1	1300	1300	1300
f of H (field lens)	80	80	100
f of O_2 (projection objective)	60	75	80
diameter of K (cone)	12.20	12.20	12.20
diameter of K_V (virtual cone)	17.70	17.70	16.23
enlargement factor	1.45x	1.45x	1.33x
K to H	25	25	25
K_V to H	36.30	36.30	33.33
H to Bl. (diaphragm)	85.14	85.14	108.16
diameter of diaphragm	7.55	7.55	9.43
diaphragm to O_2	20	20	20
K to O_2	130.10	130.10	153.16
K_V to O_2	141.40	141.40	161.49
O_2 to focus	104.20	159.71	157.76
solar diameter at focus	13.05	19.99	15.93
K to focus	234.30	289.85	310.92

The following should also be taken into account:

1. Distance measurements at lenses are always taken from the corresponding principal plane (important in multiple lens systems).

2. The fact that the secondary lens acts like a magnifying lens has to be considered when calculating O_2 to the focal point and the solar diameter at the focal point (C_v).

3. Also, distance O_2 to the focal point can be increased by around $1/3$ of the glass path with plane parallel plates ($H\alpha$ filters, prisms).

4. The stated diaphragm diameter is the point where the "blanking out" of scattered light begins.

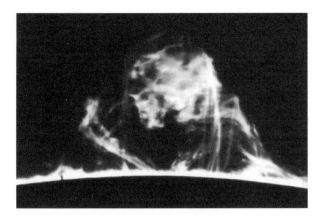

Fig. A.4.8. *Prominence taken on September 26, 1990, 14.00 UT with a AK 125/1300 mm refractor equipped with a prominence attachment. Courtesy Werner Baumann, Emsdetten, Germany.*

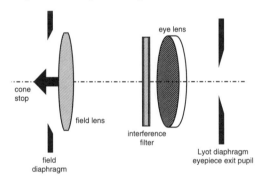

Fig. A.4.9. *Schematic illustration of a prominence eyepiece.*

A.4.3 Prominence Eyepiece[†]

In the past, prominence telescopes or prominence attachments based on the Lyot principle have been used by amateurs. Unfortunately, however, the Lyot design is relatively large and expensive to construct. The length is at least 30 cm which can place a considerable load on a small instrument. Furthermore, securely fixing such a prominence attachment to the eyepiece focusing mechanism of a small refractor is a very delicate operation. A simple and lightweight design should therefore be of interest to the amateur solar observer.

[†]Written by Jörg Dobrzewski

In this section the prominence eyepiece described by Richter (1974) will be further simplified and improved by introducing an 8 mm interference filter into the light path. In contrast to the Lyot system, elements which cause a deterioration in the image, such as the secondary lens and intermediate objective, have been eliminated. This design consists only of a Kellner eyepiece with a conical screen on the field lens, an interference filter between the lenses, and a diaphragm at the eyepiece exit pupil (see Fig. A.4.9). The elements such as the secondary lens, Lyot filter and intermediate objective which are required in the Lyot system, serve exclusively to eliminate the scattered light produced at the edge of the objective. The eyepiece exit pupil of a telescope shows only the objective image projected through the eyepiece, and here it is possible to use a diaphragm to cut out the edge of the objective and thereby the scattered light.

The following parts are required:
- one or more changeable cone stops (occulting disks)
- one Kellner eyepiece
- one interference filter
- one hole diaphragm in an axially adjustable mounting

The conical screen used to cut out the solar disk should be made of brass. In order for the rays from the objective to be reflected on the carefully blackened wall, the cone angle must be 80°–90° (Fig. A.4.10). The edge of the diaphragm should be stepped 0.05 to 0.1 mm so that the edge of the diaphragm does not appear "fringed"—it should have an evenly shaped profile. The cone surface should be slightly polished, but on no account should the diaphragm edge be rounded.

As the sun appears smaller in summer than in winter in the Northern Hemisphere, several screens are required for all but the most casual observer. Three sizes should be sufficient: one for summer, one for winter, and one for both spring and autumn. To work out the diaphragm sizes, the dimensions of the instrument's solar image should be determined experimentally with photographs (or a micrometer) when the sun is at its highest point in the sky, with subsequent calculations being made for the other times of year. To guarantee complete coverage of the solar disk, the diaphragm should be increased by about one per cent. The 1.8 mm hexagonal set screw allows the conical screen to be changed with a small "hex" wrench. The interference filter has a decisive influence on the quality of the prominence eyepiece. The Schott Company sells three interference filters of interest to the amateur: PIL with a half-width value of approximately 120Å, DPIL with a half-width value of around 100Å, and MA 3-0.3 with a half-width value of approximately 30Å. The MA 3-0.3 filter is excellent because of its narrow half-width value

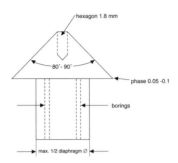

Fig. A.4.10. *Cone stop of the prominence eyepiece.*

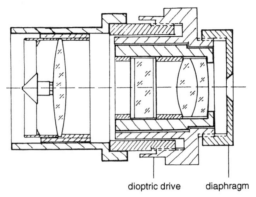

dioptric drive   diaphragm

Fig. A.4.11. *Schematic drawing of the prominence eyepiece with the diopter adjustment from a pair of binoculars.*

and high transmission of around 50% at 6563Å. A Kellner eyepiece is used as the optical imaging system. The focal length should be selected so that the exit pupil is not less than 2 mm and the conical screen takes up approximately $1/3$ of the eyepiece's field of view (magnification × 25–35).

Thus, only eyepieces with relatively long focal lengths can be considered. Also, the distance between the field lens and the field diaphragm should be at least 25 per cent of the focal length of the eyepiece. With conical screen diameters of up to 10 mm, the 28 mm eyepieces from 7x50 binoculars are suitable. All lenses must be coated. Multi-layer coatings are better still. Since the interference filter is inserted between lenses the ray path is extended by about $1/3$ of the filter strength, the eye lens must be capable of being moved axially to compensate both for errors in the conical screen position and those of the observer's eyesight. This shift is only slightly noticeable with regard to the eyepiece focal length and correction if the po-

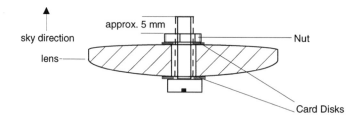

Fig. A.4.12. *Attaching the cone stop bolt to the lens.*

sition change is no more than ±20% of the distance between the field lens and eye lens. The dioptric adjustment feature found on most field glasses' eyepiece can be employed here (Fig. A.4.11).

To accept the fixing screw for the conical screen, the field lens has to have a hole drilled through its center. A lathe is ideally suited for this purpose (Gehring 1981). Drills to be used include glass and tile drills or appropriate Widia (carbide) masonry drills. The lens is first drilled about halfway through and then turned over and carefully aligned. The hole is then completed with great care just before the tool breaks through. The bit is constantly lubricated with turpentine. On no account must the drill bit be passed through the entire lens from one side because of the risk of breakage when the tool exits the backside of the lens. Finally, the boring can be opened up to the required diameter with a thin needle file lubricated with turpentine. The nut of the fixing bolt must be tightened very gently so that the lens is not put under tension. The bolt can then be secured in the boring with a two-component epoxy adhesive. To prevent reflection, the bolt head should be blackened (Fig. A.4.12).

As was mentioned earlier, the diaphragm must be in the plane of the eyepiece exit pupil. To effectively cut out the edge of the objective, it should be around 20% smaller than the exit pupil. Precise adjustment of the diaphragm position is very important; therefore, the diaphragm should be axially adjustable. To adjust the diaphragm position the objective aperture is reduced to half its diameter with an annular diaphragm. The correct position is attained when the edge of the diaphragm and the image of the objective aperture are sharp at the same time when seen through a magnifying glass. A precondition for the concentricity of the diaphragm and exit pupil is the exact centering of all the optical and mechanical components. Before the diaphragm is made, it is recommended that the position of the exit pupil be determined by projecting an image on a temporary screen made of frosted glass or tracing paper.

The conical screen is not much larger or heavier than an ordinary eyepiece and has more than proved its worth in observation. It has only two disadvantages: there is only one possible magnification and for photography the camera's lens has to be positioned very close to the exit pupil.

Professional literature on technical optics and astro-optics should be consulted for specific details on how to build an eyepiece from individual optical components.

A.4.4 Birefringent Filters[†]

A.4.4.1 Introduction

To obtain more information about areas of the sun at certain temperatures and pressures, one has to record solar spectra. The spectrum covers a broad band of energies, but it is often interesting (when observing flares, for example) to show the sun solely in the light of one line. In the past, the light of particular spectral lines was obtained directly from a spectrum (see A.4.1), but nowadays birefringent filters for various bands of wavelengths are usually employed. There is no fundamental difference between filters with a relatively wide transmission band for prominence observation (approximately 100Å= 10 nm) and Lyot filters, which are described here, with wavebands of down to 0.2Å. In addition to filters for the hydrogen alpha line, there are filters for the Ca-II line and others.

A.4.4.2 Operation

The optical effect of birefringence, which is most easily observed in calcareous spar crystals (calcite, calcium carbonate), is used for filtering purposes. If light falls vertically onto the parallel laminae of such a crystal, two separate beams of light emerge from the opposite surface with the result that objects viewed through this crystal will appear double. One beam travels without changing direction and is therefore designated the ordinary beam or o-beam: the second beam is laterally deflected parallel to the o-beam and is therefore known as the extraordinary beam, or e-beam. The only difference between the o-beam and e-beam is their direction of oscillation. If the original light beam consists of natural light which oscillates in random directions perpendicular to the direction of dispersion, then two beams with planes of oscillation perpendicular to each other emerge from the crystal. If the e-beam can be removed, the result is polarized light. Polarization filters which allow the passage of light oscillating only in a particular plane are available for removal of the e-beam.

The Lyot hydrogen alpha filter is based on the combination of two polarization filters with a birefringent crystal. The change which a beam of

[†]Written by Heinz Hilbrecht

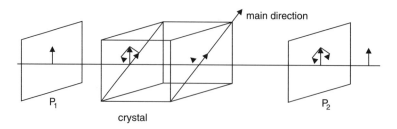

Fig. A.4.13. *Basic elements of the Lyot filter (from Behr 1951).*

light undergoes in such a device is described as follows by Behr (1951) (see Fig. A.4.13):

> If an unpolarized wave train is allowed to fall onto P_1, it is polarized, ...and it meets the entry surface of the crystal. As the crystal can be traversed only in planes of oscillation which are parallel or perpendicular to the principal direction, splitting into two components $\pm 45°$ to the original plane of oscillation occurs. Both wave trains eventually reunite through P_2. Due to the polarizing of natural light in P_1 there is a 50% loss of light. Apart from reflection losses, this is the only reduction in intensity.

The e-beam in the Lyot filter is slightly delayed with regard to the o-beam because it has to travel a greater distance. If, however, the thickness of the calcareous spar is selected so that the e-beam is delayed by half a oscillation with regard to the o-beam, when the beams join at P_2, there is a wave crest in the o-beam at the point where there is a wave trough in the e-beam. The sum of a crest and a trough is zero; therefore, the light beam is extinguished.

In the Lyot filter, however, light waves of all wavelengths arrive from the sun, but only certain ones are of interest—for example, the hydrogen alpha line. To filter out the wavelengths which are of no interest, use is made of the fact that the refractive index, and therefore the speed of propagation, depends on the frequency. If a beam of integrated light (in which all frequencies are present, i.e., so-called "white light") passes through the apparatus described above, the thickness of the calcareous spar can be selected to insure that only beams of certain frequencies cancel each other. If several series of calcareous spar laminae follow one after the other with polarizing filters between them, rays of certain frequencies will be cancelled or reinforced by "interference" as they pass through. With a lamina thickness ratio of 1 : 2 : 4 : 8 (e.g., 2.38; 4.76; ...; 73.16 mm) each lamina will suppress half of the spectrum transmitted by the preceding one. An arrangement of 6 laminae finally produces two very narrow bands of wavelengths. The band which is not required is eliminated with a simple color filter, and observation in the hydrogen alpha line becomes possible. Of course, the laminae can be calculated so that frequency bands other than the hydrogen alpha band are produced. Today filters for observing the sun in the calcium II or K line (near ultra-violet) and the green corona line are in routine use.

Filtering is therefore solely dependent on the thickness of the calcareous spar laminae, and herein lies the main problem in the manufacture of Lyot filters. For example, to achieve the minimum transmission of ± 1Å, a one millimeter-thick lamina has to be cut to an accuracy of $\pm 0.15\mu$. Obviously, there must be no change in thickness caused by expansion, for which reason Lyot filters always operate in a highly regulated temperature controlled environment. A temperature difference of one degree would shift the maximum transmission in birefringent quartz by 0.74Å and in calcareous spar by 0.42Å. Within certain limits the transmission band can also be shifted to observe structures whose radiation is not exactly in the hydrogen alpha band caused for example, by the Doppler shift. This "line shifting" must be controlled.

Polarizing interference filters must be provided with a heat protection (infra-red) filter not only to prevent image deterioration (which is annoying enough, considering the cost of such a device) but also, as can also happen, destruction of the filter.

In the past, crystals such as tourmaline were used for polarizing filters, but today the very long chain molecules found in synthetic materials make very effective filters at much lower cost. The films are stretched so that the molecules in this material align like a window grille. Light can only pass through if it is oscillating in the direction of the "bars" of the grille. The chain molecules are not heat-stable, and they eventually will break up and no longer act as polarizers.

Frequently, and despite the manufacturers' warnings, simple red filters have been used to prevent heating by infrared radiation. These filters may be inexpensive, but they are absolutely useless for this purpose. To absorb heat use filters which absorb light at wavelengths greater than 6700Å . The widely-used Wratten filter is not suitable for this purpose as, according to the manufacturers, it is not heat-stable.

A.4.4.3 DayStar Filters

This type of monochromator (Fig. A.4.14) consist of a "sandwich" made up of an anti-reflection coated optical window, a narrow-band blocking filter, an etalon window, a Fabry-Perot solid spacer crystal, another etalon

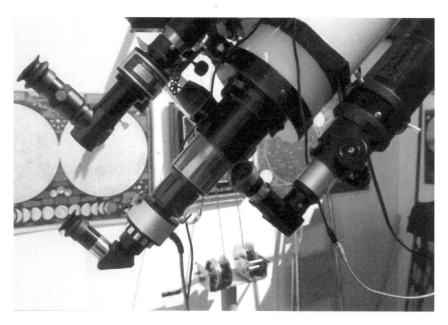

Fig. A.4.14. *Pictured left to right: A DayStar 6.0Å Calcium-K line solar filter centered at 3933.7Å. Center, a 0.6Å DayStar Type TS-II Hydrogen alpha filter centered at 6562.8Å, and lower right, a Herschel wedge prism diagonal with neutral density eyepiece filters for viewing the sun in white light. It is attached to an 80mm fl = 919mm refractor. Photo courtesy of D.E. Trombino.*

window, a broadband trimming filter, and an anti-reflection coated window. This technology results in a relatively small filter at a much reduced cost when compared to Lyot filters. In fact, this class of filters has enabled a broad community of amateur observers using small telescopes with their existing telescope mounts (Lyot filters tend to be heavy) to view the chromosphere.

Experience with these filters ranges from enthusiasm to deep frustration. As with all sophisticated equipment problems can arise when users deviate from the recommendations of the manufacturer. As a general rule commercial optical instruments can vary drastically in their quality—deviations from manufacturers' specifications can be large. The quality of a monochromator is largely expressed by the bandwidth of the filter. The narrower it is, the better the image and the higher the price. New users should familiarize themselves with how the solar image should look when observed through a filter with a given set of specifications. There is a visible difference between a 0.7Å and 0.5Å filter system. Is is remotely possible that some lucky individual might get a 0.5Å filter for the price of a 0.7Å but the reverse is also true—know what to look for!

The question "Lyot or DayStar" is mostly answered when you receive the price quotes. Lyot filters are professional instruments that are suitable for applications where very high quality images are demanded. This, however, may even be the case at public observatories. The people these institutions serve, beginners, occasional observers, and children, often need excellent quality images to concentrate on or even to see many chromospheric structures.

A.4.5 Observing the Sun by Radioastronomy[†]

A.4.5.1 Introduction

Stars, galaxies, and our sun, not only emit visible light but also radio waves. Indeed, certain objects (such as pulsars and radio galaxies) emit principally radio waves and may be invisible to the human eye. Radio waves from these astronomical sources surround us, and by using suitable equipment, it is possible to extract them from the electromagnetic spectrum, provided that we tune a detector to the correct wavelength. Most radio sources have a broad spectrum (white noise), similar to the noise of a radio receiver when the aerial is unplugged (Rohlfs 1986). Various parameters influence the *sensitivity* of a radio telescope and consequently the weakest radio source that can be picked up. These include the receiver's internal noise, amplification fluctuations, the effective antenna area, feedline losses, the intermediate frequency amplifier bandwidth, the time constant of the integrator, and so forth.

The system temperature variations T_{sys} and therefore also the weakest detectable radio signal T_{min} can be reduced by using the greatest bandwidth B and the longest integration time constant T as possible.

$$T_{min} = \frac{T_{sys}k}{\sqrt{BT}}, \text{ where } k = 1.38 \ 10^{-23} \frac{Ws}{K} \text{(Boltzmann constant).} \quad \text{(A.4.5.1)}$$

Although bandwidths greater than 1 megahertz and time constants longer than 10 seconds are preferable, the bandwidth usually has to be sharply reduced to find a portion of the spectrum free from man-made radio signals. Nearly all frequency channels have by now been at least partially taken over by radio and television stations. It is clear that reducing the system parameters means a considerable loss of sensitivity. The integration time should in practice be between 0.05 and 3 seconds for *solar*

[†]Written by Christian Monstein

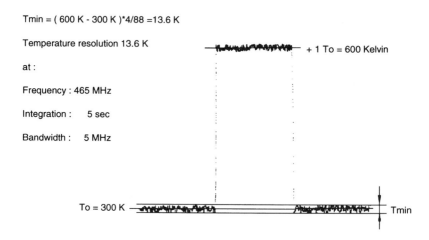

Fig. A.4.15. *The weakest signal which can be resolved by a receiving system corresponds to the width of oscilloscope trace (Heisermann 1975; Swenson 1980; Rohlfs 1986).*

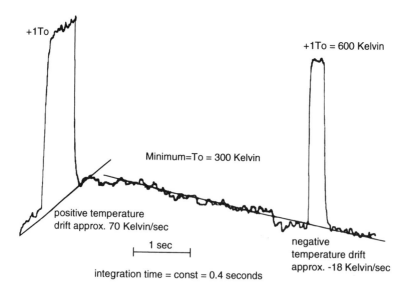

Fig. A.4.16. *Drifting calibration signal caused by fluctuations in temperature in a total power system.*

bursts (Hey 1973; Urbarz 1980) and between several seconds and possibly hours for galactic radio sources (Verschuur 1974). The choice of integration time depends on the type and intensity of interference sources on earth.

A.4.5.2 Telescope Systems

The *total power system* consists of a single antenna or a group of antennas connected directly to the receiver. The receiver output is conveyed via a direct voltage amplifier to a recording device where it can be displayed. The offset voltage caused by internal noise has to be cancelled with a suitable, stable direct voltage. The total power system is extremely sensitive as regards fluctuations in amplification caused by changes in the surrounding temperature. Problems are also caused by variations in the power supply and individual component (diodes, resistors, capacitors, etc.) characteristics. These variations usually result in a drifting oscillograph which makes it almost impossible to register very weak radio sources. Consequently, this system is still just adequate for solar radio astronomy.

In the Dicke system the antenna signal is continuously compared to a stable reference source, the latter usually being an ohm resistor linked with the wave resistance having a temperature of around 300° K (Kelvin) (Kraus 1986). The receiver is switched between the reference source and the signal approximately 100 to 1000 times a second, while the detector simultaneously separates the demodulated signals.

Two signals are created:

$$a = \text{antenna signal} + \text{internal noise} \qquad (A.4.5.2)$$

and

$$b = \text{reference source} + \text{internal noise.} \qquad (A.4.5.3)$$

In an electronic subtracter, b is subtracted from a, which in the case of the randomly distributed internal noise levels means that the basic components of the detector voltage—which are produced by internal noise—are partially compensated after sufficient filtering, and only the differential signal antenna minus reference source remains. This differential signal is then smoothed and transferred to the registering device via a rectifier.

A disadvantage of the Dicke system is that the reference temperature in smaller antenna systems is substantially higher than the antenna temperature T_a of the majority of galactic radio sources. Thus, the signal to be registered can vary considerably. Each change in amplification in the system therefore directly affects the relatively strong differential signal and causes strong drifting of the oscilloscope. Using the cold sky as a reference

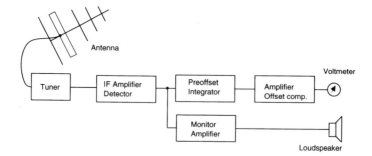

Fig. A.4.17. *Total power radiometer consisting of antenna, high-frequency tuner (receiver), intermediate frequency amplifier and detector (IF), preoffset and integrator, output amplifier and offset with registering device, monitor amplifier, and loudspeaker.*

is a good solution. The ohmic resistor is replaced by an antenna pointing towards the north celestial pole (Smith 1978). Due to the rotation of the earth, the radiation flow there is almost independent of the hour angle, resulting in a constant equivalent reference temperature of a few degrees Kelvin above absolute zero. The attainable stability of this calibration is perfectly adequate for amateur purposes.

A.4.5.3   Designing a Receiver System

It is recommended that beginners in amateur radioastronomy start with the simplest system, i.e., the total power system, so that they get the necessary feel for the subject and gain some experience before later going on to construct a Dicke radiometer. The total power system consists of the components shown in Fig. A.4.17, which will be described in as much detail as the limited scope of this article allows. Amplification between the antenna and the registering device output should be by a factor of at least 100,000,000,000,000 or 140 decibels (dB) to obtain useful readings for amateur purposes (Heisermann 1975).

$$1\text{dB} = 0.1 \log \frac{P_{\text{off}}}{P_{\text{on}}} \qquad (\text{A.4.5.4})$$

A.4.5.4   Antenna

As a general rule the antenna should be as large as possible, as received radio performance is proportional to the effective antenna surface area. However, financial considerations and problems of space frequently dictate the use of commercially available radio and television antennas. In this case it is recommended that only antennas with a minimum antenna gain of around 12 db be purchased. Several low gain antennas can be "stacked" and coupled together with impedance matching devices to increase the overall output. Another of the criteria for selection, the *apex angle,* is also of particular interest as it directly affects the angular resolution of the antenna, which should be optimum; i.e., the apex angle should become as small as possible (Altenhoff 1994; Falb 1981). Resolution for *Yagi antennas* approximately[1]

$$51 \text{ degrees} \frac{\lambda}{D}. \tag{A.4.5.5}$$

With a single antenna apex angles of 28° can easily be achieved. By properly stacking several antennas this angle can be correspondingly reduced, and angles of between 5 and 10° are obtainable. Most amateur radio enthusiasts (Hams) or radio astronomers are willing to help a beginner select a suitable antenna. Second-hand antennas are frequently sold for the scrap price or even given away free of charge.

A.4.5.5 Antenna Transmission Lines

It is a mistake to try to economize on antenna transmission line. With extremely low antenna outputs of 10^{-15} watts and less, as much energy as possible has to reach the receiver—every tenth of a decibel is needed. Transmission lines should therefore be short, low loss, and impedance matched to the input of the receiver system. Suitable transmission cable comes in 50, 60, or 75 ohms, but on no account should they be mixed, since every impedance transformation produces undesirable losses (Henne 1966). Following are recommended cable types:

> 50 ohms: RG-213/U with 12.7 dB/100m loss at 300 MHz
> 75 ohms: RG-11A/U with 13.3 dB/100m loss at 300 MHz

A.4.5.6 Receiver

The receiving device (tuner) is the most critical part of the system, for it is here that the sensitivity of the entire radio telescope is decided. The tuner should be a superheterodyne receiver consisting of a preselector stage, a mixer stage, and a local oscillator (Limann 1978).

It is usually difficult for the amateur to build such a system himself as he often lacks the necessary knowledge and test instruments. However, one solution is to cannibalize an old television for the tuner and modify it for our purposes. It is important that the set should have been in working order

---

[1]Kraus 1950; ARRL 1991

before being cannibalized to ensure that the receiver actually operates, even though the picture tube may be defective. It should also be ensured that an electrical circuit diagram for the device is available so that the supply voltage can be correctly connected at a later stage. The beginner will probably have to rely on the help of a radio amateur or television technician to make sure that the power supply, adjusting means, band selection, IF output, antenna, and tuning are all correctly connected (ARRL 1991). By way of example, the circuit diagram of a Grundig all-band diode tuner is given in Fig. A.4.18.

A.4.5.7   IF Amplifier

In the intermediate frequency amplifier (IF), the actual selection, characterized by bandwidth B, is carried out. The IF amplifier also provides the greater part of the system's total amplification. The IF amplifier can be built without test instruments, provided the builder has enough practical experience, which with today's integrated circuits, monolithic ceramic filters and detectors does not present an insurmountable problem (ARRL 1991). As an example, the circuit diagram of a Grundig image IF module is given in Fig. A.4.19.

A.4.5.8   Integrator

The purpose of the integrator is to smooth the randomly distributed noise signal impulses with a defined, selectable time constant T. Without smoothing, the chart-recorder would react far too strongly and would register the most minimal disturbance because the trace width would be too large. The integrator circuit described here can easily be constructed by the amateur using inexpensive components. A buffer stage is included before the integrator to balance out the high video direct voltage and to decouple the integrator electronically from the video section.

A.4.5.9   Amplifier and Offset Compensator

The integrated noise signal must be amplified so that it can be detected with a voltmeter, an oscilloscope, plotter, or an A to D converter for computer data capture. For special measurements the *offset* must also be moveable. This circuit too can be easily assembled by the interested amateur as there are no special precautions to be taken into account.

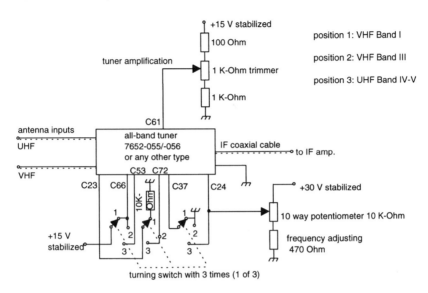

Fig. A.4.18. *Circuit diagram of a Grundig all-band diode tuner.*

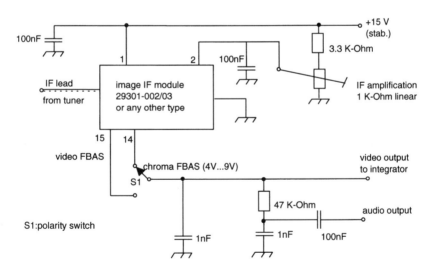

Fig. A.4.19. *Circuit diagram for an IF module with power supply, amplification control (gain), and video output. Most IF modules have complimentary outputs so that there is a choice between the two polarities of video voltage.*

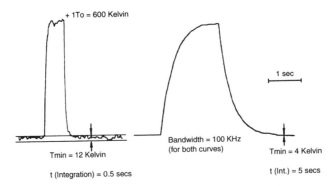

Fig. A.4.20. *Example of a noise step with a smoothing time of 0.5 seconds and 5 seconds. Sensitivity increases with the square root of time constant T.*

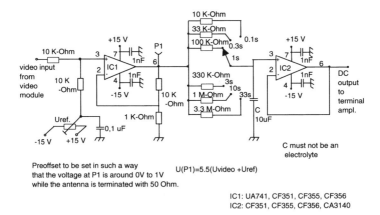

Fig. A.4.21. *Integrator circuit with selective time constant between 0.1 and 33 seconds. The second operational amplifier should have as low an error current as possible. [Electrometer amplifier.]*

A.4.5.10   Monitor Amplifier

The purpose of the amplifier is not, as is maintained in some quarters, to eavesdrop on any extra-terrestrial civilizations, but rather to distinguish sources of interference (television stations, lawn mowers, coffee machines, etc.) from solar noise storms (Hey 1973, Urbarz 1980). An experienced builder will use the sound system from a cannibalized television set or build the amplifier himself. Figure A.4.23 is intended for this purpose. Equally suitable is an old radio set with phono or tape inputs. As a last resort, a small kit which simply has to be soldered together can be purchased.

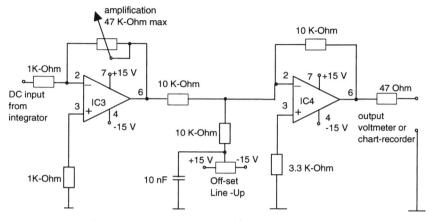

Fig. A.4.22. *Amplifier and offset compensator for connecting a voltmeter or plotter.*

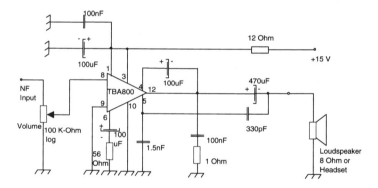

Fig. A.4.23. *Monitor amplifier with integrated circuit TBA 800 (AEG 1979/80).*

A.4.5.11 Power Supply

The power supply is just as important as all the other components of the receiving system because if the supply voltage is poorly stabilized and smoothed, it is impossible to carry out any measurement. For this reason, integrated circuit voltage regulators are used because they provide predictable results. Should a suitable transformer with three separate windings (or "taps") be unavailable, several individual transformers can be used. It is also important that an adequate line filter be installed to minimize RF and transient interference carried by the commercial power lines.

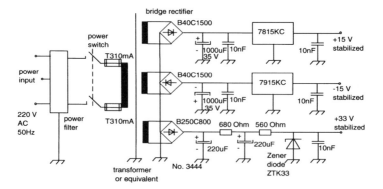

Fig. A.4.24. *Power supply circuit for receiver ±15 volts, and +33 volts for aligning.*

A.4.5.12 Assembly, Commissioning

The assembly of the components should be carried out very carefully using short connecting leads and good solder joints. Wherever possible components should be assembled on a printed circuit board or breadboard. To cancel noise the insulated power supply leads should be twisted together. High-frequency leads should be made of coaxial cable with BNC connectors. Avoid cable-to-cable connections and loose wires! The chassis should be well shielded and ventilated in accordance with good engineering practices. Particular care should be devoted to good grounding and power line bypassing.

Once all the component systems have been assembled and roughly aligned, the first measurements can be made with a noise generator and without an antenna (Swenson 1980). A 50 Ohm resister soldered into a BNC connector serves as a temperature reference of 300° Kelvin. As soon as the receiver is operational, a clear (no signal) frequency is found. Next, the antenna is directed, for example, towards the Sun or the center of the Milky Way.

A.4.5.13 Observation Possibilities

The Sun, our nearest star, provides an almost inexhaustible source for a large number of interesting observations (Heisermann 1975; Hey 1973; Urbarz 1980; Monstein 1980a; Monstein 1980b). It constitutes an intensive source of radio waves and can be located and recorded every day, even without expensive antenna control systems.

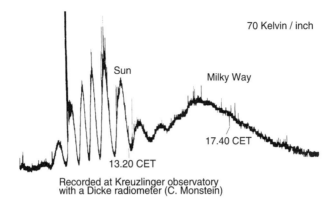

70 Kelvin / inch

Sun

Milky Way

17.40 CET

13.20 CET

Recorded at Kreuzlinger observatory
with a Dicke radiometer (C. Monstein)

Fig. A.4.25. *The Sun and Milky Way observed with a group of antennas forming an interferometer, with an interval of 12 m at 230 MHz (Kreuzlingen observatory, digital recording with microprocessor-system).*

Assuming that the first observations are not made during a sunspot minimum and at short wavelengths, the sun itself can be recorded with the simplest of radio astronomy receiving devices. The best chances of success are obtained if the antennas are steerable in azimuth and elevation so that at culmination the sun shines directly into the center of the antenna pattern. Through observation with varying polarization (horizontal/vertical), various measurements can be used to obtain very useful information about the spatial antenna pattern. In addition, once the antenna parameters are known, periodic flux measurements can be undertaken, for which an additional coaxial switch and a noise generator that can be calibrated are required (Stein 1979).

The correlation between such flux measurements and the sunspot relative numbers (see Section B.2.4) always leads to heated discussion. An almost infinite amount of time can be spent on the analysis and interpretation of such relationships and/or lack of relationships.

With the exception of measurements which can be made with a single antenna, several antennas coupled together to form an interferometer offer innumerable observation possibilities. Though the individual types of interferometer will not be dealt with here in greater detail, more on the subject can be found in the following: Swenson 1980; Monstein 1980a; Monstein 1980b; Wohlleben, Mattes 1991. Nevertheless, it is possible to localize radio sources much more precisely than with individual antennas, as the resolution of an individual interference fan can be a fraction of an angular degree, even in amateur instruments. For instance, radio storms can be localized on the sun and thus complement or even partially replace visual observations (Suzuki 1959).

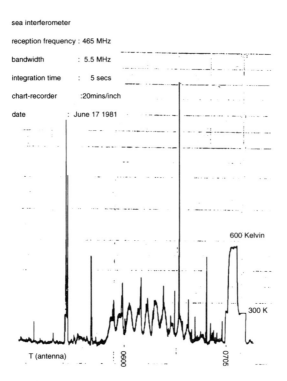

Fig. A.4.26. *Interferogram of solar radio sources produced by interference of an almost discrete radio source (sun) and its total reflection on the surface of the sea, taken at the author's station on 17.6.1981 at 465 Megahertz (Monstein 1982).*

In addition to the observations briefly described here, a large number of other possibilities include the non-thermal radio signal from the giant planet Jupiter, the precise periodic radio signals of pulsars, and the radio emissions of various objects such as Cassiopeia A, Cygnus A, Sagittarius A, Virgo A, Taurus A, and numerous other radio sources (Altenhoff 1994).

The number of objects an amateur or a group can observe depends on their own initiative and capacity for improvisation. Forming a small group to share the costs and the work involved is very worthwhile (for example: SARA). A membership at SARA (Society of Amateur Radio Astronomers) would therefore be very useful; for the address see Appendix A. At the same time relations are established between people at a local and international level, irrespective of borders and language. Technical questions are best addressed to local ham radio operators or a public observatory, where willing assistance is at hand in the majority of cases.

Chapter A.5

Photography

A.5.1 The Photographic Emulsion and its Theory[†]

Any beginner wishing to take up solar photography is going to ask, "Which film should I use? How do I develop it?" Since the various types of films and their names are frequently changing, rather than giving a list of films currently available, we are going to look at the theoretical side. That way, everybody will be in a position to select the appropriate films, according to the manufacturer's specifications (data sheet) from the range available. (The films most commonly used for solar photography in 1995 will be used as examples in this section.) We will not embark, however, upon an in-depth study of photochemistry and photophysics—a detailed bibliography is provided for those who are interested.

A black and white negative film basically consists of a synthetic film (base) to which a layer of gelatin is applied. Light-sensitive silver bromide crystals (film grains) are mixed within this gelatin layer. On the other side is an anti-halation layer, which minimizes internal reflections. It dissolves in the developer so that clear negatives are produced.

Exposing a film requires photons, which encounter the silver bromide crystals via a photographic lens system. After exposure a so-called latent image is created; however, at this stage this is neither visible nor stable. For this reason an exposed film should not be left for weeks before it is developed since the latent image may deteriorate.

The latent image is intensified during the development process by a factor of approximately 10^6 and consequently becomes visible. The developing process must be interrupted after a given time; otherwise harmful over-development begins. Plain rinsing or acetic acid stop baths are used

---

[†]Written by Wolfgang Paech

to prevent this problem. Next, the film is fixed. Fixation involves all the non-exposed silver bromide crystals being removed from the emulsion. If fixation is omitted, the negative immediately turns black under the effects of light and is completely useless.

If all the silver bromide crystals are of the same size, they constitute what is known as a line-halftone film, which can only reproduce very high contrast black-and-white images (repro film) since a silver crystal can only turn completely black under the effect of light and cannot take on shades of grey. Greys are produced by incorporating crystals of various sizes in different layers, one on top of the other. Therefore, a film layer which contains many large crystals is highly sensitive, but also coarse-grained. The film layer which contains many small crystals has a low sensitivity, but is therefore very finely grained. The yardstick used for measuring a film's sensitivity is provided by DIN or ISO values, in which case the higher the value, the greater the sensitivity of the emulsion.

Manufacturers provide numerous specifications to describe film which can help in the selection of an emulsion:

1. Characteristic curve

2. Spectral sensitivity curve

3. Gamma-time curves

4. Resolving power

5. Schwarzschild behavior

A.5.1.1   Characteristic curve

Figure A.5.1 shows a hypothetical characteristic curve, and Fig. A.5.2, a characteristic curve for various Agfa films. It is possible to determine a film's sensitivity and normal contrast behavior from the characteristic curves. The manufacturer, of course, indicates sensitivity using DIN or ISO values (except with special films). Following is a description of how such curves can be "read" in principle.

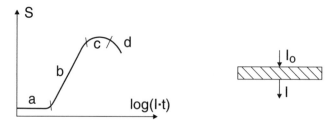

Fig. A.5.1. *Hypothetical characteristic curve (left) and I_o/I ratio (right).*

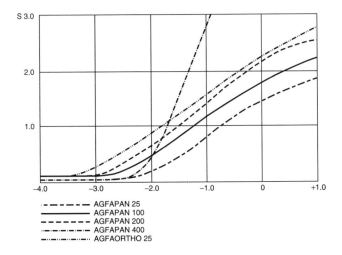

S 3.0

2.0

1.0

-4.0   -3.0   -2.0   -1.0   0   +1.0

· — · — · — AGFAPAN 25
————————— AGFAPAN 100
— — — — — AGFAPAN 200
··—··—··—··— AGFAPAN 400
—··—··—··—·· AGFAORTHO 25

Fig. A.5.2. *Characteristic curves for Agfa films.*

We can see from Fig. A.5.1 that the characteristic curve consists of four sections: under-exposure (a), linear part (b), over-exposure (c), and solarization (d). The logarithmic product of the light intensity I (brightness) and the exposure time t is plotted on the horizontal axis (Fig. A.5.1). The value t remains constant, which, strictly speaking, means that the characteristic curves (and also the DIN or ISO values) only apply for a given exposure time. The blackening S produced by $(I \times t)$ is plotted on the vertical axis. S is defined as the logarithmic ratio I_o/I (see Fig. A.5.1). If a beam of light I_o falls on a blackened piece of film the light which emerges as a result equals I. Blackening S is sometimes also called density D and is also plotted in a logarithmic scale.

We can see from the curve that each film has a grey value (film base + fog and sometimes called "veil"), even if it is developed unexposed. Furthermore, we can see that at the start of the curve (horizontal part), S does not increase, despite an increase of $(I \times t)$. The curve then begins to rise in a straight line. The further to the left the bend occurs, the more sensitive the emulsion. The linear part of the characteristic curve is the most important; work should be undertaken in this part of the film's curve wherever possible. Here we can read the angle (α). The tangent of α is called the gamma (γ) or contrast factor ($\tan \alpha = \gamma$). If α is precisely 45° (γ=1), the film reproduces all contrasts (brightness variations) naturally. If α is less than 45° (γ less than 1), they are reduced; if α is greater than 45°, the contrasts are more vividly reproduced. Gamma is heavily dependent on the film development. Therefore, we cannot simply measure the blackening

S and thereby draw conclusions as to the intensity (if t is known). So if brightness is to be determined from a negative, a characteristic curve is required for the negative concerned. This calculation requires a reference system (e.g., a "gray" or "step" wedge). The following applies, in principle, to the linear part: the more sensitive the film, the greater the γ (i.e., the "harder" the film works).

The over-exposure and solarization areas cannot be used for solar photography.

A.5.1.2 Spectral sensitivity curve

This curve shows the wavelengths of the light to which a film is sensitive (sensitized). Figure A.5.3 shows the Agfa Ortho 25 curve, and Fig. A.5.4, that of the Kodak Technical Pan Film No. 2415. The two curves differ considerably, as is clearly shown. They immediately show the spectral ranges in which photographs are taken to best effect and the filters which can be used (the filter curve must, of course, be known).

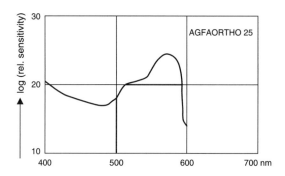

Fig. A.5.3. *Agfa Ortho 25 spectral sensitivity curve.*

The Kodak Pan Film 2415 (formerly SO–115) may be used over the whole visible spectral range (with an increased sensitivity in the red area), whereas the Agfa-Ortho 25 ceases to demonstrate any sensitivity in the red spectral range. If one were to attempt to take photographs of prominences using the Agfa-Ortho 25 (Hα=656nm), exposure could be sustained for several minutes without an image being created.

Figure A.5.5 shows how a film's spectral curve can be influenced using color filters. The shaded area shows the resulting spectral range, which is represented on the film.

Suppression of the chromatic aberration in refractors through filtering increases the sharpness of the image.

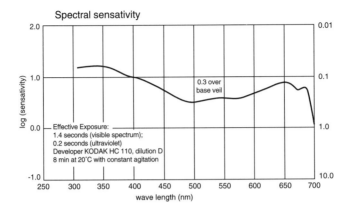

Fig. A.5.4. *Kodak Technical Pan Film No. 2415 spectral sensitivity curve.*

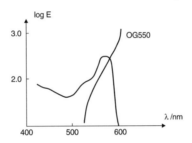

Fig. A.5.5. *Agfa-Ortho 25 and a Schott filter OG 550.*

A.5.1.3 Gamma-time curves

Gamma-time curves show us how we can influence the ascending gradient of the linear part of the characteristic curve according to our own requirements using various developers and developing times. Examples are once again provided by Kodak 2415 (Fig. A.5.6) and Agfa-Ortho 25 (Fig. A.5.7).

A.5.1.4 Resolving power

The resolving power of an emulsion is given in lines per millimeter, depending on the so-called object contrast, and should be seen as a measure of the film's sharpness and the extent to which it is fine-grained. The Kodak 2415 values lie between 125 lines/mm and 320 lines/mm, depending on the object contrast. The Agfa-Ortho value is around 350 lines/mm. It

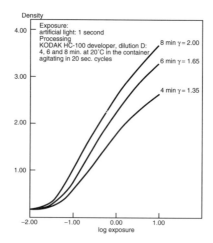

Fig. A.5.6. *Kodak 2415 gamma-time curves.*

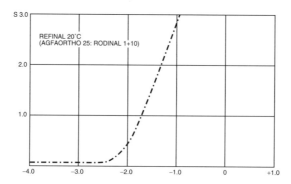

Fig. A.5.7. *Agfa-Ortho 25 gamma-time curves.*

should also be noted that an optimum level is achieved at approximately 250 lines/mm because a telescopic lens (the best to which an amateur is likely to have access) reaches its resolution limit at roughly 200 lines/mm.

A.5.1.5   Schwarzschild behavior

The Schwarzschild curve or table (depending on the developer and developing time) indicates how the film reacts to various exposure times. For example, Fig. A.5.8 shows the data relating to Kodak 2415. It can be seen that the changes with exposure times which are relevant to solar photography are of no great significance. Consequently, Schwarzschild data are also considerably more significant for long exposure times.

Fig A.5.8 Kodak TP 2415 Schwarzschild Data							
Exposure time (seconds)	100	10	1	$1/10$	$1/100$	$1/1000$	$1/10\,000$
Contrast index change	±0	$+0.08$	$+0.08$	±0	-0.06	-0.14	-0.22
Sensitivity change	-0.4	-0.2	-0.06	±0	$+0.02$	-0.02	-0.06
% exposure change	$+1.33$	$+0.667$	±0	±0	±0	±0	±0
Exposure index	64	80	125	125	125	125	125

A.5.1.6 Summary

Solar photography requires a high-resolution film, which is sensitive over a wide spectral range, and whose contrast reproduction (γ) can be controlled over a broad range through development. It goes without saying that the film may have a low sensitivity.

Films should, in principle, be stored unopened in their boxes and cartridges at as low a temperature as possible (refrigerator or deep freeze). Direct sunlight and heat irradiation must be avoided as they damage films. Before a film stored in a cool place can be used, it must be warmed to room temperature. Refrigerated films will reach room temperature within 10 to 15 minutes. Frozen films should have at least one hour to acclimate to room temperature.

A.5.2 Introduction to White Light Photography[†]

The aim of solar photography is to provide an image of the multifarious aspects of solar activity to complement observations. The simplest and most comprehensive way of doing this is to take master shots of the sun, which can be enlarged considerably. To enable amateurs to work together effectively in this area, it is recommended that a photographic network be established so that photographs of the solar disc taken from day to day can be collected and evaluated since not every day is clear at a particular location.

Solar photography does not require large aperture telescopes; refractors from 50 mm or, for instance, Newton-type reflecting telescopes (with an off-axis stop (i.e., 8-inch telescopes might use a 3 inch off-axis stop) may be used (see A.1). A reflex camera body should definitely be used. Solar photographs usually are taken with focal lengths of roughly two meters. This results in solar images measuring roughly two centimeters on the negative.

Photographs taken using eyepiece projection show more details under calm atmospheric conditions; larger granulation structures can even be

---

[†]Written by Klaus Peter Schröder

recorded with 75 mm refractors. It is advisable to use a film that is not only fine-grained, but also high-contrast to show the minute contrasts found on the sun's surface. The Agfa Ortho 25 and Kodak Technical Pan 2415 are currently available for this purpose.

There are various methods of reducing excessive sunlight. The best way is to use an evaporated metal film lens filter which completely covers the objective, which attenuates sunlight and prevents any heating within the optics (see also A.3.3). However, it is also possible to insert small neutral density filters just in front of the focus, where they do not noticeably impair the image even if they are of poor optical quality. Because the heat created by optical absorption builds up, these filters can quickly crack, which is why it is better to use them in conjunction with a partially reflective prism, the surface of which only reflects 5% of the light onto the filter while the remaining 95% passes through the body of the prism. If necessary, the aperture can also be stopped down to 4 cm; this still permits good master shots, but prevents optimum detailed photographs from being taken since resolution deteriorates because of diffraction.

With Agfa Ortho 25 film, where exposure times are minimized, master shots require filter factors of several 1000 times. On the other hand, higher ocular projections require light reduction factors of only a few 100 times. In the first case, for example, a 1:1000 (T = 0.1) objective filter is combined with a small neutral density filter close to the focus; in the second case, it is possible to manage with the same lens filter but slightly longer exposure times. Furthermore, Agfa Ortho's insensitivity to red can be utilized. If it is used with a red filter (filter factor 8), the combination results in an actual light reduction of roughly 1:100 to 1:1000, depending on the filter. The strength of the neutral density filter (which may then still be required) or else the exposure times, can be determined through sample exposures, even with various apertures. The following formula applies to the relationship between the light reduction factor, enlargement and exposure time:

$$t = \frac{N^2 D}{\text{ISO} K} \tag{A.5.2.1}$$

$K =$ constant of solar light intensity, approximately 70 million
$\text{ISO} =$ film sensitivity in ISO
$D =$ reduction number, e.g., usually 250 with a factor 8 red filters
$N =$ aperture number $\cong$ equivalent focal length/lens diameter

The difficulty in assessing haze or other bad seeing conditions also means that the exposure time (t) should be varied by at least a factor of 2 from the calculated value. The equivalent focal length, F_{eff}, is identical to the lens focal length with focal point photography or several times larger than that given by the teleconverter. With ocular projection it is approximately

$$F_{\text{eff}} = F_{\text{objective}} \cdot s / F_{\text{eyepiece}}.$$

Here, F_{eyepiece}, is the eyepiece or lens focal length, and s is the film-eyepiece spacing.

When choosing the equivalent focal length and filter, exposure times should be $1/500$ or $1/1000$ second wherever possible so that the effects of atmospheric turbulence are minimized. Following are sample results: 60/900 mm refractor, focal with $\times 2$ teleconverter, $1/20$ (5%) reflective prism (45° prism with reflective angles towards the lens, glass body *behind* the beam deflection), a factor 8 red filter, but $D_1 = 250$ on the Agfa Ortho, so that $D = 250 \times 20 = 5000$. This means that t is roughly $1/500$ second.

Since the light reduction is not as high for the human eye when using the red filter as it is with other methods over the whole spectral range, additional filtration must be fitted at the eyepiece of the camera viewfinder (see A.3.2). Otherwise the intensity of the red light is blinding!

The camera can be attached using lens adapters (see A.5.3). Even homemade clamps can be used as long as the camera is correctly positioned along the optical axis and the filter, teleconverter, etc., are coupled directly to the camera so that no stray light reaches the film. The best way of incorporating small filters close to the focus, if used, is a reducing ring. To do so cut a heavy paper mask that just fits within the adapter ring. In the center of this mask cut a hole that is slightly smaller than the filter. Tape, glue or otherwise mount the filter over this hole. The paper and internal parts of the ring should be blackened.

A.5.3 Cameras, Adapters, and Accessories[†]

A.5.3.1 Cameras

In principle any single lens reflex (SLR) camera can be used for solar photography. However, the following tips should be considered when selecting a camera. The camera is, of course, only used as a housing without a lens. If possible, the camera body should permit exposure times of up to $1/2000$ second, and times of up to at least $1/500$ second should certainly be attainable. The exposure times which are relevant to solar photography ($1/125$ to $1/2000$ second) must function perfectly. This is an important consideration when buying a second-hand camera! The best test is to take sample

---

[†]Written by Wolfgang Paech and Klaus-Peter Schröder

Fig. A.5.8. *Astro-Physics 130 mm Starfire EDT refractor with Astro-Physics eyepiece projection tele-extender, Olympus OB-1 camera, varimagni finder (Olympus), and bulb cable release. Photo by Gordon Garcia.*

photographs. The shutter release should be checked to ensure that it can be operated with a minimum of vibration (if in doubt, always work with cable release). Also check that the reflex mirror's movement does not cause vibration. The shutter should also permit "real" double exposure: in other words, it must be possible to re-cock the shutter without advancing the film (see B.3.2.4). A very important part of the camera body is the viewfinder, which, in the final analysis, determines whether the images produced are sharply defined. Microprisms, split-field or clear-vision discs in the viewfinder are not suited to focusing. Due to the low aperture ratio microprisms and split-field disc finder screens split the viewfinder image into useless bright and dark light spots; they can no longer be used to focus the camera. On the other hand, a clear screen presents the danger that the eye may easily focus outside the focal plane, causing the image on the negative to be unfocused. Very fine ground-glass screens with a central clear area have proved most effective. Focusing takes place on the ground-glass screen and the clear area can be used to assess atmosphere calmness. Of course, a camera body with an interchangeable viewfinder, which can be fitted with various screens, is most desirable since it enables the user to assemble his own optimum combination.

There are, of course, cameras which incorporate all the features listed here, but these are very expensive. Therefore, the amateur may have to compromise and select a less capable camera but one still suitable for some particular aspect of solar photography. Because of the size of the solar image, miniature cameras may not be used above a telescopic focal length of roughly 2.3 m if the objective is to include the whole sun on the film.

For focal lengths of 2.3 m and greater, a medium format camera with a 6 × 6 cm or 6 × 7 cm film is required.

A.5.3.2 Adapters

A camera adapter links the eyepiece attachment on the telescope to the camera housing. The connection must be light-tight and rigid. For commercially manufactured telescopes, ready-made adapters are usually available from the manufacturer or from telescope accessory dealers. The majority of these have an M 42 × 1 (or M 42 × 0.75 = T2) thread. Various companies also supply adapters specifically designed to mount directly to a particular camera's lens mount. The owners of home-made telescopes will probably have the metal working machinery necessary to make a suitable adapter.

A.5.3.3 Accessories

Right angle viewfinders are accessories that are attached to the normal viewfinder, and they offer two advantages:

1. The image in the viewfinder is enlarged (usually by 2.5 times).

2. The user has a vertical view into the camera. Those who have already worked with the reflex camera when the sun is high will have learned to appreciate this feature.

A motorized film advance is an advantage because many are practically vibration free. Also desirable are replaceable camera backs which record the date, exposure time, etc., directly on the film and those with large film capacities—some of which hold lengths of film up to 100 feet long.

A.5.4 Photographic observations of the Chromosphere[†]

Conducting photographic observations of chromospheric phenomena is much more difficult than visual observations because of atmospheric turbulence (seeing). While the eye is able to subtract seeing influences the photographic film cannot. An advantage of photography, however, is that more light is available—at least when using an instrument with a occulting disk. A stable and perfectly oriented mounting is a must for this kind of photography.

[†]Written by Wolfgang Paech

A.5.4.1   Shooting technique and exposure time

Photography of chromospheric phenomena is only possible using the prime focus. Eyepiece projection, while suitable for white light photographs of the sun, the moon, or the planets, would require too long exposure times (at least with a DayStar filter), and the air turbulence would smear out any details. A photographic teleconverter may be acceptable if seeing conditions are favorable. When photographing with a conical diaphragm it may be best to use a larger cone. This would make it easier to produce useful pictures and avoid reflections caused by light passing the cone if it is not perfectly centered on the solar image. To learn from mistakes and to improve your photographs, you should record the conditions for each exposure in writing.

Rough estimates of exposure times (using TP 2415) are $1/60$ and $1/500$ second for focal photography with a prominence attachment (focal ratio 1:10 to 1:15 and 10Å FWHM interference filter). The exposure time depends on the position of the iris diaphragm of the attachment and on the transparency of the atmosphere. With a DayStar filter (FWHM 0.5Å) exposure times of $1/8$ to $1/15$ second are suitable for photographs of the solar surface and $1/8$ to 1 second for prominences at the solar limb. Under favorable observing conditions (outside large cities) half of these numbers may be taken. Fig. A.5.9 and A.5.10 show example photographs.

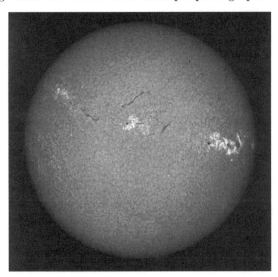

Fig. A.5.9. *Taken April 24, 1984 at 15:21 UT with a 65mm refractor, F = 1950 mm e.f.l., DayStar FWHM 0.53Å on Kodak PT 2415, $1/30$ sec., processed in D19. Photo by Wolfgang Paech, Germany.*

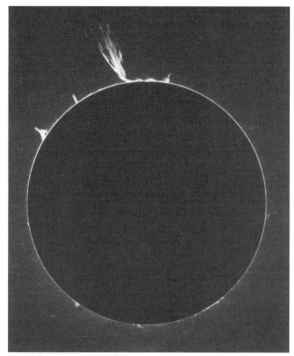

Fig. A.5.10 *Taken June 1, 1991 with a standard refractor 100/1000 mm and a Baader 10Å coronograph on Kodak TP2415 at ¹/₂₅₀ sec. Photo by Jungblut, Germany*

A.5.4.2 Choosing a photographic emulsion

At this time (1995) only one b/w negative film was available which is suitable to photograph chromospheric phenomena: Kodak Technical Pan 2415 (TP 2415). This film was an evolutionary developed from emulsions used by professional solar physicists (Kodak IV-E, V-E, SO 392 and SO 410).

TP 2415 is available as 35-mm (24 mm × 36 mm) film with 36 exposures (very expensive), manufactured on 42 m rolls (good value), as 6 cm × 6 cm roll-film, and as larger format sheet film of almost any size. TP 2415 is also the best choice for lunar and planetary photography, and when hypersensitized, it is the best material for deep sky photography. Last, but not least, it is also well suited for pictorial photography with the proper processing.

For solar photography, the sensitivity of TP 2415 in the red is important, and this emulsion is extremely fine grained. Depending on the object contrast and processing of the film, TP 2415 resolves more than 300 lines/mm. This film will record much more detail than the telescope is capable of delivering which is about 200 lines/mm.

Most emulsions for slides and color negatives are sensitive enough in the red but the images show too little contrast. This is especially true for photographs of the solar surface with a DayStar filter. The available film types are constantly changing in response to demands of the "snap shot" market and therefore, any specific recommendations made today are likely to be invalid tomorrow. The amateur will have to be willing to experiment with each new film as it becomes available and will not be surprised when he learns that even "old" proven films have been modified by the manufacturer without warning!

Whenever possible, the exposed TP 2415 film should not be handed to a laboratory for developing. Otherwise, the film would be treated in a standard process optimized for pictorial photography. Beginners will find some hints in this chapter on how they can develop b/w films and how to make enlargements from the negatives. The following table gives the data for optimum development of TP 2415.

Kodak TP 2415

Object	Developer	Dilution	Time (min.)	Tilt (sec.)	Contrast
Deep Sky	Ilford Dokumol	1 + 9	4–8	30	high
	Tetenal Dokumol	1 + 9	4–8	30	high
Sun	Tetenal Dokumol	1 + 9	4	30	high
white light	D 19	–	4	30	highest
	HC 110	1 + 9	6	30	average
Sun	HC 110	1 + 9	6	30	average
Hα	HC 110	1 + 19	8	30	low
	Neofin blue	1 + 10	about 8	10–30	average
	Rodinal	1 + 50	about 12	10–30	average
Moon &	HC 110	1 + 20	6–8	30	low
planets	HC 110	1 + 10	6	30	average
	Neofin blue	1 + 10	6–8	10–30	average
Pictorial	Technidol	–	about 10	30	lowest
photography					

The column "dilution" specifies with how many parts of water one part of developer concentrate has to be mixed. All development times are given in minutes and assume a developer temperature of 20 degrees Celsius. The column "tilt" lists the time interval at which the developer tray or cannister is to be tilted or agitated during the process. "Contrast" is the ability of the film to reproduce gray-tones. High contrast means few gray-tones (i.e. only black and white), low contrast many gray-tones.

Finally, it should be noted that the sensitivity (ASA, ISO, DIN) decreases with decreasing contrast reproduction—TP 2415 produces low contrast when exposed at 32 ISO (16 DIN) while the negative is high contrast when exposed at 200 ISO (24 Din). On average, the sensitivity and contrast range balance out at about 100 ISO (21 DIN).

The developers D 19, HC 110, and Technidol are from Kodak; Neofin blue is manufactured by Tetenal; and Rodinal by Agfa.

A.5.5 Solar Photography in Violet Light[†]

Photography in short-wave light is not necessarily aimed at higher resolution (as in microphotography), but rather at achieving visibility of the photospheric solar faculae on the whole solar disc. The sky must be very clear for the photographs to be useable. Even fine cirrus clouds will reduce the contrast substantially. The reduction in light intensity towards the limb of the sun (limb darkening) is also more pronounced than with longer-wave light.

Since most refractor lenses are not fully corrected at 400 nm, mirror telescopes are better suited for violet light photography. It is fascinating to observe this spectral range from a purely visual point of view. One problem involves the removal of thermal rays. A lens filter does not let sufficient violet light pass through. To overcome this difficulty, an *uncoated* primary mirror, which can produce double images, can be used. The reverse side can be dulled, but that results in additional scattered light (see Fig. A.3.13). An uncoated main mirror has proven most effective. The back of the mirror should be polished and the area behind the mirror should be finished with a dull black paint. (Directly painting the back of the mirror black can result in heat accumulation within the mirror itself.) UG1 glass (Schott, Mainz, Germany) is used for the eyepiece filter. Since it still transmits red light, UG1 is combined with BG38 glass. At best, both pieces of glass should be mounted in *one* holder with the internal surfaces contacted by microscope objective immersion oil or lens cement to suppress reflections.

When taking photographs of the "violet" sun on orthochromatic film material, there is no need to suppress the red, although differences may result when focusing through teleconverter lens systems.

Those who can afford them should use a UV interference filter. (This filter, with a diameter of roughly 25 mm, is supplied by Schott in Mainz.) The half-width value, at 394 nm (see B.9.1.3), is only 8 to 10 nm, and a clean violet image of the sun without areas of red light is seen in the eyepiece. Through the relatively higher transmission in violet light obtained with the filter combination, a rather bright image is seen, and solar faculae are clearly visible over the whole solar disc. It is important to bear in mind,

---

[†]Written by Wolfgang Lille

however, that it is the *photospheric* faculae which are visible. *Calcium* faculae are only visible or may be photographed at half-width values of a few Å (see B.6).

In addition to an uncoated main mirror, mirror-lens telescopes or mirror-lens telephoto-lenses available on the photographic market (over 1 m focal length) are also suitable. Also required is a UV lens filter, which is mounted in an off-center aperture mask between the tube wall and the secondary mirror holder. It has been found that 49 or 72 mm photo filters, for instance UV black filters, usually have adequately optically parallel and flat surfaces to permit good photographs of the entire solar disk to be taken at a 1 to 2 m focal length. The exposure time is roughly $1/125$ second with the emulsions now (1995) available—Agfaortho 25, Kodalith 6656, or Kodak TP 2415.

A BG38 filter or an interference filter is used in front of the eyepiece or on the camera's focus window for focusing or visual observation. However, it is a fact that older astronomers can barely see the violet image produced with the interference filter, if at all. They must either use no eyepiece or camera filter or else a *yellow filter*.

Filters should be ordered directly from the manufacturer, indicating the specific area of application (1 m focal length). The company will endeavor to supply glass which has been selected accordingly.

A.5.6   Dark Room Techniques[†]

Once film has been exposed, it must be developed and printed on photographic paper. Solar photography requires special development techniques and it is difficult to find a commercial developer willing to do this at an affordable price. The astronomer will, therefore, have to learn these special procedures which can be divided into two areas: film processing and paper printing

A.5.6.1   Film Processing

For the first few rolls of film, the developer and development times specified by the film manufacturer should be observed, or reference should be made to experimental values (Beck, Paech, Remmert 1979; Remmert, Beck 1980). Those who have mastered the actual development technique should not hesitate to experiment. To develop a film, the following procedure should be followed:

1. Rewind the film in the cartridge.

2. Remove the film cartridge from the camera.

[†]Written by Wolfgang Paech and Elmar Remmert

3. Open the film cartridge (*in total darkness*).

4. Cut off the end and trim the corners of this cut, so that the film does not become canted when it is wound onto the developing reel (*in total darkness*).

5. Place the reels with the film wound on in the developing tank and seal this by tightening the lid so that it is light-proof (*in total darkness*).

6. Developer preparation (*in light*). You will need to completely fill the tank with developer. A note of how much fluid the tank holds is usually engraved on the bottom of the tank.

7. Ensure that the developer temperature is precisely 20°C.

8. Next remove the filler cap from the tank (not the whole lid) and fill the tank with developer.

9. Replace the cap on the tank.

10. Agitate the developer tank continuously for the first 30 seconds of the developing time (also turn upside down).

11. After this lightly knock the bottom of the tank several times on the table to remove any air bubbles from the film.

12. Next agitate the tank every 30 seconds for 5 seconds to redistribute the developer fluid evenly.

13. Once the development time is complete, the developer is removed from the tank.

14. Next the tank is filled with water or a stop bath. This removes any remaining developer off the film coating. (Ensure that the water or stop bath is at the same temperature as the developer!) Duration of this process is roughly 30 seconds.

15. After the stop bath has been poured out, the fixer is added. Here, too, ensure that the temperature of the fixer is the same as the developer.

16. Place the cap on the tank and fix for roughly 10 minutes. During fixing the tank should be agitated fairly often to distribute the fluid.

17. Upon completion of the fixing, the film may be checked for the first time in daylight.

18. Next the film is washed for roughly 20 to 30 minutes (observe the temperature) under running water.

19. Once the washing has been completed, the film should be treated briefly in a bath of wetting agent (approximately 30 seconds). This process avoids film spotting from lime residue common in most water.

20. The film is then dried (if possible in a dust-free environment).

21. After drying, the strip of negative is cut into smaller strips convenient for use at the enlarger or for projection. To prevent scratching and to facilitate storage, negatives should be stored in archival "negative envelopes."

While the process sounds very tedious and complicated, it is quickly learned by developing a few rolls of film.

A.5.6.2   Paper Printing

A general description of dark room equipment will not be given here. Beginners are referred to the relevant literature (Spitzing 1979).

A.5.6.2.1 The photographic paper. Nowadays quick acting resin coated paper is used almost exclusively to make photographic prints. It is easy to process, can be dried without presses and has a relatively durable surface. This paper is available in various degrees of contrast:

Paper Grade	No.	Negative
Extra hard	5	flat
Hard	4	soft
Normal	3	normal
Special	2	full
Soft	1	hard

Since the negatives often prove to be extremely varied, it is advisable to have a whole "set" of photographic paper covering all the grades. It is often difficult for the beginner to say from the very start which grade is suitable for a particular negative; however, experience gained over a period of time gives the photographer a feel for the correct combination.

A.5.6.2.2 Adjusting the negative for sharp focus. With the negative placed in the enlarger's negative holder, the focus is set with the enlarger's lens wide open. The image is in sharp focus when the film's grain can be identified. Next the enlarger light is turned off and the lens stopped down (usually two stops). Then the paper is placed in position and exposed.

A.5.6.2.3 Exposure time. To determine the correct exposure time, a piece of paper should be exposed in stages, e.g., at 2-second intervals. Begin by covering most of the paper for the first exposure. Then move the cover to expose another strip. This process is repeated until 5 "strips" on the paper have been exposed. Since the exposure times add up, one will have a sheet with strips which were exposed for 2, 4, 6, 8, and 10 seconds. Of course, it is also possible to cut a piece of photographic paper into strips and then expose these individually. After exposure the sheet or individual strips are developed, and the piece displaying the correct brightness provides us with the exposure time for the final print. It should also be pointed out that the various paper grades also have different sensitivities; the soft paper is the most sensitive, the extra hard, the least sensitive.

Particular problems arise with negatives which show the limb of the solar disk. There are often major brightness fluctuations here, particularly with films developed with too high a contrast. If the photographer wishes to capture, in normal brightness, spots and faculae areas which do not lie in the direct vicinity of the limb of the solar disc, the real limb of the solar disc is completely "absorbed." On the other hand, if the limb of the solar disc is exposed, the print of the solar center becomes increasingly bright so that details are no longer recognizable. This situation is caused by the natural darkening of the solar limb. To solve the problem one must selectively expose various parts of the print. For example, suppose test prints reveal that the direct limb of the solar disc prints properly with a 10-second exposure, but the center of the disc only requires a 2-second exposure to show structures. To print this picture one must, either with the hand or a template, cover the solar disk after a 2-second exposure of the entire picture and then expose the remainder for an additional 8 seconds (10 seconds total). This technique ("dodging" and "burning") requires practice and experience since it is easy to create a disconcerting bright or dark strip between the solar limb and the center of the solar disc.

A.5.6.2.4 Developing the print. As with the negative, the paper is developed, stopped, fixed, and finally washed and dried. The fixer and stop bath are made up of the same chemicals, as with the negative process; however, the developer must be a positive or paper developer and the concentration of stop bath and fixer *may* be different for negatives and *paper*. Its temperature should be roughly 20° C. If it is warmer, it works too quickly and with too high a contrast; if it is too cold, it works more slowly and with little contrast.

The exposed photographic paper is laid in the tray with the developer so that the entire sheet is, as far as possible, wet at the same time. The paper or developer should be constantly moved or agitated during development. Development takes approximately 1 to 2 minutes, depending on the type of developer. Once development is complete, the stop bath follows (approximately 30 seconds), after which the print is fixed, which lasts between 2 and 15 minutes, depending on the paper and chemistry. During the final washing, the remains of the fixing bath are washed from the paper under running water for roughly 15 to 30 minutes. The drying, which concludes the positive process, presents no problems with synthetic paper. The images may be air dried or speeded up with a hairdryer. Resin (synthetic) coated paper should not be dried in a dry press designed for normal (uncoated) paper.

Finally, the photograph details or a negative number should be noted on the reverse side of the print. The printing process is thereby complete. With the exception of dodging and burning, the description given here was limited to standard methods of enlargement. In practice, however, tricks and short-cuts are soon learned or invented to solve problems which arise.

Chapter A.6

Evaluating Photographs

A.6.1 Microdensitometry/Microphotometry[†]

The following section describes a method relating to the photometry (brightness measurement) of photographs along with some examples. This method does not involve determining light intensities on the sun but densities (see A.5.1) on the negative, which is why the term "densitometry" is a more precise description of the process. High (microscopic) resolving power of the equipment used leads to the terms "microdensitometry" or "microdensitometer." Intensities may be calculated from the negative densities (i.e., brightness) and from these, temperatures (see B.2.1).

A.6.2 Principle of the Microdensitometer

The basic equipment consists of a light source, the beam of which passes through an aperture (slit, square, circle, etc.) and crosses a photographic layer where the beam is weakened, depending on the density of the negative. The remaining light intensity of the beam is measured with the aid of a photoelectric device and serves as a measure of the density of the negative at a point which the beam of light has crossed. The negative is placed on a stage which is pushed in the direction of the x-axis. If a line is scanned with a predetermined number of steps, the stage then moves one step in the y-direction and records the densities in the next line. The brightness received by the recording device is converted into a voltage and either printed on paper or, better still, stored on magnetic media. With the aid of magnetic tape or floppy disc and a computer, the wealth of information obtained can be rapidly processed. This computerization is not absolutely necessary,

---

[†]Written by Heinz Hilbrecht

however.

A.6.3   Working Sequence

To carry out evaluations with the aid of the microdensitometer, high resolution photographs should be used unless the aim is simply to determine dimensional ratios in a sunspot, as for instance, with the Wilson effect (section B.4). Once the slit width and step size (i.e., the resolution) have been fixed, possibly after consulting professional astronomers familiar with the equipment concerned, the negative is placed in the movable stage. The starting point and number of steps in the x and y directions are determined by testing so that the field of interest may be scanned. Fully automatic microdensitometers cover the field without assistance, but should, nevertheless, be monitored to prevent errors. It is often sufficient to record individual lines, and thus reduce the quantity of data and amount of time required considerably. The "veil," i.e., the zero offset created by the film base which can be determined at an unexposed point nearby, is measured for each recording to determine the inaccuracy of the measurement and the zero point of the density curve (see A.5.1).

Entering density curves to convert the densities into intensities, a tedious task with the old photometers, has been made very simple by digital methods. By contrast, calculating the density curve itself is more difficult. For calibrating photographs of a light source with various filters, a neutral wedge or pictures of the stars are used for calculating the density curve.

A.6.4   Data Medium

With the objective of the investigation in mind, a suitable data medium for storing the density measurements must be chosen. Customary methods include recorders, which produce the microdensitometer recording on paper by analogue means, or magnetic tapes, where the information can be stored digitally for subsequent evaluation with the aid of a computer.

1. **Recorder.** An analogue recording is recommended when measuring dimensions in the spot. Figure A.6.1 shows a recording which was undertaken using a microdensitometer belonging to the Kiepenheuer Institute (Freiburg, FRG). Dimensional ratios can easily be measured, but may also be determined under the measuring microscope. The disadvantage of this method is the mechanical inertia of the recorder. Modern apparatuses have a coordinate display (in micrometers), which means that analogue recording is redundant.

2. **Magnetic tape or disc.** Scanning the corona (C.2.3) easily requires several tens of thousands of steps, the information content of which can no longer be used with the recorder method. Consequently, the user should

have experience dealing with computers. One thousand microdensitometer steps are usually sufficient for spots, which means that electronic data processing is not always strictly necessary.

Programs written to evaluate the data are usually available at professional institutions devoted to this speciality. The more powerful versions of the nearly ubiquitous personal computer can often run adaptations of this software.

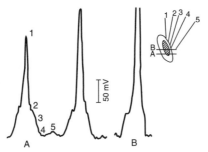

Fig. A.6.1. *Density trace of an H-spot. 1 = umbra, 2 = inner bright ring, 3 = penumbra, 4 = outer bright ring, 5 = photosphere.*

A.6.5 Tips on Preparation and Implementation

Because time and equipment are limited, detailed preparation in advance is necessary. First, the goals and method of the investigation should be precisely thought out and set down in writing. Next, the work schedule is reviewed with the scientists at the institute, who assess its feasibility and suggest improvements. Unless there are powerful arguments to the contrary, astronomical institutes support effective programs. A powerful argument may be large-scale utilization of the equipment by institute members; however, spare capacity is often available during the summer astronomy season.

A.6.6 Microdensitometry Applications

If the size of a picture element is greater than the grain size of the film being scanned, the grain noise is suppressed and extensive areas of faint densities become visible. Equidensities achieve this in principle, but the digital method is the most flexible and permits the grain noise to be subsequently reduced, if necessary. Weak structures which are not visible on the original negative, such as coronal streamers (see Part C) (Martinez 1978), lunar formations with total solar eclipses, or the

Fig. A.6.2. *PDS microdensitometer: Width of slit 50μ, point interval 30μ, original dimensions 15 × 15 mm, 501 times 501 points. Computer: Cyber 172 MPIfR, K. Reif, P. Steffen (Bonn University). Original Izaña, Tenerife Oct. 13, 1979, 09.33, 40 cm Newton reflecting telescope belonging to the Kiepenheuer Institute Freiburg, pos: 10 N, 25 W (U. Grossmann-Doerth, W. Schmidt).*

two bright rings in sunspots, become visible (see B.2.1). Following are further possible applications for digital picture processing: color charts of the corona or sunspots made by combining photographs in various spectral ranges; digital evaluation of rapid changes, e.g., young sunspots, prominences, flares; automatic evaluation of the area and number of spots in a group of sunspots; enhancement of faint details in umbra and penumbra by increasing the contrast.

In many cases, digital microdensitometry permits the resolution of very close structures which converge into one image on the original negative. If the diffraction pattern of a pointed structure, e.g., that of a star, is known, the image of a planar structure can be "developed" in a computer so that the individual components become visible. If the grain noise is to be suppressed without a loss of resolution, several photographs must be digitally combined. For example, if several photographs of the solar photosphere are taken at about 5 minute intervals and digitally combined, the granulation "noise" can be suppressed to make the white light network visible.

To calculate the distribution of the polarizing degree and angle in the solar corona (see Section C.2.3), photographs taken using a polarizing filter which can be digitally scanned and combined in a computer must be available.

The most varied displays can be obtained from a digitized photograph: isophotes (lines of the same intensity), black-and-white charts or colored charts. The various images on a television screen can be used to produce an animated sequence on tape or film.

A.6.7 Final Observations

Since computer programs are available for work in astronomy institutes, the main problem facing the amateur is probably gaining access to the equipment. The path to follow is via the local astronomy association, which then contacts the astronomy institute. That organization usually lends a sympathetic ear because all the projects referred to above are of scientific value.

The reason for the emphasis placed on computers in the final part of this section is the wealth of opportunities which they provide. Many of the evaluations may also be achieved photographically (noise suppression, equidensities, trick film), and recorders are often completely adequate for investigations into sunspots (see Section A.6.17). Our sole aim is to obtain data—the sunspot itself can be viewed to greater effect through the telescope.

Chapter A.7

Digital Image Processing[†]

This chapter introduces basic aspects of image processing systems and their application in amateur solar observation. There will be no detailed discussion of today's products (software and hardware) because the technology is evolving so rapidly that what is written today almost certainly will soon be out-of-date. Here I will deal with the fundamental considerations of image processing which should remain constant during most, if not all of this book's lifetime.

A.7.1 Introduction

Image processing systems need to be tailored exactly to the needs of the user. Therefore, the first step in planning a system is to answer the question "What do I want to do with image processing?". Standard processing includes simple gray scale operations like contrast enhancement or color coding, filter operations (smoothing, sharpening of the image), and geometric measurements. These functions are all available in standard image processing software. Dedicated hardware (signal processors) provides such functionality at very high speed (for a price) which is only necessary in real time image processing, i.e., manipulation of images at video rate (24 images or more per second). This is usually not required in amateur solar observation. Therefore, the standard image processing system of the amateur consists of five parts: the image generating system, the frame grabber that digitizes the image, a personal computer, archiving devices for the digitized images, and image processing software. The general design of such a system is shown in Fig. A.7.1.

[†]Written by Heinz Hilbrecht

99

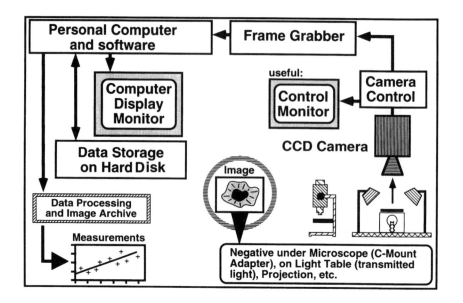

Fig. A.7.1. *A PC-based image analysis system*

A.7.1.1   The Image Generating System

This part of the system has nothing to do with image processing but it should be considered with great care because the quality of the processed image depends on the quality of the image you begin with. No scientifically legitimate system can add resolution or details to the image that have not been recorded. Some of the myths in image processing include that images can be "improved" with this technique. This is nonsense. Strictly speaking images can be altered in various ways. They look different after processing, relevant information can be effectively extracted, other features can be suppressed.

Most images will be generated using photographic techniques or with a CCD camera attached to a telescope. Digitizing photographs is a technique with unique considerations. For example, the range of gray levels in a negative is compressed when printed on photographic paper. Thus, one should use the negative and not a print because it will contain more data. To image a negative one should use a light table (essentially a diffuse light source coming from "below" the negative placed on a glass plate), and/or a microscope (low magnification) with light again coming from a microscope illuminator through the negative. Other methods might also be practical as long as the light can be projected through the negative to the imaging

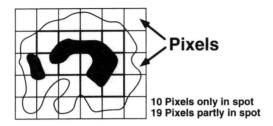

Fig. A.7.2. *Resolution and precision of measurements depends on the number of pixels in an object. Under low magnification only a small amount of pixels fall in a feature on the sun, e.g., a sunspot. Finally, areas will not be determined very accurately and in the extreme case shown here most pixels will cover the feature only partly. The resulting image is blurred. Such problems occur when the entire sun is digitized and measurements shall be performed (total sunspot area on disk). It is better to measure every sunspot separately and to add areas of individual sunspots after geometric correction for distance from the center of the sun.*

device. Once evenly illuminated the image on the negative can be captured to a CCD video camera. The biggest problem in this procedure is to achieve even illumination across the entire negative. As a rule, more even illumination can be achieved over smaller fields of view.

Uneven illumination can occur if the light source is smaller than the image. The image processing system can be used to determine inhomogeneities in illumination through analysis of the brightness distribution of the image, of the light table, or along lines across the image. Some compensation for uneven illumination results when a negative is digitized and the background (without negative) is subtracted from this image (image subtraction). This technique is sufficient for analyses of morphologic features in the image but densitometric or photometric results remain unreliable.

Heat emitted by the light source can destroy a negative. A cooling fan or "cold light" should be used. The negative is sandwiched between glass plates (from photographic or microscopic equipment) to hold it parallel to the camera's focal plane and to absorb heat.

The CCD camera is a critical component. Its geometric and photometric accuracy sets an overall limit to the accuracy of image processing results. There probably are inexpensive cameras on the market which may produce good results, however, they were designed for home video and in a home video camera demands on photometric accuracy are lower and damaged pixels go unnoticed by users. However, for our purposes, damaged pixels are CCD elements with unreliable output values. Ideally, a

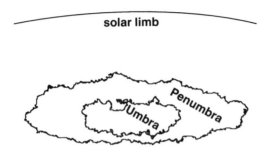

Fig. A.7.3. *Outline detection for umbra and penumbra of a sunspot with the Wilson effect. Automated measurement procedures can find the center of gravity of each feature easily and will return more reliable results than manual measurements. Ideally, such measurements are made from photographic negatives with a CCD camera attached to a microscope. The amount of magnification depends on the object's size on the negative and the required pixel resolution.*

CCD camera for image processing should be free of geometric distortion (square pixels, but most video CCD chips run in a rectangular pixel mode) and nearly all the pixels should be working to specification. The relevant data covering these and other considerations should be available in the CCD chip data sheets (not necessarily in the camera specifications; find out the chip manufacturer and type). An acceptable camera costs about $1000 (in 1994) but one should not rely on price to determine suitablity—check the specifications and test the camera with the same care one would do with a cheaper camera.

Most cameras have automatic gain control and automatic black level adjustment. These convenient features are problematic in photometric applications because the camera will change its characteristics between the images. This becomes a serious problem when you move the negative after density calibration (gray wedge exposed on the film) to a solar feature exposed on another part of the film. Automatic cameras can be used in analyses of morphologic features but still problems may occur. Manual adjustment of camera characteristics is always preferable. Ideally you will have a camera with a simple switch that allows you change between automatic or manual mode—all too often this switch is sacrificed only to make the camera smaller (which is prestigious in the consumer video market).

A.7.1.2   The Frame Grabber

Images have to be converted into digital format for processing with the computer. This may be accomplished with a scanner or frame grabber. The latter provides the most convenient way. Scanners, because they are mechanical devices, are susceptible to geometric distortions and falsifications of the brightness relationships within the image. Scanners are therefore a second choice for quantitative applications (geometric measurements, densitometry).

Frame grabber cards are plugged in to the computer bus and convert the analogue electric signal from a camera to a digital form understood by the computer. Recently (about 1993) very inexpensive frame grabbers have appeared on the market which should be regarded with caution. Often they produce images of reduced resolution, geometric distortions, noise, or alter the gray level relations within the image. Good frame grabbers cost about $1000 and more in 1994. The frame grabber is central in an image processing system. Note that many of them have gained their reputation in desk top publishing applications. Excellent frame grabbers exist which, however, produce a constant reduction in distances in one direction in the image. Two lines of equal length are then different in x- and y-axis in the digitized image and will be treated that way by the computer. Finally, you will find that your sunspots are always a little oval in shape by a few percent. We have higher demands on geometric correctness of the image. Make tests and ask for exact specifications! Possibly you can correct for such inaccuracies in your image processing output if the error is constant. However, how many tests do you need to confirm this constancy?

A.7.1.3 The Personal Computer

The faster the computer the more convenient the image processing. Eight to ten megabytes of RAM should be available—more is always preferable. Virtual memory may expand the possibilities but it is very slow. Some older machines do not have a floating point processor which is essential for compatibility with many image processing applications. A large hard disk makes life easier—a typical image is several hundred kilobytes but it does not take long to accumulate megabyte size directories with only a few individual files. Often the numeric output from automatic measurement procedures eats up much disk and RAM space. Finally, a gray scale monitor (8 bits or more) is the essential minimum. My advice is not scrimp when choosing a monitor—a big screen with a stable image is expensive but you will work with it for hours on end—bad monitors cause headaches and are hard on your eyes.

A.7.1.4 Archiving Images

An archiving system is essential because numerous images have to be stored. This may be on disks but the normal 1.4 MB disk will only hold about 3–4 images. Over the long run disks will be expensive and frustrating storage media. The alternatives are magnetic tape or magneto-optical disks. These media provide capacity of several hundred megabytes and the "price per megabyte" is low. Review the amount of images you take, the price for disks and mass storage systems and find out which type of archiving system is the most cost effective for your purposes. Magneto-optical disks ("rewritable CD's") are the most flexible. Tapes or magneto-optical disks may also be used for backups of your hard disk. Data compression software is very efficient on images and should be part of the archiving system for those images that are not frequently used.

A.7.1.5   Image Processing Software

Software is the most dynamic part on the image processing market. Take time to make comparisons—one can easily spend large sums of money on software that does not meet your purposes. A good program provides you with the functionality your specific work requires—make this the first consideration when you explore the market. Other factors to consider are the on-line software support and the documentation should be excellent and easily accessible because image processing software tends to be complicated and not very "user friendly." You will have questions and you can spend weeks working out the answers by yourself if nobody gives you the right answers on the phone.

I have not yet found the ideal image processing software. There is always something I need that is not available in an application. Therefore, do not buy a product that is not expandable. Modern image processing software allows the user to write code and to attach its functionality to the commercially distributed software product. "Programmable" in this sense is not the macro feature which is standard in competitive products. Macros allow the user to record steps in an image processing procedure (which may consist of the application of many features in an application) and to repeat them automatically. This recording should be done automatically by the software. Macros in a strict sense, however, do not allow the user to add new algorithms to the software. You need an interface to your self-written software and documentation of links to your commercial product. Many applications provide an interpreter that allows you to write code in a specific interpreter language. Some like this approach—I hate it. Why should I learn an inefficient and slow programming language that is only useful in combination with a single program in a particular field of application? Do you learn Chinese for a one-week holiday trip? Extensive libraries of image processing algorithms exist that can not be plugged into your system! Most popular programming languages in image processing are PASCAL (good) and C (better, because it is faster).

How much money you spend on software depends on your specified needs. Demo versions of the software often provide sufficient insight into how a product works upon which to base a purchase decision. We can take advantage of market place competition. Prices tend to be high (but I have never bought an image processing program at list price). Discounts for educational institutions (schools, universities, public observatories) are often a software supplier practice.

The alternative is NIH-Image. This software runs on a Macintosh computer and is distributed as freeware by the National Institute of Health of the United States of America. As these programs go, it is very user friendly and has all functionality that is characteristic of a professional image processing application. This includes filtering and object segmentation algorithms, image stacking, animation of successive series of images, and graphics. It can handle look-up tables very easily. Look-up tables are used to convert gray values into calibrated units, e.g., densities of a photographic image into brightness, brightness into temperatures. It provides tools for geometric characterization of areal objects, such as sunspots, and landmark measurements (distances, angles) with simple mouse clicks in the image. The program can be expanded with code that can be written in a well documented programming language derived from PASCAL. The documentation is provided with the software as a computer file and is therefore available on the screen or as a printed hardcopy.

NIH-Image supports Data Translation and Scion frame grabbers. The Scion frame grabber may have geometric problems. NIH-Image requires a Macintosh with at least 2 megabytes of memory, but 4 megabytes or more are recommended. It requires a monitor with the ability to display 256 colors or shades of gray.

NIH-Image is written for the Macintosh computer. You can get the latest version through the World Wide Web or anonymous ftp from `ftp://zippy.nimh.nih.gov/pub/nih-image/` including sourcecode, macros, and extensive documentation.

I regret to say, after much investigation, that similar freeware is not known to me for other hardware platforms. Systems running under UNIX may be an exception because many user groups provide software or algorithms that can be compiled with freeware compilers (mostly C). Such software needs skill and time for evaluation. I am amazed by NIH-Image because it is a professional software that is user friendly and allows the user to concentrate on the scientific problem rather than the handling of the computer system.

A.7.2 Planning an Image Processing System

"What shall I buy?" is a frequently asked question. My answer is: "What do you need?". If this question is properly answered, the decision is made easy and a system tailored to your requirements can be designed. In this phase ask many people for their experiences and try to obtain "hands-on" experience with image processing systems. First, you should know the basics of image processing which you may start to learn from the books referenced in this chapter. Buy as late as possible—computer-related equipment tends to decrease in price and you may be able to buy at a lower price if you purchase hardware that the market regards as obsolete. If possible do not buy at all and try to use existing systems that are properly maintained (maintenance is important and time consuming).

Image processing requires a system and should be planned as such. The various components interact with each other. This is most obvious in the software component which does not support all frame grabbers available on the market and will run on a specified hardware platform. Therefore, the planning should start with the selection of the software and all other components should be assembled around it. Prices can be surprisingly low. If you consider NIH-Image, you need a Macintosh computer plus a frame grabber (about $1000) and a camera (about $1000 for a good camera) to be operational. Other computer systems may be less expensive but the price of the software (you may not find a good freeware for other platforms) must be added to the hardware costs. Prices need to be evaluated as system costs rather than as prices for single components. Because image processing software can be rather expensive, you may even decide to buy a new computer to run cheaper software to reduce your system costs.

The other aspect is also economic: how often do you use your system? Most computers are used sporadically because the image processing happens rather quickly. Obtaining images at the telescope and data processing are the common bottlenecks. Consequently, the computer should also have data processing software installed on it (i.e., statistics and spreadsheet software). Some graphics programs still can not handle images stored in TIFF format. This is essential—it is the most widely used format because it does not alter the gray levels in an image. Other formats, e.g., PICT, may have problems in the accurate handling of gray level information. If you are linked to a network that gives you access to information systems via gopher or world wide web you can obtain satellite images in GIF format from many sources. The software you need for the transfer is available via Internet ("ftp," consult a handbook on networks).

Image archiving software (image database and access software) will become essential over some time. Good software exists as freeware and can be obtained through freeware services or networks. Be aware that all software evolves and the hardware requirements increase rather quickly so it is often wise to have a few more megabytes of RAM, a larger hard disk, and a really good monitor capable of moving with this trend. The multi-tasking capabilities of modern personal computers allow you to handle image processing, the software manual or help feature, data processing software, and file handling all simultaneously (provided you have enough RAM). On a big monitor this can be real fun when you have all windows open and can switch quickly between applications to see what is happening.

A.7.3 Applications

The potential of an image processing system for amateur solar observation is large. The occasional user, however, needs advice or time consuming testing. Serious applications should be planned according to the normal scientific procedure:

1. specification of scientific goals,
2. selection of methods,
3. definition of the work schedule including observational aspects, data extraction and evaluation procedures.

Image processing helps in the data extraction process. It may be useful during observation (CCD camera on the telescope) but usually it is more fun to obtain many images when the conditions are good and to reserve the processing to a cloudy day.

Most image processing systems are quite capable of spectacular image manipulations. For example, if you like color, the raw images can be color coded by transforming gray values into color. If this is your objective you can save a lot of money by writing a simple program that performs this operation—certainly this procedure does not justify a sophisticated image processing program.

Professional color coding extracts physical information. Imagine a photographic image with a gray scale wedge on the same film. If you extract the density variation and correlate it with the photometric brightness variation across the wedge you can define an input look-up table for your image processing system. The software transforms densities into brightness and thus physically meaningful units. Ideally, brightness can be transformed into temperatures and finally you may create a temperature map of the sun. The limitation lies in the effects of seeing and the telescope which

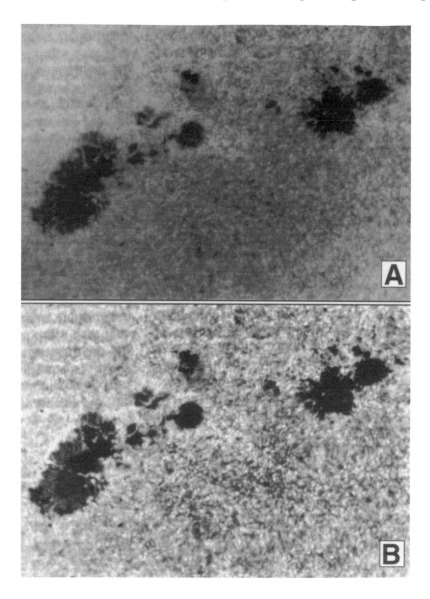

Fig. A.7.4. *Photograph with strong variation in background brightness caused by various artifacts (A). Image after background homogenization with NIH-Image 1.52 software. Note better contrast and definition of features in the granulation and penumbrae. Printed with Laser printer. Original photo: Oct. 7, 1993, by W. Lille, Stade/Germany.*

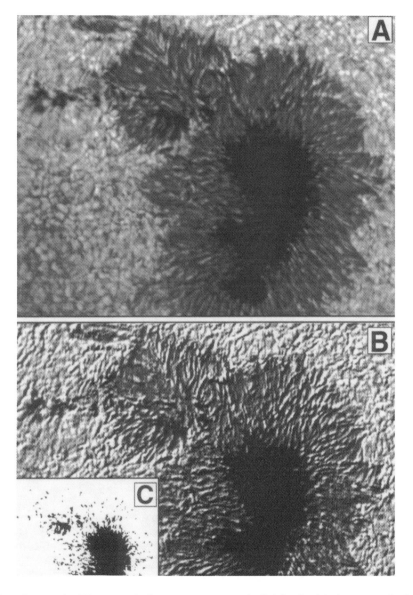

Fig. A.7.5. A: *Photograph (positive, on paper) digitized with image analysis system (CCD camera); B: Shadow filter increases visibility of structure in the image; C: Binary image after thresholding (black: all gray values below a certain level to detect umbral objects). Original photo: May 22, 1992, by W. Lille Stade/Germany (photographic processing by E. Slawik).*

introduce artifacts to the image. It is possible to reduce these effects to a minimum but this is not trivial even for professional scientists.

The most powerful application that I see for amateur solar image processing lies in the extraction of geometric measurements. While "playing" with colors is possible in any software that calls itself an image processing system, large differences exist in their ability to measure either landmarks or shape parameters in a user-friendly way. Landmarks are point coordinates, distances, or angles in arbitrary units. The basic unit in image processing is the pixel. It should be possible to quickly calibrate the system in real world units, e.g., arc seconds or kilometers on the sun. Some software displays an "electronic ruler" on the image which can be placed between points of measurements with the mouse. This is often very time consuming. It is more convenient if the user specifies "distance measurement" or "angle" with a mouse click on a symbol and then clicks on the points in the image between which the measurement has to be performed. The result should be displayed in a data window and saved to a file.

Computer-support is very useful when geometric properties of areal objects shall be analyzed. The area of sunspots or prominences can be measured within seconds. The procedure is simple: you specify the gray value that defines the margin of the feature, the software marks all pixels above or below this threshold and returns geometric measurements, such as area, center of gravity (good basis for determination of positions), diameter, and much more to describe shape. This technique allows one to discriminate between umbra and penumbra which can be measured separately. On the focal image of the sun on a photograph you can extract areas of sunspots and faculae in two steps: first, detect (segmentation in the language of image processing) dark objects on bright background first (sunspots) and second, bright objects on dark background. This may be even done "on line" with the camera mounted on the telescope. The only problem in such application is resolution. Calculate the number of pixels that cover the objects of interest to estimate your resolution. If you cover the sun with an image 512×512 pixels wide you achieve a resolution of about the diameter of the sun divided by 512. This is not very much. You can achieve higher precision with higher magnification.

If you wish to correct areas for limb foreshortening you can segment the sun and determine the center of gravity and its diameter in the image. With the center of gravity of the sunspot you have all numeric values available. The coordinates are transferred to a spreadsheet and corrections can be done. A similar procedure may be applied for measurements of the Wilson effect.

The photographic negative contains a wider range of gray values than can be captured on photographic paper. In a sunspot photograph printed to paper you will usually see a dark umbra that is just black (all information lost) while the penumbra, and the photosphere will be partly overexposed, however, these same phenomena will be displayed in much greater detail on the negative that made the print. Photographic techniques, e.g., "unsharp masking," exist to overcome this problem but it takes time in the photographic laboratory. In principle this is much easier done with image processing. The major limitation, however, is the 8-bit range of gray levels available in most systems. The 256 gray levels are nothing compared to the sensitivity of the human eye. Systems show up on the PC market that provide 16-bit or 32-bit image processing but the processing of the data requires fast processors and file handling. Recent advances in computers demonstrate that this bottleneck in image processing on personal computers will eventually be reduced or eliminated.

Until you have your new 16- or 32-bit number cruncher you may use the following procedure to overcome your 8-bit limitations. With a manually adjustable camera you take three images, each ideally exposed for features in the umbra, the penumbra and the photosphere. The software can isolate these features either manually or with a gray level based algorithm and the rest of the image is removed. Then you perform a histogram equalization that would stretch the gray levels in each image over the entire 8-bit range. When you have done this with all three sub-images you can combine them into one image where each feature covers the same gray level range, and structure in them will be equally well visible. Such photographs show gradation and interaction between features in the umbra, penumbra, and the photosphere that is otherwise seldom extracted from a negative to a photographic print. In the same way, you may superimpose images of the chromosphere (filter observations) and the photosphere (white light) to see relations of structures in the different height levels of the sun, or corona images in combination with structure on the disk.

Chapter A.8

Recording Solar Structure Movements[†]

A.8.1 Introduction

There remains one further, more "exotic" field of amateur solar observation: the recording of the movements in the solar photosphere and chromosphere by photographic means, i.e., taking a series of sequential photographs and then rephotographing the resulting prints on cine film by the single frame technique.

A.8.2 Areas of Application

To begin with, I would like to point out that the animation techniques I will describe are not restricted to making movements on the sun visible. Of course, they may be used for all such undertakings with integrated light pictures (changes in position within a group, the development of light bridges, sunspot separation, eclipses, etc.) and Hα pictures (prominences/filaments [Völker 1980], chromospheric faculae, flares [Völker 1978], etc.). There are, however, further applications: for lunar observers, the appearance of mountains at the terminator, lunar phases, the course of lighting in individual craters, lunar eclipses, star and planet occultations, etc.; for planet observers, planet rotation with large instrument photographs, moon movements (for Jupiter a 2-inch instrument is adequate), changes in the openings of Saturn's rings (over 15 and 29 years), phases of Mercury and Venus, etc.; even the apparent rotation of the sky about the poles can be filmed (a photographic camera without a telescope is sufficient). The reader no doubt can extend this list of ideas.

[†]Written by Peter Völker

A.8.3   8-mm Movie Cameras[†]

Brägger and Moser (1964) have demonstrated how films of prominences can be produced on 8-mm reversal film using commercially available Super-8 cameras. As those amateurs having decided on this option will find everything they need to know in this still up-to-date article, I will not go into this method again.

Lille describes here how an 8-mm camera can be attached to the telescope:

It would be best if a camera, such as a cine-camera, could be used in the same way as a common 35-mm still camera. Unfortunately, the objective lenses of most Super-8 cameras cannot be removed except for a small number of expensive models. Nearly all 16-mm cameras do not have this limitation. With cameras having permanently mounted objective lenses, an additional optical device has to be inserted between the telescope and the camera to get a properly sized image of the sun on the film. With this intermediate lens in place, the new focal length is determined as follows:

$$\frac{\text{Telescope Focal Length}}{\text{Focal Length of Intermediate Optical Lens}} \times \text{Super} - 8 \text{ Zoom Focal Length}$$

For example, with a 60/700 mm telescope and an intermediate optical lens

1. objective 85 mm focal length, diaphragm 1:1.5 or

2. achromatic 85 mm focal length 40 mm diameter

The camera's zoom lens has a focal length of 8 to 48 mm; in this case, with the above formula and the telescope's focal length of 700 mm, we have:

$$\frac{700}{85} \times (8 \text{ to } 48) = 66 \text{ to } 396 \text{ mm is the new zoom range.}$$

This combination, therefore, provides only a good half of the focal length of the main instrument. The full telescope focal length is reached only if the additional optical device has the maximum focal length of the zoom lens. A 50 mm photographic objective could achieve this effect, but the small diameter of the zoom's front element produces strong vignetting, particularly in combination with the lower focal length ranges of the zoom

---

[†]Throughout the world 8 mm is virtually unobtainable and Super-8 is almost so. Processors for the films are also few. However, we include this section from the original edition because some people will overcome these problems and because the technical problems (removable objectives, etc.) are the same with video cameras. Further, today only film cameras operate properly in frame by frame technique. Video cameras now only allow steps of 6–8 frames (no smooth movement). Eventually this problem will be overcome and video will allow smooth animation.

lens. Only very fast 50 mm objectives with an aperture ratio of 1.2 to 1.4 can be used. Better still would be an equally fast 80 to 100 mm focal length lens. A reduction in the size of the picture cannot, however, be avoided. Some long focal length zooms have larger front elements but the last element is a long way away from the front element and consequently these lenses usually produce strong vignetting. The additional optical device and zoom lens are joined together front lens to front lens using filter rings.

The simplest procedure would be to use short focal length achromats with a diameter between 40 and 50 mm. The inlet and outlet apertures are equally large in this type lens, and the short distance between the front and rear elements produces hardly any vignetting. However, the picture quality is not good. With the achromats' short focal lengths (under 150 mm), only the center of the image is more or less sharp.

It would be better to use a camera without its lens, which would make it possible to preserve the full focal length of the telescope. Such a camera could also be used with a prominence attachment to film active prominences. The camera should also have a single-frame mechanism and, possibly, a range of operational speeds. Additionally, a cable release mechanism is important. I have converted very simple cameras without a cable release and subsequently attached a cable release mechanism. For slow motion shots, the 18 f.p.s. speed has to be released as quickly as possible. Simpler cameras do have the advantage that the distance between the front of the lens mount flange and the film is approximately that of a 35-mm still camera.

The objective lens is removed from the camera body and a short 42 mm photographic intermediate ring is attached to the front lens mount flange so that an objective set for infinity shows a sharp image on the film of a distant object (chimney, lamppost). To make the film plane image visible, a small matte disk is taped to the film stage (matte side towards the objective), and the camera is set for continuous operation.

Now comes the most difficult part of the process—conversion of the finder system. Since a beam splitter has to be inserted into the optical path, the diaphragm system and color film conversion filter, neither of which is necessary for filming, are usually removed. For normal filming with photographic objectives, a color film conversion filter is attached in front of the optics. The diaphragm for the corresponding film speed is determined by using the camera's internal light measuring device or with a standard hand held exposure meter. It is best if the finder's image emerges from the top or side of the housing. Focusing is accomplished by adjusting the optics until the object is sharply defined in the finder (aerial view, therefore a matte focusing screen cannot be used).

With larger cameras with zoom lenses, the distance between the front plate and the film is bridged with a fixed teleconverter. The existing beam splitter is then altered in the following manner.

Usually a two part system is present. Light for the finder and light for the photographic cell are deviated. This second separator is dismantled (we retain it in the simple camera). The first separator is turned through 90° (light now goes upwards). The housing is bored out and the finder optics from the rear of the camera are used as the finder system. Somewhat more difficult is the removal of the basic optics (just in front of the film stage). Usually they can be unscrewed and the approximately 20 mm focal length lens used as a finder eyepiece.

Once one understands the optical design of a zoom lens and if the converted camera is to be used for filming without a telescope, the following can be attempted in addition to telephoto lenses. A 60 mm photographic objective is located in front of the camera. The built-in converter provides a focal length of 120 mm. This combination is now nothing other than the new basic optics (vis-á-vis an original 20 mm which is now six times longer). In front of this combination there is a small photographic intermediate ring with a built in iris diaphragm to which is attached the previously removed zoom. The basic optics increase the zoom range by a factor of 6, which is now 48 to 288 mm, and supplements the normal focal length range of a Super-8 camera.

Maximum light intensity is determined by the rear lens opening (around 11 mm) of the zoom, which in turn becomes the inlet opening for the 60 mm photographic objective (system focal length with converter 120 mm). The diaphragm is thus $120/11$ = aperture 11. By reducing the size of the iris diaphragm, which is located in the parallel path of rays, smaller apertures can be set (16 and 22). As the zoom part is now heavily overloaded optically, filming should only be with f/16 or f/22.

For filming the entire solar disk (with attached grey filter), for solar eclipses, and for animal and landscape pictures in sunshine, f/16 and f/22 can be used. However, if the additional features found on expensive Super-8 cameras are to be utilized, tele-attachments can be employed (similar to wide angle attachments). With a front element diameter of about 110 mm and an enlargement factor of 1 : 1.7 these multi-lens attachments (weighing over 1 kg) are extremely expensive and not very effective. The light intensity of the basic optics is preserved, however, and films of lunar eclipses can be made. Solar eclipse films with reproduction of the middle and outer corona are also quite possible. A polarization filter can be rotated to emphasize the polarization of the corona.

A.8.4   Film Type Availability

Color reversal films do not record the full range of information which can be obtained by a fine grain black and white material (photosphere) or Kodak Spectroscopic material (chromosphere). All professional solar observatories use 35-mm film: it is available both as 35-mm cassettes or in 150-ft rolls for 35-mm cine-cameras. Dürst (1969) and Müller (1965) describe the equipment and operation of such apparatus. Kodak will not supply the special emulsions in Super-8 format, even if large quantities are ordered; therefore, if the amateur wishes to film using this material, there are three possible courses of action. The first of these can only be used for 16-mm and 8-mm films, and is not practical for Super-8 (due to the spooling of the material on a cassette). A splitting and perforating machine is built which "cuts" 16 or double 8-mm films from the 35-mm film. Making or purchasing such a machine is worth considering for those desiring a wider range of film emulsions, despite the fact that all film processing (after construction of the actual machine) has to be carried out in the dark.

A.8.5   35-mm Cine-camera

The second option is the most elegant—a 35-mm cine-camera. This equipment can cost thousands of dollars; however, it is possible to work with this medium for a much more modest expenditure. All we require is a 35-mm film advance and film cassette system (the heart of the camera). We do not need an expensive objective lens as our lens will be the telescope. Even an old camera made of wood with a hand crank drive will do. The movement of the individual pictures takes place manually in this example, and exposure is through an old-fashioned shutter. The exposure time is determined by a series of test exposures.

Many camera dealers sell a reasonably priced complete 35-mm system, consisting of a camera housing, three cassettes, objectives, batteries, motor and metal case. Even bought second-hand, they usually include complete documentation and a guarantee. Simpler equipment can be found at even lower prices with a little luck by dealing directly with the individual owners.

Using a 100-foot role of film, you can record events which will run for 1.5 minutes when projected at 24 frames per second. Since commercial film developers cannot process your film, you must do it yourself. Therefore, you will have to purchase special 20 or 30 m tanks and use the appropriate chemistry.

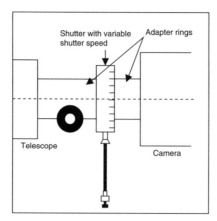

Fig. A.8.1. *Connection of a 35-mm camera housing to a telescope with a shutter as an intermediate piece.*

Once you have assembled your equipment, exposed the film and developed it, you can use the film in a variety of ways:

1. The individual frames can be evaluated with a measuring microscope to measure movements within an activity center. If necessary, this can also be done by projecting the negatives frame by frame and copying the positions to evaluate them at a later stage.

2. At any time photographic enlargements can be produced as the cine-film format is half that of the 35-mm format so that the grain does not cause problems. Even equidensitometric or photometric evaluations are possible.

3. Finally, the movements of the activities recorded in slow motion can be viewed in projection. For those without a 35-mm projector, the negative has to be copied to 16-mm, Normal 8 or Super-8. However, this process is inexpensive as it involves black and white film, and the copying labs will only charge for the regular price of the end product (30 m of 35-mm film = 12 m of 16-mm film or approximately 6 m of 8-mm film).

A.8.6   Sequential Photographic Prints

If a 35-mm cine-camera cannot be acquired, there is a third option for producing a film for which available 35-mm equipment can be used. Extensive darkroom work will be required, however, as frame by frame animated techniques are used to produce the final film strip. The advantage for the amateur is that he can capture the full information of the 35-mm negative and shoot prepared solar photographs directly on Super-8 film. I will describe the exact procedure. Once an interesting activity center has been observed through the telescope where it is suspected that noticeable changes will occur within the next few minutes or hours, a large number of pictures are taken in the usual way. Precise details of the time should be noted for each picture as it is easy when making many pictures to lose track of the details which would render all the work useless with regard to subsequent evaluation.

The number of pictures required and the interval at which they are taken depends on the intended running time of the film. The calculations for this process are described below. These pictures form the starting point for our animated series. Once the 35-mm pictures have been developed in the usual way, we can begin working on them.

First, each negative's density should be checked. Since the pictures have been taken close together, you will probably find that the densities are more or less identical. However, you may detect a continuous change throughout the sequence which is the result of the varying height of the sun above the horizon—this should not be a problem. What you should be particularly alert for are defective frames (fuzzy exposures from shaking, aircraft in front of the sun, etc.). These should be removed (marked) beforehand. If you find great variations in density from one frame to another (e.g., due to unfavorable weather), further processing is not recommended. Rapid changes in frame density will produce strong flickering when the film is run. Density variation-caused flicker cannot be "masked" or "averaged out" by the 18 to 24 frames the eye "sees" per second during projection. If the negatives are in order and if there was "enough" activity on the sun to make a film interesting, production of the animated film can begin. Basically a paper enlargement of each picture is made, and these positives are then filmed again with the Super-8 camera in the same sequence as the images were obtained at the telescope. On projecting the finished Super-8 film, we see the processes in motion.

A.8.6.1 Peg Bar

The most important prerequisite for steady movement is that all the images are registered *exactly* to each other. If they do not, the picture will dance and jerk about and all your work will be in vain. Therefore every picture has registration holes punched in it, and a peg bar ensures that the positions of the individual prints can no longer be displaced with regard to each other. To construct a peg bar, a strip of rigid card stock is punched with a paper punch and the holes measured. We next must purchase two rivets which tightly fit these holes. Rivets usually can be purchased at the hardware store. You should take your punched card to the store since the rivets are mass produced and are not identical, at least not to the degree of accuracy we require. You will probably have to sort through a number of "identical" rivets to find several that meet your requirements. Once

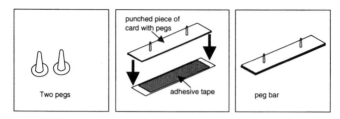

Fig. A.8.2. *Making a peg bar.*

two have been found, the heads are passed through the perforations and a second card strip (with no holes) is stuck underneath with double-sided tape to make the projecting pegs acquire the necessary rigidity. Our peg bar is ready (Fig. A.8.2). Anyone possessing a lathe can produce the pegs for the peg bar. The unexposed photographic paper on which the photographic sequence is to be produced is then punched using the same punch (in the dark or with suitable safety lights).

A.8.6.2   Template

Now comes the most important part of the work. We have to choose the point in the negative which is later to be in the film and produce a holed template (see Fig. A.8.3) containing the following information:

1. Camera field (dependent on the size of the photographic paper used, which in turn depends on the camera. The closer we can get, the smaller the format can be).

2. Safety field (format for important parts of the picture. All important phenomena have to be contained here).

3. Fixing points for subsequently placing the negatives under the enlarger, if necessary with a "guide line."

Certain points must be made with regard to the third item. The activity center in which we are interested will not always be in exactly the same position on the negatives (poor guiding, moving of telescope, imprecise film feeding inside the camera). In addition, every negative has to be slid into the enlarger individually. By using our template and the fixing points, we precisely position the picture before exposure and minimize these effects.

The height of the enlarger during processing must not change if there is to be a smooth flow of images in the final sequence. The negative is then installed by moving the peg bar back and forth which forms a rigid unit together with the template and photographic paper.

It has been shown that with increased subsequent enlargement, the rotation of the sun can be clearly observed after only a few hours. This

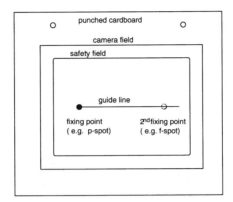

Fig. A.8.3. *Template for precise alignment of positives.*

means that if it had been the intention to establish two fixed points for p and f spots, only one can be used (e.g., the p spot) while the f spot is established according to a "guide line." In projection this produces a steady picture, although the p spot is fixed at one point and the f spot moves steadily and continuously along the "guide line."

A.8.6.3 Sequencing the Photographic Prints

Once these preparations have been completed, our animated film sequence can be produced. A sheet of punched photographic paper is placed on the peg bar; on top of this goes the format guide, and the negative is installed in the enlarger. If everything is exactly in order, the template is removed and the photographic paper is exposed. It is then developed, fixed, rinsed, and dried. This process is the same for each picture. The finished paper prints, which are all marked on the back with a serial number, constitute our image sequence, which is then shot using our Super-8 camera.

A.8.6.4 Shooting the Animation Sequence

For the entire duration of the shooting, the camera must be rock steady. Even a slight shift in position will be readily apparent when projected. There are four basic ways of filming our images (which, of course, allow for a multiplicity of variations):

1. Using an animation stand (Fig. A.8.4, Top Left). This is the best solution, as the camera can be mounted very rigidly, lighting is most easily adjusted at its most stable position, and the picture to be taken is in an upright position before the cameraman.

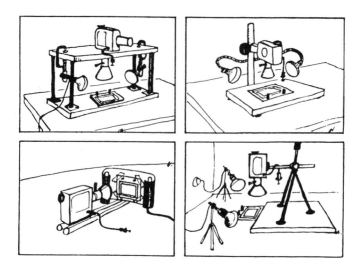

Fig. A.8.4. Top Left: *Animation stand,* Top Right: *photo-repro device,* Bottom Left: *titler device,* Bottom Right: *tripod for shooting a image sequence.*

2. Using a photographic repro-device (Fig. A.8.4, Top Right). Here lights are usually mounted on the column, but the column is often shaky, and the position of the camera forces the cameraman to position the images the wrong way round (peg bar at the bottom, pictures upside-down).

3. Using a titler device (Fig. A.8.4, Bottom Left). Usually titler devices are horizontal, and the images have to be additionally secured with adhesive tape so that they stay exactly in position on the peg bar.

4. Using a tripod (Fig. A.8.4, Bottom Right). This is a solution which is used only if absolutely necessary as it causes the greatest danger of unsteadiness. The legs of the tripod should be held as stable as possible by placing them in bored holes in a wooden board.

Shooting is carried out in the following manner. The picture is positioned in the camera's viewfinder and the peg bar is attached to ensure that each photograph is positioned correctly. Lighting is arranged at an angle of 30° to 40°, optimally four 100 watt photo flood lamps, but two 150 watt lamps will do. If the photographs are not absolutely flat, it is recommended that a sheet of glass be placed on top. The lighting should then be checked for reflections.

The diaphragm is then set in so that a color photograph (landscape picture from a magazine) containing the average light and dark values is placed in the template with the lighting switched on. The aperture is determined automatically and is then kept constant (switch off the automatic aperture); if not, a flickering effect may be noticeable because of various complex secondary effects that are beyond the scope of this discussion.

Now the actual shooting can begin. Each of the photographic images is placed one after the other onto the peg bar in accordance with the numbering on the back, and between one and no more than three individual photographs are taken. Even before taking the pictures with the telescope, a decision must be made on whether one, two, or three picture filmings are to take place. We will discuss this shortly. All the photographs are made with a cable release to avoid shaky pictures. Once the complete image sequence has been recorded, we can look forward to successful motion pictures, provided that the work has been carried out as precisely as possible. A properly colored filter can be placed in front of the camera objective to "color" black and white photographs to create the impression of actually looking through a telescope.

A.8.6.5 Calculating Time Periods

Before taking any pictures at the telescope, we have to be clear about two time intervals:

1. How much time is there for shooting or photography? In summer there will be a maximum of 10 to 12 hours; in winter correspondingly less.

2. How long should the running time of the film be? For a slow motion film 15 to 60 seconds would be adequate. Anything longer would show the movement too slowly and would cease to be instructive.

The following formula applies.

$$\text{Exposure interval} = \frac{\text{Real time duration of the process in seconds}}{\text{Projection speed} \times \text{ projection time in sec}}.$$

$$(A.7.1)$$

Two examples:

A solar observer wishes to record an activity center for eight hours. The final film is to last 30 seconds. He has a 35-mm cine-camera but wants to copy the film to Super-8 to allow a projection speed of 18 frames/second. According to the formula

$$\text{Real time duration of the process}: \ 8 \text{ hours} = 28,800 \text{ seconds}$$

$$\frac{28,800 \text{ sec}}{18 \text{ frames/sec} \times 30 \text{ sec}} = \frac{28,800}{540} = 53. \qquad (A.7.2)$$

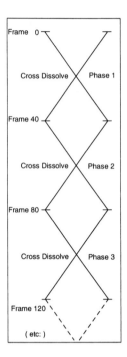

Fig. A.8.5. *Schematic diagram showing cross dissolving.*

The observer therefore has to take one picture every 53 seconds. Another observer also wishes to work for eight hours with a film duration of 30 seconds at 18 frames/second, but only has a photographic camera to do the job with. To save photographic images the observer wants to take the animation image sequence in triplicate. Triple exposure and a relatively small position change from frame to frame will ensure continuous motion in projection. In 20 seconds 540 pictures pass through the projector at a speed of 18 frames/second. Therefore, 180 pictures have to be taken in eight hours, i.e., one every 160 seconds (2 minutes, 40 seconds).

If the camera has a cross dissolve system, fewer pictures are needed. Each picture is cross dissolved onto the following one without a gap between them. Although "real" movement can no longer be observed as in full animation, changes are still readily apparent. Assuming that cross dissolving covers 40 pictures, only 14 individual photographs are required in eight hours for the 30 second film (540 frames), i.e., only one photograph every 35 minutes at the telescope. The method of producing photographic image using a peg bar, template, and fitting of the punched photographic paper remains the same as described above except that filming using the

Super-8 camera is carried out as demonstrated in Fig. A.8.5. Pure full animation is preferable to this method, but it is adequate for samples or preliminary tests.

If it is possible to observe an activity center for more than just one day during a period of fine weather, with photograph sequences being obtained over half a rotation (east to west limb), the above method also allows the production of films. The only gaps in the movement will be those caused by the night intervals. If one has the necessary patience and stamina both at the telescope and in the dark room, it is possible to produce a slow motion film of around 30 seconds for each day of half rotation directly connected to the activity of the succeeding day. This scenario could result in a film of 13×30 seconds = 6.5 minutes.

A.8.7   Video

Recently video has become of interest to the solar observer, although it has been a routine technique in many professional institutes for a long time. What would make the use of video feasible for amateurs? The financial outlay is less than might be assumed. Everyone possesses a television set nowadays, and many, a video recorder as well. Tape is also much less expensive than film, especially when the subsequent costs of photography or filming are taken into account—i.e., dark room, chemicals, photographic paper or printing laboratories, etc. Also, an unsuccessful video tape can be reused for new recordings at any time. The only additional requirement is a video camera.

Günther Appelt of Kaufbeuren, Germany and Donald F. Trombino in Florida, have accumulated a great deal of experience with video systems.

With a guided telescope the solar activity can be continuously monitored on a television screen indoors without the need to "be near" the telescope all the time. Also, many more people can watch at the same time (certainly of interest for public observatories).

Should the monitor be installed in the immediate vicinity of the telescope, it is recommended that it be in a darkened room (garage, shed, tent). The screen should be as large as possible so that fine structures can be picked out more easily.

If rapid changes start to occur, e.g., pore formation, light bridges, active prominences, flares etc, the video recorder is switched on so the events can be less hurriedly evaluated later.

Even medium-priced 4-head VCRs are capable of producing clear, crisp stills if used with a high grade VHS tape. If used in conjunction with a frame grabber digitized images can be printed which reveal 2 arc second

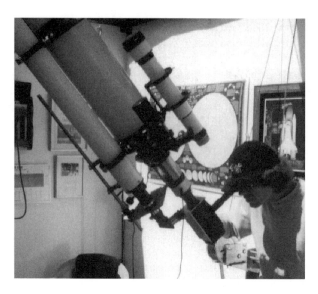

Fig. A.8.6. *Recording Solar Structure Movements—Video. Using a standard Sony home video camcorder, Central Florida solar observer, Ernie Sangraw, constructed a simple aluminum camera to telescope adapter plate. With it he recorded dramatic changes in a large solar flare near the solar limb together with nearby prominences on 12 March 1993 at 1715 UT. He used the 15 cm refractor with a 0.7Å Hα filter. Date and time in hours, minutes, and seconds were superimposed on the video tape using the video camera's built-in electronic digital clock. This camera is also particularly well-suited to recording the normally dark Calcium-K line solar features in 'real time'. The Calcium-K line located in the 3933.7Å region of the solar spectrum is often beyond the range of visual perception but is easily seen with such cameras having one lux low light capabilities which are common in home video cameras. Photo courtesy D.F. Trombino, Deltona, Florida.*

details. Moreover, 10:1 or 12:1 zoom lenses on camcorders will enable the observer to make either full or partial close video records in real time. Many of these camcorders also feature date/time information, which is very helpful when played back at later date. They are also furnished with remote "mike" cables which can be plugged into a shortwave radio receiver for recording audio WWV or CHU time signals directly onto the VHS video tape. At normal playback speeds, however, the recorder will only reproduce a picture of the sun at a time ratio of 1:1. As most flow phenomena on the sun take place relatively slowly (minutes, hours) a playback speed control is desirable. Although some machines have such a device up to a maximum of 1:10 (visibly faster forward and rewind), it is often accompanied by interference in the form of lines across the screen.

There are professional machines (Betacam SP, Betacam Sp digital or the "classic" 1-inch magnetic tape for broadcasting) which do not have this problem (perfect pictures in fast forward and slow motion), but they are beyond the reach of most amateurs. We can be sure, though, that most home video recorders will be appropriately equipped in the future.

Before starting to use a video system, it must be determined that the pre-filtering (light damping to protect the chip) is correct. Camcorder CCD chips are very sensitive and subject to damage. A rough rule of thumb is that light damping should be such that if photographs were being taken with a camera, the exposure time should be $1/30$ second (See A.5.2.). A variable polarizing filter will do well and even increase contrast.

Modern camcorders are excellent (in most cases) for "seeing" and recording the deep violet Calcium-K wavelength not easily observed visually by older individuals with the monochromator. Hence, they are excellent for real time monitoring of Calcium plage regions on the sun.

In contrast to photography, video images are lower in resolution.[1] The finest details are lost, and a negative can be "tweaked" better in the dark room. Also, video can be used adequately only if the atmospheric conditions are good. However, the system does offer the significant advantages that it is a more convenient method for continuous monitoring of the sun, and it is possible for simultaneous observation by a group of people. Video need not be limited to solar observation, the moon and many of the planets are also interesting targets for this medium.

---

[1] However, based upon recent experience with the new "electronic world" it seems safe to predict that video cameras are certain to continually improve to the point that within the near future this may no longer be true.

Part B

Solar Observation

Chapter B.1

Observation

B.1.1 Observation Program and Note-keeping[†]

B.1.1.1 Introduction

Part B of this book sets out the scope of amateur observation of the sun in terms of its principles, problems, and results. The reason for observing the sun, whether it be purely for pleasure or the fun of discovering uncharted territory and "amateur research," is quite irrelevant as there is always the same problem at the outset, i.e., what should be observed and how should the observations be recorded?

But at the outset an even more important question has to be answered: why should observations be recorded anyway? Why should the amateur objectively observe the sun, if astronomy is only a hobby?

The answers are as follows:

1. Every observation is unique and cannot be repeated. Everything that is not noted will be lost forever.

2. Objectives can change. Who can say that one will not require a particular piece of information for evaluation or only to help others some time in the future?

3. There are long-term changes taking place in the sun which can be observed only by looking back through records.

4. The exchange and gathering of observations by national and international groups is made possible.

B.1.1.2 Recording Observations

Keeping a log-book has proved to be the best method of documenting observations over long periods of time. Entries should note the time

---

[†]Written by Heinz Hilbrecht

and place of all observations, instruments used, external influences such as turbulence (see B.1.2), and other factors.

However, inexpensive methods of printing and copying (photocopiers) mean that the bound book is being increasingly replaced with the previously, and justly, scorned single sheet of paper. Blank forms, set out in accordance with the objectives of observation, are being filled in throughout the country and are easily obtainable. They save time, as the corresponding explanation does not have to be written down for each observation, and they ensure that observations are not omitted since they are divided into sections.

Figure B.1.1 shows the most common layout of such a form. There is enough space for entering the name of the observer; the instrument; the seeing conditions; the time; and, in the lower section, a plan for determining the sunspot number. The middle section is for a general drawing of the sun to facilitate the recording of such important information as the approximate position of sunspots and faculae. When recording an area of sunspots, information such as the type of group and number of individual spots (i.e., C7, F58) should not be omitted. These data are required for calculating the sunspot number. Throughout Part B the appropriate forms for specialized observation are illustrated and explained to allow the observer to record information for participation in an observation program.

B.1.1.3   Observation Programs

As the amateur astronomer's own interests develop, so will his resolve to participate in observation groups. Appropriate information can be obtained from the solar sections of national and international organizations. Only a small number of essential comments about amateur observation groups will be made in this section of the book.

Unless it is related to a certain small number of phenomena, specific observation of the sun makes sense to an amateur only if carried out under amateur conditions. As a rule, only comparatively small instruments are used by the amateur, often in atmospheric conditions which are not always ideal and with limited resolution. However, in comparison with astrophysical institutes and their highly developed methods of observation, the amateur has one distinct advantage in that he can make use of his instrument at any time. The amateur is, therefore, able to gather together observations in the long term and to evaluate this information. The disadvantage of limited quality can often be compensated for somewhat by quantity if the data are consistent.

The objective is, therefore, to collect as much information and to leave as few gaps in observation as possible. The only way of doing so is to work

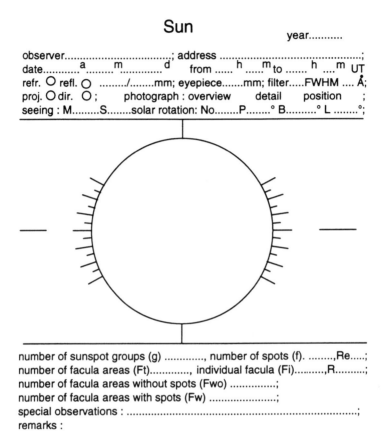

number of sunspot groups (g) ...., number of spots (f). ....,Re.....;
number of facula areas (Ft).............., individual facula (Fi)..........,R..........;
number of facula areas without spots (Fwo) ....;
number of facula areas with spots (Fw) ....;
special observations : ....;
remarks :

Fig. B.1.1. *Observation form as explained in the main text.*

with other amateurs. On a regional level such groups could be established in public observatories, on a national level there are many groups which are constantly looking for new observers. A good way of making contact is through the conferences held by solar observers and other amateur astronomers.

Whatever the amateur astronomer's goals and activities, he should always be aware that he is an amateur. Imagining oneself to be a researcher may well be an attractive thought, as everyone feels a need to explore, but all too often too much ambition results in disappointment in one's own capabilities. Quite a number of amateur astronomers have given up their hobby because they discover that they are not solar physicists after all. Part B is based on the premise that the most important aspect of astronomy for the amateur is taking part.

B.1.2   Seeing[†]

B.1.2.1   Introduction

This section will deal with essential aspects of atmospheric influences on image quality and will present a number of ways of reducing this interference. The references and text have been compiled to avoid the often complex mathematical approach to this subject.

B.1.2.2   Appearance

In the same way as it causes the stars to twinkle at night, the atmosphere causes blurring of the image and undulation at the solar limb. These two forms of atmospheric turbulence are known as

1. directional scintillation, which changes the apparent position of a light source located beyond the earth's atmosphere, and

2. blurring, which causes the image to become indistinct.

In short, the factors causing the interference are turbulence and variations in the density of the air. These alter the optical properties of the air in the same way as a lens which changes its focal point and adjustment several times per second. The effects on the image of the sun are, among other things, reduced contrasts, reduced resolution, position shifting, and variations in brightness. Light is diffused in the atmosphere. This "scattered light" overlays dark structures on the sun's surface and produces an almost uncontrollable uncertainty factor in the calculation of brightness and temperature (B.2.1.5).

B.1.2.3   Defining Turbulence

The costly technical methods used by professional astronomers (e.g., seeing monitors) are needed by amateurs only in special circumstances. Instead, the Kiepenheuer scale is used for everyday observation, both as an assessment scale and as a basis for measuring the quality of the air. Kiepenheuer (1962) defined the units for measuring the sharpness of the image of the sun (S) and the image motion at the limb and on the solar disc (M). In amateur circles a modified version of the Kiepenheuer scale is widely used (Tables B.1 and B.2). In addition, the deviation from the average observing conditions should be recorded using the scale given in Table B.3.

[†]Written by Heinz Hilbrecht

Table B.1

Motion (M) Description

1	No image motion visible, neither at the limb nor on the solar disc.
2	Image motion $\leq 2''$ only detectable at the limb, but almost undiscernible on the disc.
3	Image motion $\leq 4''$ well visible at the limb and on the disc, solar limb undulating or pulsating.
4	Image motion $\leq 8''$ almost prevents distinction of umbrae and penumbrae (and thus judging the sharpness), solar limb strongly undulating or pulsating.
5	Amplitude of image motion $> 8''$ reaches diameter of sunspots, solar limb heavily undulating or pulsating.

Table B.2

Sharpness (S) Description

1	Granulation very conspicuous, structure of penumbrae recognizable.
2	Granulation well defined, penumbrae well visible, but almost without fine structure, sharp boundary between umbrae and penumbrae and sharp transition to the photosphere.
3	Only traces of granulation visible, but structure of solar surface still easy detectable when solar image is displaced. Umbrae and penumbrae still well separated, but without fine structure, transition to the photosphere hardly defined.
4	No granulation structure detectable, umbra and penumbra only distinguishable in large sunspots, transition to the photosphere blurred.
5	Granulation not visible, umbra and penumbra undistinguishable even in larger spots.

Table B.3

Quality (Q) Description

E xcellent	Reserved for days with exceptionally clear details being visible.
G ood	Average visibility of details on the solar surface according to the individual circumstances of the observer.
F air	Seeing below average, but observation not adversely affected.
P oor	Considerable image distortions which badly reduce the value of the observation.
W orthless	Conditions so bad that the observation is not useful for reductions.

B.1.2.4   The Causes of Seeing

The "atmospheric turbulence" perceived through a telescope is the result of atmospheric movement due to uneven heating. Temperature differences between the ground and the air, and in the air itself, produce layers and cells of air at various densities some of which are rising and falling. If a large air mass is moving across the observation point there is hardly any turbulence, e.g., over large areas of grass, forests or larger lakes. But if there are one or two trees on the grass area, a complex micro-climate is formed and the quality of the air deteriorates. An observation point should therefore be selected so that the visual line to the sun is over a homogeneous area. Strong turbulence occurs in the first 3–10 m above the ground. It is, therefore, a distinct advantage to set up the telescope above this zone. However, the wall of a house will also heat up; thus if it is at all possible, the objective should project beyond this layer of rising air (30–50 cm). This reduction in turbulence can, however, also be achieved with extended eaves.

A strong source of turbulence is the telescope itself. The air in the tube heats up and results in turbulence. This source can be reduced only if the air is totally removed from the tube (vacuum telescope), but for amateur purposes a large screen (e.g., strong cardboard or thin wood) around the front lens is enough to shade the telescope. Increased wind-shake is another problem. Screening the telescope for a few minutes during observation, say, every 15 minutes often controls the heat problem. As heating of the front lens is also a frequent source of turbulence, it is advisable to cover it.

There are no hard and fast rules. Protecting the telescope against heating is usually a matter of the observer's own judgement and has to take into account local circumstances.

B.1.2.5   Daily and Annual Cycles and Other Effects

As every observer knows, air turbulence changes throughout the day. Shortly after sunrise it is at a minimum, rising to a maximum at midday and then falling again towards evening. Figure B.1.2 shows various daily cycles and the importance of scheduling observations. The midday observations carried out by so many amateur astronomers coincide precisely with the period of least favorable seeing conditions. Whenever possible, observations should be carried out shortly after 6 a.m. since the atmospheric conditions tend to be good to very good almost everywhere (and what is more, sensing the awakening of nature is a wonderful start to the day). However, Figure B.1.3 should be taken into account.

If it is impossible to make your observation during these morning minima, the afternoon minima often produce good data, but they are less precisely determinable. It would therefore be worthwhile (say, during the weekend,) to carry out observations until shortly before sunset and record the turbulence as in Figure B.1.3.

Figure B.1.2 shows that, for various other reasons, it is important to have precise information about the seeing conditions. The start of the afternoon minima (in this case) is subject to periodic shifting which must be taken into consideration as the shifts can involve several hours.

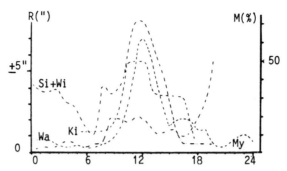

Fig. B.1.2. *Daily scintillation cycle observed by various authors, actual local time. (D. Paperlein)*

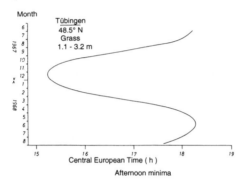

Fig. B.1.3. *Annual cycle of afternoon minima of terrestrial scintillation for a test area varying between 1.1 m and 3.2 m in height. (D. Paperlein)*

B.1.2.6 Place of Observation

The choice of a location for your observations also has a great effect on the seeing conditions. No new observatory (e.g., new outer stations of public observatories) should simply be built "out in the country" without site-testing, as is the case in professional astronomy where it is absolutely essential in the selection of a suitable location. Site testing involves a series of test measurements aimed at obtaining precise information about the seeing conditions at the location under consideration. Such test observations are, if possible, carried out in parallel with comparable telescopes so that results obtained in similar weather conditions can be compared with each other. Müller (1962) describes some typical locations based on work by Kiepenheuer.

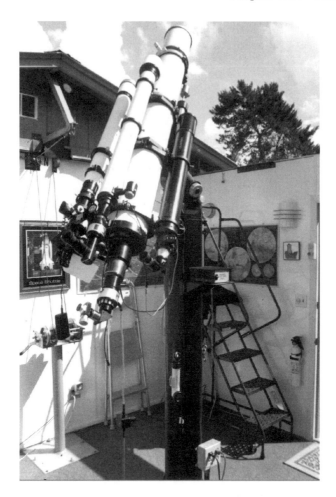

Fig. B.1.4. *The interior of Donald Trombino's Davis Memorial Solar Observatory is especially designed for solar observing. The walls of the building are made of treated wood and paneled with white Formica sheeting since brick, stucco, concrete block or stone material tend to "hold" heat and radiate it upward. Although the floor of the observatory is made of reinforced steel and 18-inch thick concrete, it is covered with insulated indoor/outdoor carpeting which prevents the formation of heat waves (turbulence). Note: one of the roof vents (top left) with the roof rolled off toward the north. The white enameled telescope tubes reflect unwanted heat. The unobstructed light path of refracting telescopes also helps to prevent the annoying heat waves within the telescopes which sometimes happens in compound SCT or Newtonian type telescopes.*

1. Only in the early morning are the seeing conditions good with telescopes all at one level at a height of approximately 5 m.

2. Placing the telescope on a 20 m high tower adds considerably to the number of hours of good seeing conditions after sunrise.

3. Locations on hills of over 500 m in areas with steep slopes are unsuitable.

4. A good location is one with a slope of at least 50 m in height descending in a S or SW direction in a higher mountain range.

5. The best conditions are obtained if the observatory is surrounded by a lake (or the sea).

B.1.2.7 Concluding Remarks

This chapter is intended to show that a large and expensive telescope is not the be-all and end-all in solar observation. Every observer should be familiar with his local seeing conditions (daily and annual cycles), and the emphasis is on "local," as conditions vary too much for making consistently valid rules. The individual has to be willing to experiment, but often it is just a question of pushing the telescope a little farther out to reach beyond the flow of air around the walls of the house. For the owner of a smaller instrument, it is encouraging to know that with an objective diameter of over about 100 mm (4 inches), turbulence becomes greater than the resolution which depends on diffraction. Using a larger telescope for solar observation is worthwhile only if there are excellent seeing conditions at a particular site (see Fig. B.2.22).

Chapter B.2

Sunspots

B.2.1 The Structure of Sunspots[†]

B.2.1.1 Introduction

This section is an introduction to sunspot phenomena which are not dealt with in detail elsewhere in this book and is restricted to white light objects and their physical properties. For those requiring more detail reference is made to the appropriate literature.

B.2.1.2 Nomenclature (see Fig. B.2.1)

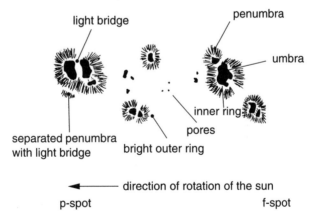

Fig. B.2.1. *Nomenclature of phenomena related to sunspots.*

[†]Written by Heinz Hilbrecht

B.2.1.3   Pores

Pores are sunspots without a penumbra which are characterized by rapid changes. They can mark the position of newly forming sunspots or appear in groups. The amateur astronomer should be familiar with their properties as pores are not included in sunspot statistics (B.2.4.).

1. Pores have diameters of $1''$ to $10''$ (usually 2–$5''$). In sunspot statistics, sunspots smaller than $3''$ count as pores.

2. They may last between a few hours and one day.

3. Their intensity is between 0.2 and 0.4 I_{phot} (see Section 2.1.5 on umbrae).

4. Pores have no penumbra.

The amateur astronomer could perhaps study motion of the pores which may indicate flows or changes in the sunspot's magnetic field, or the development of young sunspots.

B.2.1.4   "Void Areas"

Not to be confused with pores are the "void areas." These are areas in which granulation (B.7) is missing, but reforms again within a few minutes. These void areas can, however, also change their brightness and then become the first stages in the development of pores. Following are significant data about void areas:

1. Void areas are regions in which granulation is missing.

2. Their diameter is $1''$ to $5''$ (usually $2''$ to $3''$).

3. They usually only last a few minutes.

4. Their intensity is 0.7 to 0.75 I_{phot}; in other words, they are brighter than pores.

B.2.1.5   Umbrae

Umbrae are the dark "cores" of sunspots. Normally about 10,000 km in diameter, they vary in color from black to reddish-brown. If they are observed directly (e.g., through an objective filter) in good seeing conditions, differences in brightness will typically be indicated by a saddle structure. Darker centers are separated by brighter areas. The stronger the magnetic field, the darker the umbrae will be. Also, they are darker during a sunspot maximum than during a minimum (see B.2.3).

Brightness on the sun is usually described in terms of the photosphere's radiation intensity (I_{phot}) which is given as 1. The intensity of the umbrae is approximately 0.1 I_{phot}; in other words umbrae are only $1/10$ as bright as the photosphere. However, as in all solar features, brightness is dependent on the wavelength or color of the light being observed.

The temperature can be calculated using Boltzmann's equation:

$$\frac{I}{I_{\text{phot}}} = \left(\frac{T_e}{(T_e)_{\text{phot}}}\right)^4. \tag{B.2.1.5.1}$$

With a photosphere temperature $(T_e)_{\text{phot}}$ of 5780 Kelvin (K), the temperature of the umbrae works out at around 3300° K. The typical magnetic field strength in umbrae is 2000 Gauss (G) (compared to the earth's magnetic field of 0.5 G).

B.2.1.6 Umbral Dots

Umbral dots appear in the umbra in the form of brighter, blurred points with apparent diameters of approximately 0.5″ (500 km) and an intensity of 0.13 I_{phot} (i.e., only a little brighter than umbrae). Their size and intensity are distorted by atmospheric turbulence and scattered light, but after appropriate correction, a diameter of 150–200 km and a brightness similar to that of the photosphere can be calculated.

The most noteworthy aspect of energy transportation in sunspots is convection, which can be observed using a spectroscope (see B.3). It is still not known why there is a magnetic field in the umbral dots which is 1400 Gauss weaker than in the surrounding umbra.

B.2.1.7 Bright Points

Bright points, like umbral dots, appear in umbrae, but are much brighter and can be identified with 80 mm telescopes if observed directly. In the same way as umbral dots, bright points exhibit convection but are rather more like granulation in terms of brightness. However, whereas an individual granule lasts on average six minutes, bright points are stable for several hours. The strong magnetic field probably has a stabilizing effect, as even "ordinary" photospheric granulation tends to last somewhat longer in the immediate vicinity of sunspots. Bright points probably form a network of 5″–10″ and accompany light bridges (see B.5) in the initial phases of their development. However, this relationship has not been studied in detail.

B.2.1.8 Light Bridges

There is a separate Section (B.5) on light bridges in this book, but it is interesting to note at this point that with a sunspot diameter of around 30,000 km, the development of light bridges stagnates and the spot decays more slowly (see B.2.2). The spot has then attained the diameter of a supergranule (a chromospheric convective cell) and is probably particularly stable in this state. The so-called bright rings are at their brightest during this phase.

B.2.1.9 Inner Bright Ring

Between the umbra and penumbra there is a narrow zone, the existence of which was first proved photometrically in 1932 after disputed visual observations. The inner bright ring is a brightening of the penumbra and should not be confused with light bridges in which granulation similar to that in the undisturbed photosphere occurs.

B.2.1.10 Outer Bright Ring

Between the penumbra and the "undisturbed" photosphere is the outer bright ring with an intensity of 1.03 to 1.075 I_{phot}. Temperatures are therefore approximately 50 to 100° K higher than in the photosphere. However, the increase in temperature is not related to the granules but to the intergranular lanes (see B.8). Bright rings are thus overheated at lower levels, and for this reason it is assumed that energy which cannot pass through the sunspot from below is diverted. As a rule, its area is two to three times greater than that of the sunspot itself, and the number of granules per unit of area is also greater than in the remainder of the photosphere. The stronger the magnetic field, the smaller the granular cells and the longer their lifespan.

The characteristics of the outer bright ring can be summarized as follows:

1. All sunspots, irrespective of size, have rings.

2. Rings are features of the sunspot, not of the group.

3. The rings have a distinct boundary with the photosphere.

4. The rings often have filaments running towards the center of the sunspot which reach into the penumbra. The brightness of these filaments exceeds the average brightness of the rings.

5. The rings can be complete or broken into separate sections.

6. The shapes of the rings and the sunspots exhibit a greater similarity the nearer they are to the solar limb.

7. Faculae (Chapter B.6) avoid the bright ring areas and often surround them.

B.2.1.11 Penumbra

The penumbra surrounds the umbra as a dark corona with bright filaments which are radial to the umbra and consist of longitudinal cells. The

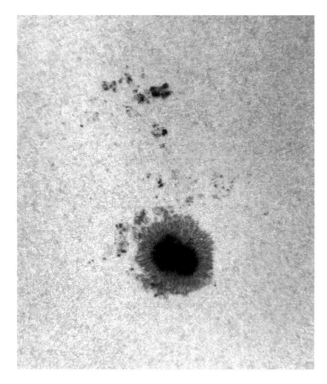

Fig. B.2.2. *The large sunspot at the lower center of this photograph by Gordon Garcia shows the dark umbra and the bright filaments which surround it. Photo taken using Kodak 2415 on August 16, 1992 with a 130mm f/8 refractor (e.f.l. 9520 mm) using a Tuthill SolarSkreen and #58 green filters.*

width of the filaments is around 0.3″ (approximately 200 km), and they last about 45 minutes. Changes and divisions can even be detected after periods of only 12 minutes.

Brightness is around 0.8 I_{phot}, but it is strongly dependent on wavelength. The average magnetic field strength is 1000 Gauss. Flows can also be observed in the penumbra, particularly by using a spectrograph. Line shifting points to a flow away from the umbra at a velocity of 7–10 km/s in the bright filaments, with an opposite movement towards the sunspot at a speed of 5–10 km/s in the dark filaments. The Evershed effect, as this phenomenon is called, may be identified by the movement of bright nodal points (points where bright filaments cross or nodes in individual filaments) at a velocity of 1–2 km/s which can be directly observed in white light. It is likely that this movement is also the result of convection along the almost horizontal magnetic field lines.

B.2.1.12   Other Characteristics

One observation which is still not really understood is the east-west asymmetry of sunspots. The number of sunspots on the eastern half of the sun's disc appears to be greater than the number on the western half. This situation is complicated by the fact that the opposite applies for sunspots whose maximum period of activity has passed.

The ratio of the penumbra diameter to the umbra diameter shows changes which can also be of interest to the amateur astronomer. If small or medium sunspots are observed, the penumbra is significantly larger with regard to the umbra in observations near the limb. In the case of larger sunspots, the opposite applies, and the differences in size are smaller. The relationship between the radii of the penumbra and umbra depends on the stage the sunspot has reached in its development, particularly on the increase in area of the umbra.

It can be seen that in relation to the penumbra diameter, umbrae are larger during maximum sunspot activity than during minimum activity. At the same time, umbrae are on average darker during sunspot maxima than during minima, and it is probable that there are also changes in the sunspot's magnetic field as a stronger magnetic field can be observed when brightness is lower (see Figs. B.2.10).

B.2.2   The Development of Sunspots and Sunspot Groups[†]

Development of sunspot groups means temporal changes in characteristic measurable features, and it is these changes which make the observation of sunspot groups an attractive proposition. This section will be dealing with ways of systematically recording them.

B.2.2.1   Typical Development of a Large Area of Activity

The appearance of a sunspot group is connected with wider-ranging phenomena such as faculae, filaments, flares and—the cause of all these—magnetic fields. The development of the phenomena takes place at different rates and is different for each area of activity. A description can only cover a few general features of the developments which are typical of a large area of activity. Detailed descriptions can be found in Newton (1958), Bray and Loughhead (1964), Bumba (1967), Wilson (1968), and McIntosh (1981). Following is a general description:

> **Day 1:** A flux tube of the magnetic field reaches the photosphere. If the magnetic field flux density there exceeds 0.1 T, an initial small facula becomes visible in Hα (also in white light if it is in the limb area).

[†]Written by Rainer Beck

Day 2: The initial small sunspot appears at the western edge of the facula. The facula increases in size and brightness. The section of magnetic field continues to rise; the observed field strength increases.

Day 3: One or more sunspots appear at the eastern edge of the facula with magnetic polarities opposite to the initial sunspot. The area of the magnetic field and facula continues to increase.

Day 4: Small sunspots dissolve into larger ones. The western preceding (p-) spot of the group forms a penumbra. The facula surrounds the sunspot group but remains compact. The magnetic field shows a distinct bipolar structure. The first Hα flares are observed. Small filaments in the vicinity of the p-spot are not yet stable.

Day 5–13: On day 5 the eastern following ($f-$) spot forms a penumbra. Then follow numerous small spots between the two principal spots until the group attains its greatest extent. The brightness of the facula increases, as does the area of the magnetic field. The flare activity attains a maximum.

Day 14–30: All of the sunspots, apart from the principal p-spot disappear. The facula is extensive but begins to shrink. Flare activity decreases. The magnetic field strength is at a maximum but the area it covers begins to decrease. A stable filament of around 50,000 km in length points in the direction of the p-spot.

Day 30–60: The p-spot too begins to shrink and disappears. The brightness of the facula decreases and the facula divides into smaller individual areas. The magnetic field becomes weaker and irregular. The filament increases regularly in length (around 100,000 km per rotation of the sun) and divides the area of activity into two halves.

Day 60–100: The chromospheric facula disappears, and the photospheric facula dissolves. The filament reaches its greatest length and runs almost parallel to the solar equator.

Day 100–250: No more faculae are observed. The filament gradually breaks up along with the magnetic field.

While the sunspot group in this example lasts only 60 days, the magnetic field can be detected for around 250 days. The magnetic field is the cause of solar activity. A flux tube of magnetic field lines reaches the photosphere and expands into an arch due to the lower pressure. The two points at which it penetrates through the photosphere mark the two magnetic poles in a sunspot group (see Fig. B.2.8). The details of the formation of sunspots remain unclear, particularly the formation of the sharp boundaries between the umbra, penumbra and photosphere, as does the origin of solar magnetic fields (Schüssler 1980).

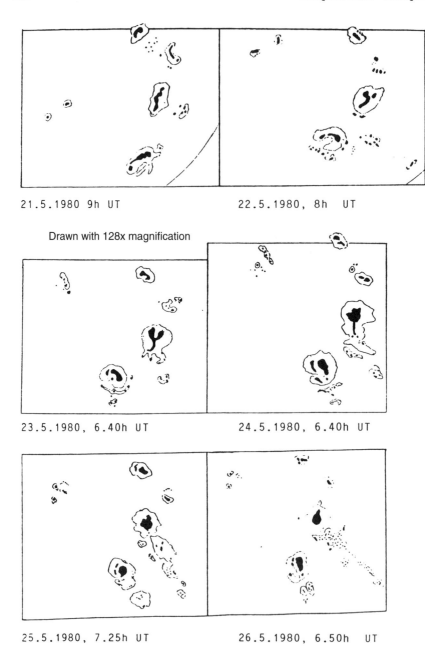

21.5.1980 9h UT   22.5.1980, 8h UT

Drawn with 128x magnification

23.5.1980, 6.40h UT   24.5.1980, 6.40h UT

25.5.1980, 7.25h UT   26.5.1980, 6.50h UT

Fig. B.2.3a. *Development of large sunspot groups (A. Reil).*

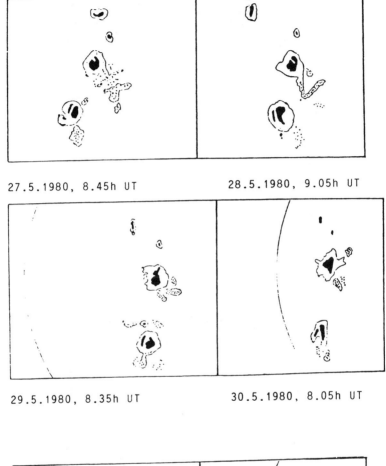

27.5.1980, 8.45h UT   28.5.1980, 9.05h UT

29.5.1980, 8.35h UT   30.5.1980, 8.05h UT

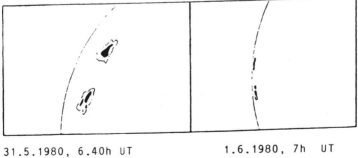

31.5.1980, 6.40h UT   1.6.1980, 7h UT

Fig. B.2.3b. *Development of large sunspot groups (A. Reil).*

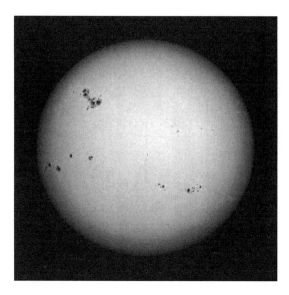

Fig. B.2.4. *Sunspot group taken on July 11, 1989 with TP 2415 using a 6-inch f/12 refractor and a B&L N.D. 5 solar filter. Lee C. Coombs.*

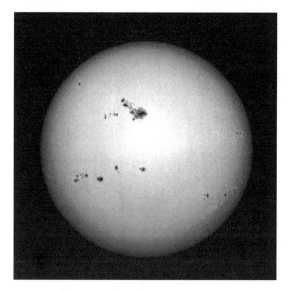

Fig. B.2.5. *Sunspot group taken on July 13, 1989 with TP 2415 using a 6-inch f/12 refractor and a B&L N.D. 5 solar filter. Lee C. Coombs.*

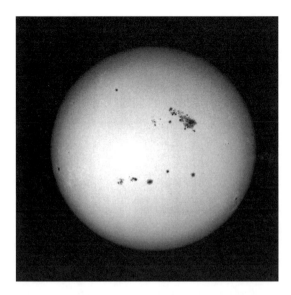

Fig. B.2.6. *Sunspot group taken on July 15, 1989 with TP 2415 using a 6-inch f/12 refractor and a B&L N.D. 5 solar filter. Lee C. Coombs.*

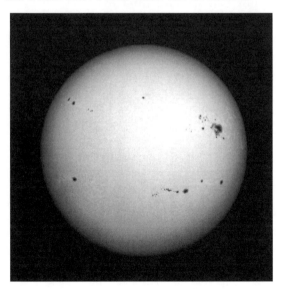

Fig. B.2.7. *Sunspot group taken on July 17, 1989 with TP 2415 using a 6-inch f/12 refractor and a B&L N.D. 5 solar filter. Lee C. Coombs.*

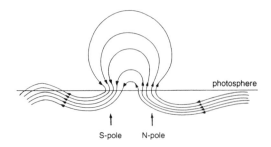

Fig. B.2.8. *Course of the magnetic field in a bipolar area of activity.*

Following the development of a large sunspot group is one of the most fascinating observation opportunities for an amateur. Solar photography (Section A.5) is particularly suited to this endeavor, but even drawings are of great value (see Figs. B.2.4–7). The series of 4 photographs (B.2.4–7) taken by Lee Coombs spaced two days apart illustrates the rotation of the sun but also how these groups of sunspots change over this period of time.

B.2.2.2   Sunspot Classes and Lifetime

The sunspot classifications (see Fig. B.2.15) introduced by Waldmeier (1947) are based on the above typical development of a large sunspot group: appearance of a pore; growth to more than 2000 km in diameter (class A); appearance of the f-spot (class B); formation of a penumbra around one of the two main spots, usually the p-spot (class C) and then the second main spot (class D); a sharp increase in area and spot number in the group (class E and F); breaking up of the spots between the two principal spots (class G); breaking up of one of the principal spots, usually the f-spot (class H); decrease in the area of the remaining main spot (class J) and breaking up of the penumbra of this spot (class A, or better still A^*).

Only a few sunspot groups attain class F or pass through all the Waldmeier classes. By far the majority of groups reach their maximum extent during one of the earlier classes and go back via classes G, C, or J. Possible development paths are given in the following diagrams (see Fig. B.2.9) by Kiepenheuer (1953). The curves show the number of individual spots in the group against time (in days), with the large letters indicating the Waldmeier classes. The maximum sunspot number is usually reached during the first third of a group's lifetime (curve group a), less frequently during the second third (b) or the last third (c). Symmetrical curves are

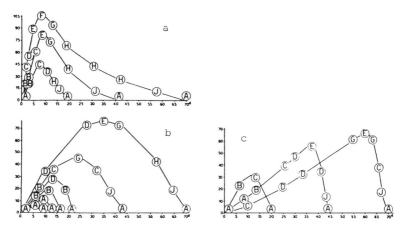

Fig. B.2.9. *Typical development curves for sunspot groups (number of spots vs. time).*

more common in groups with a short lifetime. The asymmetry of the development curves presumably increases with the maximum development stage—surprisingly like Waldmeier's first law on sunspot cycles (see B.2.5.4).

The development curves show that the higher a sunspot's development stage, the longer its lifetime. For the period 1944–1954, Künzel (1960) looked into the percentage of observed groups which attained a maximum development in classes A to F. (Classes G, H, and J are stages related to breaking up and were therefore not taken into consideration.) Sunspots are a short-lived phenomenon with 90% of all groups disappearing after 10 days at most and 50% after only 2 days. On the other hand, the largest groups last for months. The longest lasting group of all was observed from 15 March to 3 August, 1979. According to Kopecky (1967), the average lifetime of a sunspot group is 10 days with a long-term change which presumably follows the "long sunspot cycle" (see B.2.5.5).

The f-spot achieves the longest lifetime in approximately only 10% of all groups while the p-spot dominates 40% of the time. (The remaining 50% does not allow any clear conclusions to be drawn.) The area of the p-spot is on average 40% greater than that of the f-spot (Yilmaz 1964).

Statistics on the lifetime of groups show why naked eye observations are rare. A prerequisite for such an observation is that a sunspot has a minimum diameter of over 30,000 km. Even the principal spots in F groups do not always reach this size.

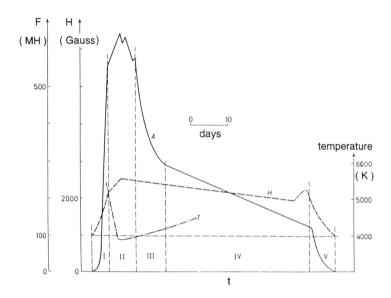

Fig. B.2.10. *Temporal course of area A, magnetic field strength H and temper-ature T in a large sunspot group.*

B.2.2.3   The Area of a Group

The area taken up by the sunspots in a group is one of the most im-portant values used to describe its development (see B.2.4.7 with regard to measuring this area). The area of a sunspot is closely connected with the magnetic field strength at the center of the spot, and so the development of the sunspot area consequently reflects the development of the magnetic field. Examples of such development curves are given by Newton (1958, p. 101).

The connection between the maximum area $A_{\max}$ of a group measured in millionths of the visible solar hemisphere and its lifetime t, in years, (Gnevishev 1938) is shown in the following formula:

$$A_{\max} = 8.5t. \qquad (B.2.2.3.1)$$

Like the sunspot number curve, the area of a group increases more quickly at the beginning of its development the higher $A_{\max}$ is. According to Kopecky (1953) the following applies:

$$\Delta A = 0.094 A_{\max} + 9.3, \qquad (B.2.2.3.2)$$

where ΔA is the average daily increase in area. The area of a group increases particularly rapidly during the first few days—by a power of 4 with regard to time according to Bumba (1963).

After the development maximum, the number of sunspots quickly decreases while the area defined by the long-lasting principal spot decreases only slowly in accordance with the slow decrease in the area and strength of the magnetic field. At the end of the group's development, the area decreases exponentially, while the magnetic field strength stays almost constant and then decreases rapidly (see also Bumba 1967). Area A, the magnetic field strength H, and the temperature T of the group show the course schematically in Fig. B.2.10.

The main problem in measuring a development curve is the rotation of the sun. Continuous observation of a group is possible only over two weeks at most, as it then disappears at the western limb of the sun. The two week gap in the development curve until it reappears at the eastern limb cannot be bridged by interpolation as substantial changes can take place within the space of only a few days. Only superimposing the development curves of many similar groups can reasonably reproduce the typical course. Important parameters in characterizing the development curves are given below:

- the lifetime of the observed class of sunspot groups
- the maximum area attained $A_{\max}$
- the area below the development curve $A = A(t)$ as a measure of the average activity of the observed class
- the mean gradient of the rising section
- the mean gradient of the falling section

Statistical evaluation of development curves should at first be directed towards the following parameters: connections, differences between the sunspot classes, comparison with the development curve of the sunspot number (see B.2.2.4). Examples of such studies are given by Götz (1977, 1978). Longer-term observations make it possible to become involved with several problems:

1. Does the lifetime of a class of sunspot groups change during the 11 year cycle?

2. Do the typical shapes of the development curves change during the 11 year cycle?

3. Are there links between the development curves and other features of a class of sunspot groups, e.g., the inclination of its principal axis with regard to the solar equator, the number of light bridges, the size and brightness of associated faculae, the frequency of flares (see also the appropriate sections)?

The professional literature contains detailed studies only of the first item in our list (Kopecky 1967). According to these studies the lifetime during the

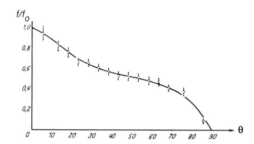

Fig. B.2.11. *"Visibility function" of sunspots.*

11 year cycle does not change, although it does during the 80 year cycle (see
B.2.5.5). The question of whether the lifetime is adequate to characterize
a sunspot group is not dealt with.

B.2.2.4   Number of Individual Sunspots

The simplest measure for an amateur to determine the development
stage of a group is the number of sunspots. Counting the number of
sunspots depends more strongly on instrumental and earth atmospheric
conditions (see Section B.2.4.6) than does area measurement because these
conditions can reduce their reproducibility and therefore usefulness for systematic investigations. Furthermore, the number of sunspots is subject to
"perspective foreshortening;" i.e., it appears to fall if the group moves from
the center towards the limb. While for the sunspot area this effect can be
easily corrected through multiplication with $1/\cos\theta$ (θ = heliocentric angle), the "visibility function" of the sunspots deviates clearly from a cosine
law (Roggenhausen 1952) (see Fig. B.2.11). Between angular distances of
$0°$ and $30°$ the number of sunspots first falls more rapidly and then more
slowly than function $\cos\theta$. The reason for this deviation is considered to
be the depth of sunspots. The mean value of the cos function between 0
and $90°$ is $2/\pi$; i.e., we only see approximately 64% of the sunspots on the
facing hemisphere.

Another source of error in determining the number of sunspots (Kiessig's
experiment of 1949) lies in the fact that the observer, remembering a normal
group rich in sunspots, tries to find more sunspots in the limb area.

If all the factors affecting the viewing and counting of sunspots are taken
into account, it becomes possible to draw the development curve for sunspot
numbers in a group. For evaluation purposes, the points in Section B.2.2.3
apply. Of particular interest are comparisons between the development
curves for area and sunspot numbers, if possible taking into account other
observations (faculae, filaments, flare activity, magnetic field structure, light

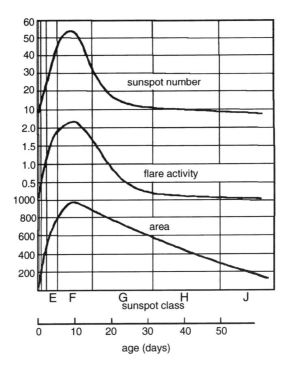

Fig. B.2.12. *Typical course of Wolf number, flare activity, and area of a large sunspot group.*

bridges). Such investigations are seldom found in professional literature (e.g., Waldmeier 1955, p. 167; see Fig. B.2.12).

B.2.2.5 Axis Inclination (see also B.3.3.4)

During the development of a bipolar sunspot group, the angle between the line connecting the p- and f-spots ("axis") and the lines of constant latitude exhibits a typical change. With an increasing sunspot area this angle decreases, reaches a minimum during maximum sunspot development, and increases again as the number of sunspots falls. The development curve for the axis inclination is symmetrical to the minimum for large and small groups. The mean axis inclination depends on the heliographic latitude of the group (Bendel 1980; Gilman and Howard 1986). The change in the axis inclination indicates that the principal spots in a group have a systematic proper motion. During the period before the maximum spot development the p-spot rotates more rapidly and the f-spot more slowly than the photosphere. As the group breaks up, this tendency is reversed (Bendel 1980).

However, Gilman and Howard (1986) could *not* find a rotation about the group center. A precise investigation of this phenomenon would be desirable. Sunspot position determining methods (Section B.3.2) could be applied.

B.2.2.6 Relationship between the Umbra and Penumbra Areas

Each sunspot group begins its development as a small individual spot, an umbra without a penumbra. The penumbra increases in significance as the sunspot group increases in area. Large *F* groups often exhibit enormous penumbrae which surround numerous sunspots. As the group breaks up, the penumbra area shrinks more than the umbra area. The relationship between the umbra and penumbra areas is thus a possible way of describing the development stage of a group (Deszö and Gerlei 1964). The published observation material is not sufficient to provide a typical development curve—again amateur observers are needed!

B.2.2.7 Brightness of the Umbra

The brightness of the umbra is linked to the magnetic field strength in the sunspot (Abdussamatov 1973) and should therefore change during the development of the spot. The maximum area and the minimum umbra brightness in a sunspot group coincide. To estimate the umbra brightness, scales of "very dark" to "very bright" are often used. However, the use of such scales is inadvisable as (*a*) the eye subjectively perceives large sunspots as darker and (*b*) the proportion of scattered light in small spots can exceed 50%. Studies of the umbra brightness are therefore of value only if photoelectric measuring devices are available and the proportion of scattered light can be determined.

B.2.2.8 Rapid Development of Sunspot Groups

During the lifetime of a large group, there are phases in which its appearance changes rapidly. Sunspots appear, others disappear, penumbrae and light bridges are formed, sunspots change their relative positions. Such changes are classed as "rapid" if they are observed within an interval of a few hours. Sometimes developments even occur within minutes. These usually involve the appearance and disappearance of small spots (e.g., Hilbrecht 1977). Since the human eye is easily fooled, photographs of rapid changes in sunspot groups are more convincing than drawings (e.g., Remmert 1979). However, care should also be taken with photographs as atmospheric conditions can give the impression of structural changes. A moment of optimum atmospheric conditions can reveal features in the sunspot group which could not be observed before.

The best way of studying rapid developments is a series of photographs taken at intervals of about ten minutes (extremely rapid developments), one hour (very rapid developments) or one day (development of active groups). To overcome the effects of atmospheric turbulence, three or four photographs should always be taken one after the other with the best one being selected. Details of the penumbra should be clearly visible. Photographing extreme or very rapid changes is an ideal observation program for the weekend and holiday observer. A single summer's day can provide enough information for weeks of evaluation. Although many observers may find the amount of time involved very high, the results obtained make the trouble seem more worthwhile. A series of photographs of an active sunspot group is of scientific and aesthetic value.

Hedewig (1979) indicates the value of such a series of photographs when he enumerates the following data which can be obtained:

1. The speed at which individual spots approach or move away from the center of the principal spot (in km/h)
2. The speed of increase or decrease of the sunspot area of a group (in km^2/h)
3. The speed of light bridge formation and change
4. The speed of development and decay of large individual sunspots

All these measurements can be carried out with a pencil, ruler and graph paper, providing that the scale is the same in all the photographs. To determine the inherent motion of small spots, only the relative positions are required without the absolute values of heliographic coordinates having to be known (see also Pfister 1975).

Following the development of the smallest spots in a group can be a particularly successful activity. Mehltretter (1979) observed sunspots which penetrate into the penumbra of larger sunspots or leave them, whereby inherent motion of up to 250 m/s ($1.''2/h$) occurs. These movements are not known to follow a regular pattern. The answers to the following questions remain open.

1. Is the movement of small spots in the vicinity of large penumbrae slowed down or accelerated?
2. At which phase in the development of the group do the highest rate of inherent motion and other rapid changes take place?
3. Is there a link between proper motion (or other rapid changes) and flare frequency (see also Dezsö 1984, Kalman 1984)?

Examples of evaluating a series of photographs are given by Kalman (1984) (see Fig. B.2.13) and Künzel et al. (1961), who describe the remains of an old sunspot group melting into a new active group, and Waldmeier (1963), who studied the division of a sunspot (see Fig. B.2.14).

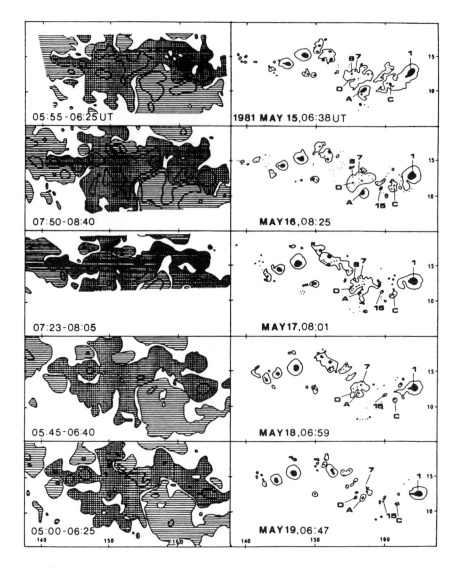

Fig. B.2.13. *Magnetic field maps and sunspot drawings in Hale region 176.
(Kalman 1984).*

B.2.3   Classification of Sunspots and Sunspot Groups

B.2.3.1   Waldmeier Classification

In 1938 Max Waldmeier (Director of the ETH Zürich Observatory between 1945 and 1979) introduced an eight step classification system for sunspot groups which takes into account polarity, the formation of penumbrae and longitudinal extent. In 1939 a further class was added (Brunner 1939). This nine step system is still widely used by both professionals and amateurs (see Fig. B.2.15). According to Waldmeier, the complete classification of a sunspot group consists of a letter for the class and the number of individual spots in the group. For example, a single spot without a penumbra is classified as $A1$. A spot with two umbrae and a common penumbra is classified as $J2$ or $H2$ if its diameter exceeds 2.5 heliographic degrees. $C8$ is a bipolar group with eight sunspots and one penumbra around one of the main spots. The largest sunspot groups could develop right through the Waldmeier classification; smaller groups usually skip classes E, F, G, and H (see also B.2.2.2).

A) An individual spot or a group of spots without a penumbra or bipolar structure

B) Group of sunspots without a penumbra in a bipolar arrangement

C) Bipolar sunspot group, the principal spot of which is surrounded by a penumbra

D) Bipolar group, the principal spots of which have a penumbra. At least one of the two principal spots has a simple structure. The length of the group is in general $< 10°$.

E) Large bipolar group in which the two principal spots, which are surrounded by penumbrae, generally exhibit a complex structure. Numerous smaller spots between principal spots. Length of group at least $10°$.

F) Very large bipolar or complex sunspot group. Length at least $15°$.

G) Large bipolar group without small sunspots between the principal spots. Length at least $15°$

H) Unipolar spot with penumbra; diameter $> 2.5°$

I) Unipolar spot with penumbra: diameter $< 2.5°$

One task for the amateur is to determine the frequency of sunspot groups in the individual Waldmeier classes since professional literature contains little information on this subject. The results of Kleczek (1953), who evaluated observations between the years 1938 and 1950, are summarized in the following table. The second line gives the average proportion of a class (in percent) in terms of the sunspot groups in one day; while the third line

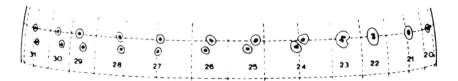

Fig. B.2.14. *Changes in a larger group of sunspots (Waldmeier 1963).*

A				
B				
C				
D				
E				
F				
G				
H				
J				

0°   10°   20°   30°

Fig. B.2.15. *Waldmeier classification system.*

gives its proportion of the daily Wolf number (see B.2.4.1). The fourth line gives the fraction of flare activity (see also Section B.10.5).

Class	A	B	C	D	E	F	G	H	J
Fraction	28.7	11.2	12.3	11.1	7.6	2.0	5.1	8.0	13.8
Fraction R	20.4	10.0	13.1	13.8	13.5	5.9	6.3	7.1	9.8
Fraction FA	3.3	5.4	9.4	16.3	26.2	20.4	7.7	8.6	2.4

The difference between lines 2 and 3 is a result of the different average sunspot number in each class. It is noteworthy that the greatest flare activity is not during the greatest extent of the group (class F), but in class E.

A worthwhile amateur observation program is to determine the temporal changes in the frequency of individual spots (see Schambeck 1979,

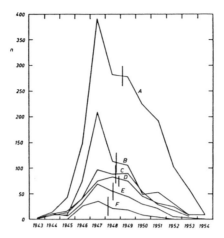

Fig. B.2.16. *Frequency distribution with geometrical center position for sunspot groups of classes A to F in the 18th activity cycle (Künzel 1960).*

Beck 1982, Gericke 1983) throughout the entire course of a sunspot cycle if possible (Künzel 1960, Ventura and Tanti 1988). Further studies are needed.

B.2.3.2 McIntosh Classification

The Waldmeier system is popular among amateurs, for a practiced observer who is using it can usually identify a sunspot group at first glance. However, there are sometimes problems. The allocation of class *G* is often only possible if the previous history of a group is known, and the difference between classes *H* and *J* is of little significance with regard to their development. Finally, there are cases in which the Waldmeier system is inadequate for classification purposes, e.g., in complex groups. Because of these problems the Waldmeier system was altered and extended in professional astronomy. The new system, called the "McIntosh Classification" (McIntosh 1990), is used, for example, in *Solar–Geophysical Data* by the NOAA (National Oceanic and Atmospheric Administration, Boulder, Colorado). The goal of the revision was to discriminate "active" from "inactive" varieties of sunspot groups. This was achieved as demonstrated by correlations with x-ray flares (McIntosh 1990).

The *initial letter* corresponds to the Waldmeier system but without classes *G* and *J*. (Depending on extent Class *G* is included in *E* or *F*; while classes *H* and *J* are combined in *H*, which now covers all the unipolar groups with a penumbra.) According to the NOAA, unipolar groups are individual spots or individual groups of spots in which the maximum

distance between two spots does not exceed 3 heliographic degrees on the
sun. (In *H* groups this distance is measured from the outer penumbra limit
of the largest spot to the middle of the most distant spot.) The appearance
of new large spots in the vicinity of an *H* usually involves the birth of a
new bipolar group, and the new spot is considered as a separate group (see
B.2.4.2).

The *second letter* (small) of the McIntosh classification indicates the
appearance of the penumbra of the largest spot in the group:

x — no penumbra

r — rudimentary (incomplete) penumbrae, irregular boundaries, width only
around 2000 km (0.2° on the sun or 3″ in the sky); brighter than normal
penumbrae, granular fine structure (*r*-penumbrae are a transition between
photospheric granulation and normal penumbra filaments.)

s — symmetrical, almost circular penumbrae with a typical filament
structure which is directed outwards, diameter less than 2°5 on the sun
(30000 km). (The umbrae of the sunspot form a compact group in the
vicinity of the center of the penumbra. Included in this class are elliptical
penumbrae around a single umbra. Spots with *s*-penumbrae change only
slowly.)

a — asymmetrical or complex penumbrae with filament structures, diameter less than 2°5 on the sun (The boundary of an *a*-penumbra is irregular
or elongated, and within it there may be two or more umbrae. Spots with
a-penumbrae change their appearance from day to day.)

h — symmetrical penumbrae like type *s*, but with a diameter of more than
2°5.

k — asymmetrical penumbrae like type *a* but with a diameter of more
than 2°5 measured in N-S direction to avoid elongated leaders which are
decaying and inactive. [If the diameter exceeds 5°, it can be assumed with
certainty that both magnetic polarities occur within a penumbra (bipolar
group) so that the group can be classified as *Dkc, Ekc,* or *Fkc* (see also
Section B.9).]

The *third letter* (small) indicates the distribution of the spots within
the group:

x — individual spot

o — open distribution. The area between the *p* and *f* principal spots is free
of sunspots so that the group clearly comprised two parts with a differing
magnetic polarity. (The gradient of the magnetic field strength along the
line of connection between the two principal spots is correspondingly low.)

c — compact distribution. (The area between the main spots is populated
with many large spots, of which at least one has a penumbra. In extreme
cases the entire sunspot area can be surrounded by one huge penumbra. In
groups with a *c* distribution, there are steep local gradients in the magnetic
field strength.)

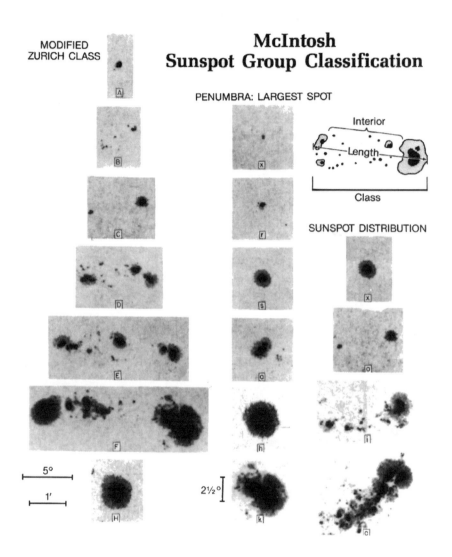

Fig. B.2.17. *McIntosh classification.*

i — intermediate type between o and c. (Some sunspots without a penumbra can be observed between the principal spots.)

Figure B.2.17 further amplifies the McIntosh classification, which makes for more precise descriptions of a sunspot group than the Waldmeier classes.

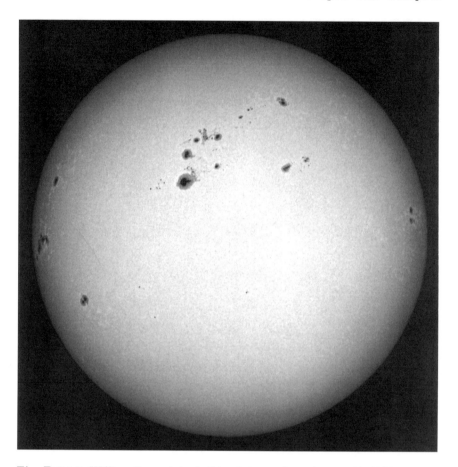

Fig. B.2.18. *William Benesch took this photograph on August 24, 1990 at 15:56 UT using his homemade 5¼ f/15 Daley Solar Telescope.*

"Even this figure belies the great variety that seems among groups. The most complex situations arise when two or more spot groups form close to one another." (Comment by Patrick McIntosh 1995.) The second and third letters of the McIntosh class provide rough information on the magnetic field structure in the group. Statistical investigations based on this classification therefore contain physical information. For this reason amateurs should also become acquainted with the McIntosh classes, despite the slightly longer time spent on observations.

B.2.3.3 Künzel Classification

Another modification of the Waldmeier classification system was proposed by H. Künzel of the Potsdam Astrophysical Institute in 1964.

1. During the final stage of sunspot group disintegration, one of the principal spots (usually the p-spot) returns from being a spot with a penumbra (type J) to a spot without a penumbra, classified as A^*.

2. Uncertain classifications of a group should be marked with *brackets,* e.g., [C]8.

3. It is important to indicate whether a sunspot group is still growing or whether it is decreasing again. To do so requires observations on several consecutive days. The *development tendency* should be indicated by prefixing the letters d (developing) or r (reducing). If no trend can be recognized from the available observations, no letter is prefixed.

4. The number of individual spots in a group should be followed by further details of flare activity, the strength of Hα emission, the type and size of faculae linked to the group, and details of the magnetic polarity (see also Sections B.7, B.9, and B.10).

Künzel's proposals 1, 2, and 3 can be recommended to amateurs without hesitation. However, 4 must be discussed with a view to finding a uniform system for the additional information which is suitable for amateurs.

B.2.3.4 Area Classification

The criteria of most previous classification systems are largely qualitative; i.e., they cannot be measured, but (with a little experience) they can be estimated using the appearance of a group. Mistakes due to a lack of experience or poor observation conditions cannot be excluded, however, and it is clear that a *more* objective yardstick for the sunspot classes needs to be used.

The *total area* of a sunspot group in millionths of the visible solar hemisphere (see also B.2.4.7) is such a yardstick as it is closely connected with the magnetic field strength in the group (see also B.2.2.3). An investigation into the average area of the Waldmeier classes (Beck 1977) showed that the area of class A to class F increases. In other words, the area could be used for classification purposes. In subsequent classes G, H, and J, the area decreases again. Therefore, area alone is not sufficient for classification as for each value there is an early and later class. The role of the second parameter could be played by the *development tendency* (see also B.2.3.3). For each Waldmeier class, the following table shows the variation of the area A and number of individual spots f, and the quotients of mean values A/R and A/f (R is the contribution of the group to the Wolf number (see

B.2.4.1) calculated in accordance with $R = 10g + f$). The number of individual spots f is not a suitable means of classification for two reasons: the ranges of variation for the individual Waldmeier classes overlap (one group of 10 spots can belong to classes B, C, D, G, or H), and secondly, the counting of the spots is disrupted by a number of external influences (see B.2.4.6). The classification of sunspot groups on the basis of area should be widely used in amateur studies.

Class	A	f	A/R	A/f
A	2–20	1–5	1	4
B	20–50	5–15	2	4
C	50–200	10–20	5	8
D	200–500	10–30	12	18
E	500–1000	20–40	19	25
F	1000–(3000)	30–(80)	31	36
G	500–1000	10–20	30	50
H	200–500	1–15	19	44
J	20–200	1–5	8	37

B.2.3.5   Magnetic (Mt. Wilson) Classification

In professional astronomy, sunspot groups are often classified according to their magnetic polarity (α for unipolar, β for bipolar, γ and δ for complex groups, with subclasses; see Bray and Loughhead (1964), p. 234). For amateurs this system is not attractive as measurements of the magnetic field cannot be made directly. Some inference from H-alpha structure is possible from DayStar filtergrams and direct visual observation (see also Section B.8).

B.2.3.6   Schulze's Umbra Classification

In 1978 German amateur W. Schulze studied the question of whether the size of umbrae follows a particular distribution pattern. He based his study on approximately 2000 observations from the years 1960 to 1976.

The area of the umbrae was estimated on the projection screen using a sunspot for comparison and classed according to a 5 point size scale (see table below), taking into account perspective foreshortening. The lower limit for size class 1 (0°25 on the sun or $4''$ in the sky) is roughly the borderline between a pore and a sunspot (see also B.2.4.3). With a small refractor, as used by Schulze, pores can only be picked out in quiet atmospheric conditions, a situation which distorts the statistics. The sunspot numbers of class 1 are also largely subject to the observation conditions; Schulze (1978) multiplied them by factor k (B.2.4.5).

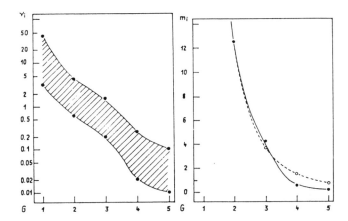

Fig. B.2.19. *Average annual number of umbrae (left) and fractions m_i (right) in the individual classes.*

The average annual number of umbrae in the individual size class G is shown at the left-hand side of Fig. B.2.19. The distribution is given by the second singular highest and second lowest value in the observation period. On the right is the fraction m_i in the classes related to class 1 (= 100%). The broken line shows function $m_i = 100G^{-3}$. The average proportion of umbrae in the various classes during the observation period is given below:

Class:	1	2	3	4	5
Prop. %:	85.2	10.6	3.5	0.5	0.2

It is important to study whether the distribution of the umbra size-classes changes during the eleven year sunspot cycle. According to Schulze, umbrae in classes 2 and 3 occur immediately before and after the sunspot minimum much more frequently than during the minimum or in the maximum years. Furthermore, umbrae of these classes are more frequent during the decreasing part of the sunspot cycle than the increasing part. To date it has not been possible to comment on variations of frequency in classes 4 and 5 due to the infrequency of these umbrae.

It is instructive to compare the frequency of umbra sizes with that of the total area of the sunspot group (see B.2.3.4). Does the Wolf number of the groups in an area class decrease in the same way as the umbrae in Schulze's size classes? Does the maximum frequency of the highest and lowest area classes coincide with the maximum of the highest and lowest umbra classes, or does phase shifting take place? These and other questions await an answer.

Schulze's Sunspot Classification (MH indicates millionths of the hemisphere ($3.0435 10^6 \ km^2$))					
Magnitude scale G	Diameter on the sun in degrees	in km	Area A_U in MH	Mean value A_U in MH	Diameter of comparison spot in mm
1	0.25 – 0.8	2840 – 9060	2 – 21	5	0.5 – 1.6
2	0.8 – 1.2	9060 – 13590	21 – 47	30	1.6 – 2.4
3	1.2 – 1.6	13590 – 18120	47 – 84	55	2.4 – 3.2
4	1.6 – 2.0	18120 – 22650	84 – 132	95	3.2 – 4.0
5	>2.0	>22650	>132	150	>4.0

B.2.4 Measurements of Sunspot Activity

Solar activity is best measured by the intensities in the radio, UV or x-ray spectral ranges—all of which are not available to the owner of an optical telescope.

B.2.4.1 The Sunspot Number

The "sunspot number" (also known as the Wolf number in English) which was introduced by Rudolf Wolf in 1848 is a simple and globally used means of characterizing solar activity though somewhat inexact and of limited use for physical investigations. The Wolf number is a basis for numerous investigations into solar-terrestrial relationships. In amateur astronomy, determining the Wolf number is one of the most popular observation programs and is one which can even be carried out with the smallest telescopes. Wolf intended to verify the sunspot frequency cycle which had been suggested by the amateur astronomer H. Schwabe and determine, if necessary, the exact period length. To do so he had to collect numerous, very scattered, and highly dissimilar observations of sunspots and reduce them to a uniform measure. To bring together the old and future observations, Wolf introduced the number R, based on the following formula:

$$R = k(10g + f) \qquad\qquad (B.2.4)$$

where g is the number of sunspot groups on the sun (see B.2.3.1) and f, the total number of all sunspots in these groups. If there is just one spot on the sun, $R = 11$. In a group of five spots, $R = 15$; 5 independent individual spots, on the other hand, yield $R = 55$.

Wolf determined his number by observation using a Fraunhofer refractor with an 8 cm aperture and a focal length of 110 cm with an magnification factor of 64. This instrument is still in use today for solar observation on the roof of the Zürich observatory 20 m above the ground. To obtain as complete Wolf number statistics as possible, observations made by other astronomers using different instruments were included. To reduce these observations to a uniform scale (i.e., his own), Wolf introduced the "reduction factor." For his instrument and his way of counting the spots, Wolf used $k = 1$. On journeys he used hand-held telescopes where $k = 1.5$.

Using his method, Wolf was able to start a complete series using earlier observations dating back to 1749. Between 1848 and 1893 all observations were reduced to Wolf's; between 1894 and 1926, to A. Wolfer's; and from 1927 to 1944, to W. Brunner's. M. Waldmeier then continued the observations until 1979. H.U. Keller now determines the Wolf number using the Fraunhofer telescope. At the beginning of 1981 the task of collecting, evaluating and publishing Wolf numbers went to the Sunspot Index Data Center in Uccle, Belgium.

Despite several changes of director at the Zürich observatory, the scale of Wolf numbers has remained more or less constant for over 200 years (see B.2.4.7). From a sixteen year long series of parallel observations carried out by Wolf and Wolfer, the result was a reduction factor of $k = 0.60$ for Wolf; while Brunner's, Waldmeier's, and Zelenka's numbers showed no systematic difference to Wolfer's. The jump from Wolf to Wolfer occurred because Wolfer had introduced a new method of counting the sunspots. Wolf counted a large sunspot consisting of several umbrae with a common penumbra as one spot and did not take the smallest, barely visible spots and groups into consideration. Wolfer and his successors counted every umbra as a spot and did not ignore the smallest spots (see also B.2.4.3). Until 1979, apart from Prof. Waldmeier ($k = 0.60$), there were four assistants ($k = 0.58$ to 0.63) engaged in determining the Wolf number in Zürich. In addition to this, the station in Locarno made observations by projecting the solar image to 25 cm diameter ($k = 0.60$). Outside stations and amateur observations were taken into account if observations from Zürich or Locarno were not possible or were unusable due to poor atmospheric conditions. The new center in Uccle has democratized the process in that all collaborators are considered. The principal observer is S. Cortesi in Locarno. (For the history of the Wolf number see Gleissberg 1952, Waldmeier 1978a; Beck 1980; Taylor 1991.)

The use of the reduction factor $k = 0.60$ results in the smallest Zürich Wolf number which differs from 0 being $R_Z = 7$ and not $R = 11$. On 24 and 25.12.1957, $R_Z = 355$ was the highest number since 1749, with the highest monthly average being $R_Z = 254$ in October, 1957 (see Waldmeier 1961). In the maximum year 1979, the Wolf number only reached 300 on one day (10.11.1979); the monthly averages were all below 200. The simplicity of

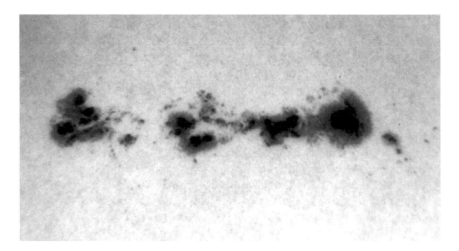

Fig. B.2.20. *Sunspots taken by Gregory Terrance on TP 2415 with a 7-inch Astro-Physics refractor.*

determining the Wolf number disguises the problems which can occur in practice. The following sections will deal with these problems.

B.2.4.2   Group Number g

Sunspots mainly occur in bipolar groups (see B.2.2.1 and B.2.3.1). In the early and late stages of a group, only one magnetic pole (usually the western one) is marked with a spot. Such single spots should also be considered as groups. The division of the sunspots on the sun into groups becomes difficult with groups of spots having a complex structure, such as those which occur during periods of great activity. Here further observations are useful, e.g., day-to-day observations of group merging or splitting, observations of inherent movement, Hα structures or magnetic field measurements (see also Sections B.3, B.9, and B.10). Certain rules can help, even without such measurements (Künzel 1976).

1. Sunspots within an area of around $5° \times 5°$ on the sun (around 60000 km $\times$ 60000 km) are generally counted as a *single* group if no bipolar arrangement can be detected.

2. Bipolar groups, on the other hand, can reach lengths of $20°$ and more. Thus the following applies:

    (a) Two individual spots up to $15°$ apart are considered as *one* group if they are the remainder of a large, once continuous group.

(b) A bipolar collection of spots is seen as *one* group if the western section has the same heliographic latitude as the eastern section or a smaller one. The mean inclination of the longitudinal axis of a sunspot group is 1° to 2° in ±10° latitude and around 4° in ±30° latitude (see B.2.2.5).

In other unclear cases of group allocation, it is permissible to add further rules based on one's own experience. Although different observers' varying rules are generally compensated for by the k factor, uniformity should be sought. For this reason, solar observers with many years of experience should allow their personal rules to be openly discussed so that they can then be recommended for possible general acceptance.

B.2.4.3 The Individual Spot Number f

To answer the question of what conditions a sunspot poses greater difficulty than the question of what defines a sunspot group. The physical conditions which lead to the formation of a sunspot are still not sufficiently known (see also B.2.2.1). A spot develops in the region between the granules (see Section B.8), but an exact time of birth cannot be given. In very still air the sun appears to be covered with small A groups caused by enlargements of the intergranular space with a lifetime of a few minutes. These enlargements are usually known as "pores" to distinguish them from sunspots (see B.2.1.3 and B.2.1.4).

Waldmeier (quoted in Husar 1967) defines a sunspot as follows:

1. A sunspot has a diameter of at least 3 angular seconds in the sky (around 2000 km or 0°16 on the sun).

2. A sunspot has a lifetime of at least 30 minutes.

According to McIntosh (1981), a sunspot has to have a size of at least 2500 km. These definitions ensure that in good atmospheric conditions a sunspot can be seen with a 2 inch telescope and that shortlived increases in thickness of the intergranular space do not affect the Wolf number.

Unfortunately the terms "pore" and "sunspot" are not used uniformly in the professional literature because the visibility of small spots critically depends on the spot's darkness and the resolution of the telescope. In the *Solar Physics Glossary* (Bruzek and Durrant 1977), "pore" is taken to mean a sunspot without a penumbra having a diameter of 1″ to 5″ and a lifetime of up to one day, whereas a sunspot in the narrower sense of the word has to have a diameter of at least 10″ and a lifetime of one day. This definition is not really suitable for amateur astronomers as it deviates considerably from the method of determining the sunspot number practiced in Zürich.

Very large sunspots cause new problems in determining the Wolf number. Often a penumbra will contain several umbrae; umbrae are separated by light bridges; penumbra filaments show thickening. The following rules apply.

1. Each umbra within a common penumbra is counted as a spot.

2. Only after complete separation of an umbra by a light bridge are two spots counted.

3. Thickening of penumbra filaments are *not* counted as spots.

At the Swiss Observatory in Zürich the same large spots are counted as two, three, or five spots (Waldmeier 1968). This method of counting appears arbitrary, however, and is not used among amateurs.

The sunspot number in a group generally falls as the group approaches the limb. This reduction does not follow the laws of perspective foreshortening (see B.2.2.4), and the effect is *not* corrected when working out the Wolf number. As sunspot activity on the far side of the sun is not taken into account for obvious reasons, the Wolf number contains *a sunspot activity weighting in the direction of the earth*. This feature of the Wolf number is entirely desirable if it is to be used for solar-terrestrial studies. On the other hand, the reduced significance of the daily Wolf number for describing solar activity becomes clear; for this only the monthly or rotational mean values of the Wolf number are of use (see B.2.5.2).

B.2.4.4   Weighting Factor 10 for the Group Number

In the formula for determining the Wolf number (see B.2.4.1), the number of sunspot groups is weighted by a factor of 10 when entered; i.e., the appearance of a new group is valued 10 times higher than a new spot within an existing group. This arbitrary factor introduced by Wolf has been shown to be useful (Waldmeier 1968). During the period 1945 to 1967, the mean relationship between the annual average of the Zürich Wolf number R and the annual average of group number g was 12 ± 1. The values for the years after 1967 are also in this range. From R/g the relationship between the mean values of sunspot number f and group number g can easily be calculated:

$$f/g = (R/g)/k - 10. \qquad (B.2.5)$$

As $k = 0.6$ is used in Zürich, $f/g = 10$. Ten (10) sunspots per group are observed when averaged out over decades. The factor 10 weighting for the group number in defining the Wolf number therefore means that a group, and the sunspots it contains, on average make the same contribution to the Wolf number. This correlation applies not only to the Zürich Wolf number but to all observers who determine the same group number g as in Zürich. However, this correlation cannot be guaranteed in observation with much smaller or larger telescopes than the one in Zürich (8 cm aperture, 110 cm focal length) (see B.2.4.5). Determining the Wolf number should therefore be carried out using an instrument similar to the Zürich standard telescope if possible. Whether equal consideration should be given to groups and sunspots in the Wolf number remains open to question. If solar activity is described through observation of sunspots alone, then in addition to the number of spots, their size and the structure of the groups (complexity, "density" of spots) also play an important part. To date there have been no statistical studies of size and structure of groups in relation to their activity.

The "inventor" of the Wolf number wrote in 1856 that he would have preferred to introduce area measurements rather than sunspot numbers. The instruments which had been available to him, however, had not enabled him to make area measurements. Also, only by using the sunspot numbers was he able to bring the numerous but dispersed sunspot observations prior to 1848 together into a form which would make statistical recording possible.

The fact that the size of a sunspot is not taken into account is a further reason for the limited importance of the daily Wolf number. A tiny A-spot contributes just as much to the Wolf number as a huge H-spot with a diameter of 50,000 km. As large sunspots occur infrequently during the minimum period but relatively more often during the maximum, the Wolf number during the minimum reflects too much solar activity, whereas during the maximum it reflects too little. To balance out these effects, the value of the weighting factor for the group number would have to be made dependent on the area of the group in question, as has been done in the "new area number" (see B.2.4.8). However, the simplicity with which the Wolf number could be calculated, the factor which undoubtedly led to its being widely used, would disappear.

B.2.4.5 Reduction Factor k

To be able to compare and average out the Wolf numbers of various observers, the reduction factor between the series of numbers has to be worked out. To do so the Wolf number-mean value relationship over a certain period between a "standard series" (up to 1980 Zürich, then the Sunspot Index Data Center in Uccle) and the observer's series is calculated

$$k = R_I / R_{\mathrm{obs.}} \qquad (B.2.6)$$

Standard series R_I amateur solar observers in the German *Sonne* network
use the Wolf numbers of several observers who observe frequently and under as similar conditions as possible (Karkoschka and Reinsch 1982; see
also B.2.5.1). The k factors of other observers are calculated every quarter
and published in *Sonne*. The k factor is often known as the "correction
factor" in literature. The expression is misleading, however, as it suggests
the existence of "true" Wolf numbers. In reality it involves matching one
series of data with another, one of which is used as a standard, even though
both are subject to random and systematic errors. Systematic errors can
be reduced by investigating what the k factor depends on (see B.2.4.6).
Random errors, on the other hand, are a fundamental feature of all measurements and can only be limited by several observations, providing that
systematic errors have been previously eliminated.

The value of the k factor says *nothing* about the "quality" of the observer. A low k factor can possibly mean that "eagle eyed vision" has been
at work or that the atmospheric conditions were excellent, but also that
groups and sunspots were counted more generously than a standard observer would expect. On the other hand, a high k factor is no reason for
giving up solar observation—perhaps only for improving the quality of the
solar filter. Of far greater importance is *consistency* of the k factor. Stable
k factors are an indication of the reliability of a Wolf number series.

The k factor is the quotient of two figures whereby it can happen that
one or both numbers are equal to zero. In two cases ($0/0$ and $R/0$), no
k factor can be calculated for mathematical reasons. Such cases are rare,
however, as annual means for the Wolf number should be used for calculating the k factor. In the history of regular solar observation, there has been
only one annual mean of $R_Z = 0.0$, and that was in 1810 (see Waldmeier
1961).

In amateur circles the calculation of k factors from daily Wolf numbers
is common. Apart from the limited information content of the daily Wolf
number (see B.2.4.4), this method leads to a too high dispersion of the k
factor with low Wolf numbers. By attempting to average out daily k factors,
considerable deviations from the methods indicated above can occur (Beck
1978b). The calculation of daily k factors is not recommended.

For evaluating the *Sonne* observers' network (see B.2.5.1), a third
method of calculating the k factor was tried (Reinsch 1980). For each
observer the pairs of values (R, R_I) for the period in question are balanced
out using a regression line through the coordinate region. This line is calculated by a computer using the "least squares" method; i.e., the sum of
the squares of the deviations of all points from this straight line has as
small a value as possible. The mean k factor is the *slope* of the regression
line. As a by-product, the computer provides the *correlation coefficient* r

as a measure of dispersion between the observer and the standard series. With perfect correspondence $r = 1$, but good correspondence is also given by $r = 0.7$ to $r = 0.9$.

The correlation coefficient is also unsuitable as a measure of the quality of an observation series as there is no possibility of determining which of the two observers has caused the deviation. Only if several observers are compared with the mean of *all* Wolf numbers can the mean deviation of an observer from the mean value be estimated, and thus the quality of his Wolf number series (Karkoschka 1982). Karkoschka's studies have also shown that equation (B.2.6) best takes into consideration the dependence of the k factor on the Wolf number (see B.2.4.6). This method has been used by the *Sonne* observer network since 1982 (Karkoschka and Reinsch 1982).

B.2.4.6   Influences on the k Factor

The determination of the Wolf number is affected by a number of observation conditions which can be split into four groups:

1. Atmospheric conditions: Motion and sharpness of images (see B.1.2), air temperature, wind, cloud, haze, elevation of the sun, location of the telescope.

2. Instrument: Aperture of the objective, focal length, optical quality, enlargement, filter, projection system, mounting, stability of the tripod.

3. Observer: Eyesight, sitting position, physical and psychological state (tiredness, illness, pressure of time, distraction, etc.), care during observation, experience.

4. Level of solar activity.

In principle, all but three of the features on which the Wolf number depend, and therefore the k factor, can be measured. In practice, however, very few such studies have been successfully carried out so that the majority of the above influences are included among random errors in determining the Wolf number. To reduce these errors, care has to be taken that the observation conditions vary as little as possible. If changes have been made to the instrument (new optics, new filter, new eyepiece, new location), the k factor has to be redetermined from that point on. The greatest influence on the homogeneity of the Wolf number series is a variation in the *atmospheric conditions* (visibility) which is worked out from the motion and image sharpness and is classified on a five point scale (see Section B.1.2). Schulze (1978) studied the variation in visibility throughout the year (see Fig. B.2.21).

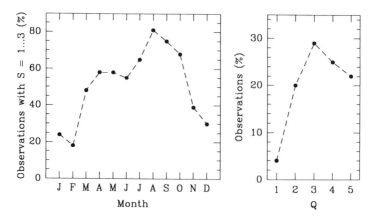

Fig. B.2.21. *Course of visibility conditions during the year (left), distribution of visibility conditions (right).*

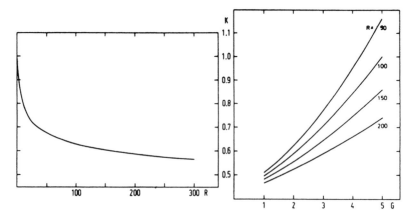

Fig. B.2.22. *Relationship between the k-factor of the atmosphere G and the Wolf number R.*

There have been several investigations into the relationship between the k factor and "quality" (average of motion and sharpness) of the atmosphere G, which Beck (1978a) has summarized and discussed. Despite considerable variations between the results, there appears to be an exponential increase in the k factor with atmospheric quality as is shown in Fig. B.2.22. Since k is also dependent on the Wolf number itself (see below), curves are given for various values of R. The other k factor relationships are in its absolute values; in the figure the value of $K = 1.10$ with $G = 5$ and $R = 100$ was determined at random. More recent investigations by Karkoschka (1982) and Dreyhsig (1985) show that there is no significant relationship between the k factor and atmospheric quality. Further studies are urgently required.

Reducing all the Wolf numbers to atmospheric quality $G = 1$ assumes that all the observers use the same scale for evaluating the quality of the atmosphere. The only possibility is to measure air motion at the solar limb, for example, using an eyepiece micrometer or on the projection screen (Schulze 1980). Estimates of atmospheric quality in their usual form cannot be used. A "spoilt" observer with completely still air would allocate a higher G value to much poorer atmospheric quality than a "window observer" would.

Many years of observations have shown that the k factor depends on the *level of solar activity,* i.e., the Wolf number itself. With an increase in activity the k factor decreases (see Fig. B.2.22). This relationship can, according to Beck (1978a) and Bendel (1976, 1978a, 1979), be expressed as an exponential function or a power law. Figure B.2.22 shows a power law $k = k_0 R^{-0.1}$, normalized to $k = 1.0$ at $R = 0$.

An explanation for this seemingly confusing relationship is given by Schindler (1981): high Wolf numbers are mainly caused by a large sunspot number f and less so by group number g, i.e., f/g increases with increasing activity. For this reason an observer's Wolf number will increase more sharply with better optics or better atmospheric conditions than that of a standard observer as the observation conditions affect the spot number more than the group number. To the standard observer, however, a lower k factor is obtained by reduction than during a period of low solar activity.

From the above we can conclude that the relationship between R_I and R is *not* linear as assumed in B.2.4.5. The deviations from direct proportionality can, however, only be determined during periods of high solar activity. The reason for this effect lies in the definition of the Wolf number itself, which assumes a constant relationship f/g (see B.2.4.4).

Detailed studies into the relationship between the k factor and *aperture D of the instrument used for observation* (refractor) were undertaken by Seeck and Hinrichs (1977). These observers distinguished between the k factor for groups k_g and the k factor for spots k_f for which the following applies:

$$R_I = kR_{\mathrm{obs}} = 10k_g g + k_f f. \qquad (\mathrm{B.2.7})$$

The results are shown in Fig. B.2.23 in which the absolute values of k have again be chosen at random. The k factor for groups (broken curve) is more or less constant for apertures of more than 6 cm; i.e., the number of observed groups no longer increases. This is not so for the spot k factor (full curve), which decreases slightly above 10 cm. Even with a 10-cm refractor some small sunspots escape observation, as do pores which are often erroneously included in the counting (see B.2.4.3). The theoretical resolution of a

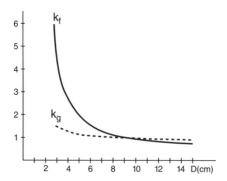

Fig. B.2.23. *Relationship between the k-factor for groups (k_g) and spots (k_f) and the objective aperture D.*

4-inch instrument is 1″2; that is substantially better than the diameter of the smallest pores which is 2″. Atmospheric turbulence, which is much greater during the day than during the night, in practice, reduces the attainable resolution during solar observation (see B.1.2.7).

For large apertures D, both k factors approach an asymptotic value; i.e., the group and sunspot number determined with large refractors approaches a maximum value which cannot be exceeded even with a significant increase in the size of the aperture. Even with periods of great atmospheric disturbance, all the spots are found. (Pores of less than 3″ diameter must not be counted as spots; see B.2.4.3.) In practice, maximum sunspot visibility is reached with a 4-inch instrument so that there is no point in acquiring a larger instrument for determining the Wolf number.

With very small objective diameters the curves approach a vertical asymptote. Below a certain value $D_{\min}$ no more sunspots are found on the sun; i.e., the spot and group number is zero, and the k factor increases beyond all bounds. $D_{\min}$ is around 0.3 cm as the naked eye can just pick out sunspots on the sun if their diameter is over 30,000 km (Keller 1980). The relationship between the sunspot k factor and the aperture (full curve in Fig. B.2.23) makes it possible to determine the size distribution of sunspots (Seeck and Hinrichs 1977). Values $1/k_f$ are plotted against resolution A. $1/k_f$ is proportional to the relative frequency of all sunspots which are larger than A. Resolution A is calculated according to the equation

$$A = \frac{A_o}{D} \ (\text{cm}). \tag{B.2.8}$$

A_o is theoretically 12″, but in practical solar observation A_o is around 25″ so that a resolution of 3″ is only reached with an aperture of 8 cm (see above).

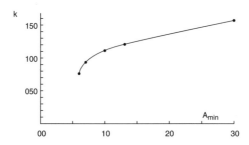

Fig. B.2.24. *Relationship between the k-factor for area A of the smallest spot still visible with the observation instrument (in millionths of the visible hemisphere).*

Seeck and Hinrichs (1977) showed that the relative frequency of sunspots decreases with size. This study should be continued and extended as it enables the size distribution of spots to be determined without necessitating direct measurement of the diameters. Spot counts using various sizes of refractors are sufficient for this procedure. A similar study of the size distribution of spots was carried out by Hotinli (1951). He found a relationship between the k factor and the area A (in millionths of the visible hemisphere; see B.2.4.7) of the smallest spots still visible through the observation instrument (see Fig. B.2.24).

$A = 2$ corresponds to a spot with a diameter of $3''8$ which, in accordance with the above formula, is only seen with an objective diameter above 7 cm. $A = 1$ is a spot with a diameter of $2''7$ seen from $D = 9$. The precise limit of visibility of small spots depends, as with the k factor, on a number of conditions (see above). Changes in one or more of these conditions will also change the limit of visibility; the effect of the k factor can be read directly from Hotinli's curve (1951). This method can be used to reduce the mean deviation of a Wolf number series and should be tested in detail. If, in addition to the k factor of the Wolf number, the k factor for spots k_f is known, the size distribution of the spots can be derived using $1/k_f$ being plotted against the area or diameter of the smallest visible spot.

The Wolf number depends on the *quality* of the entire optical system, that is, the solar filter and projection screen in addition to the objective lens and eyepiece. To date there have been few studies on the relative importance of each of these elements. Wagner (1979) showed, in a simple test, that the spot number of a group increases with a *larger eyepiece magnification*. What is unknown is the change of the k factor, e.g., in changing from a Mylar to a glass filter, from projection of the solar image to direct observation with a filter, from a reflector to a refractor with the same aperture. A study of these effects by amateurs would be an important contribution.

While the effects of atmospheric turbulence and the optical system on the Wolf number and k factor can in principle be measured and therefore reduced to "standard conditions," the observer himself can hardly be made uniform. There will be sharp deviations in the k factor for a beginner until he has arrived at his own personal method of distinguishing groups and counting spots (see B.2.4.2 and B.2.4.3). Thereafter the k factor decreases as the eye subsequently becomes trained. However, deviation of the k factor is unavoidable as the actual physical and psychological state of the observer play an important part in counting sunspots. Hence the following recommendations:

- Do not carry out observations if pressed for time.
- Ensure a comfortable observation position.
- Switch off any distracting acoustic or visual sources.
- Do not engage in observation while ill or under the influence of medicines or alcohol.
- Try to ensure that the observation conditions remain as similar as possible (instrument, filter, eyepiece, location, time; see also Figures B.1.2 and B.1.3).

Of course, these recommendations apply not only to determining the Wolf number but to *all* visual astronomical observation programs.

B.2.4.7   Area Number A

From Sections B.2.4.4 and B.2.4.6 the conclusion can be drawn that the Wolf number may be a simply determined measure of solar activity, but it is not the only one. The presence of sunspots alone is not sufficient to characterize solar activity which is expressed in phenomena which vary in every spectral area. The trend in solar physics is to replace the Wolf number by radio flux at 11 cm wavelength as a measure of solar activity which reflects the magnetic field strengths on the sun particularly well. Magnetic fields are assumed to be the origin of all solar phenomena (B.2.2.1).

If the recording of solar activity is limited to observation in white light, i.e., essentially to sunspots, the measurement to be used should be as closely linked with the magnetic field strength on the sun as possible. This is the case with regard to the *area* of a sunspot (Houtgast and van Sluiters 1948). The magnetic field flux density in the center of a spot B_m (in Gauss) is linked with the area of the spot A_i (in millionths of the visible hemisphere, see below) as shown in the following formula:

$$B_m = 3700 \frac{A_i}{A_i + 66}. \tag{B.2.9}$$

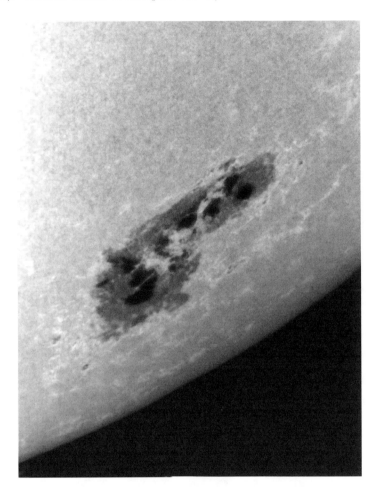

Fig. B.2.25. *Gordon Garcia photographed this massive sunspot using TP 2415 on June 14, 1991 with a 120mm refractor, Mylar filter and #58 green filter at an e.f.l. of 11400 mm, f/95.*

This equation applies to "stable" spots (e.g., Waldmeier classes H and J), not to spots which are in the development or disintegration phases.

Even Wolf suspected that the area of sunspots is a better measure of solar activity than the sunspot number (see B.2.4.4).

From 1874 to 1976 the Royal Greenwich Observatory used solar photographs from various observatories to determine the area A_i of each sunspot and corrected this with regard to perspective foreshortening (through division by $\cos\theta$ if θ is the heliocentric angle). The areas of all the spots were added together and the sum divided by the area of the visible hemisphere of the sun ($2\pi r_o^2$ if r_o is the radius of the solar image used to determine A_i). Finally, the result was multiplied by 1 million to obtain a handy figure. The result is the *area number A* in units of one millionth of the hemisphere (MH) (for details of Greenwich area measurement, see Newton (1958) p. 65):

$$A = (\Sigma_i(A_i/\cos\theta))100000/2\pi r_o^2. \tag{B.2.10}$$

The area numbers were published annually until 1955 in the *Greenwich Photo-Heliographic Results*. More recently the area data has come from Mount Wilson. In the weekly *Solar Geophysical Data* (NOAA, Boulder) the areas of all sunspot groups on all observation days are given. Due to their limited accuracy, these data should be used with care.

An area of $A = 1$ corresponds to a circle of only $2''7$ (2000 km) in diameter on the sun, the size attained by a large granular cell or a pore, for example. Large spots of 50000 km diameter have an area of $A = 650$, i.e., 0.065% of the visible hemisphere. The largest spot yet recorded, in May 1951, reached an area of $A_i = 4865$, and the largest group, in April 1947, reached $A_i = 6132$ (Newton 1955). The highest area number observed in Greenwich was $A_g = 8382$ on 8 April 1947.

Sunspot groups with an area of over $A_i = 1500$ are rare. In the twenty-first sunspot cycle, twenty five of them were observed, the largest reaching $A_i = 3350$ (12 July 1982). During the entire twentieth cycle (1964–1976), there were 23 groups over $A_i = 1500$, the largest being $A_i = 3202$ on 1 February 1968. According to Tang et al. (1984), the distribution of sunspot areas varies with the phase of the cycle. Newton (1958, p. 86) found the mean frequency of sunspot groups in various area classes is as follows:

A_i:	1–250	250–500	500–750	750–1000	1000–1500	1500–2000	>2000
Fraction:	85.6%	9.2%	3.0%	1.0%	0.6%	0.4%	0.2%

Bumba (1965) determined that groups occur mainly in "quanta" of 190, 310, and 570 MH.

As both the area number A and the Wolf number R apply as a measure of solar activity, there has to be a relationship between the two figures averaged out over a period of more than one month. Waldmeier (1941) found a linear relationship between the annual means of area number A_g from Greenwich and the annular means of the Wolf number R_Z from Zürich for the period 1874 to 1938. This relationship is expressed in the following equation:

$$A_g = 16.7R_Z. \tag{B.2.11}$$

As was shown in the following sunspot cycles (nos. 18 and 19), the relationship between A and R during a period of increased solar activity is no longer linear: the area number increases more rapidly than the Wolf number as large spots dominate during increased activity (see B.2.3.1). For the period 1907 to 1970 the following was found (Waldmeier 1978a):

R_Z	20	40	60	80	100	120	140	160	180
A_g	280	580	920	1300	1660	2070	2500	2960	3440
A_g/R_z	14.0	14.5	15.3	16.3	16.6	17.3	17.9	18.5	19.1

In minimum years A_g/R_z falls to 11.5 (Giovanelli 1964).

In defining the area number A, it is assumed that sunspots are flat objects on the "surface" of the sun. The Wilson Effect (see Section B.4) shows that this assumption is false; i.e., the spots have a "depth" (even if not in a geometric sense). Indeed, Archenhold (1940) found that the area of a regular spot (without development) does *not* decrease with $\cos\theta$, as would have been expected with perspective foreshortening, but much more quickly. At $\theta = 70°$ the area is around 15 MH; at $\theta = 75°$, around 25 MH and at $\theta = 80°$, around 45 MH smaller than expected, depending slightly on the spot size (MH = millionths of the hemisphere). The measured area A_i of a spot has to be corrected as follows:

$$A(\text{MH}) = \frac{A_i}{\cos\theta} - \frac{10}{\cos\theta} - 13. \tag{B.2.12}$$

The two correction terms in this equation indicate the additional foreshortening, which is also known as "physical foreshortening." Physical foreshortening was also measured in the group spot number (see B.2.2.4).

A second study of physical foreshortening in sunspot areas by Hotinli (1951) indicated that this foreshortening does indeed depend on the size of the spot, thereby contradicting Archenhold's work. Hotinli gives the following equation for total foreshortening:

$$A_i = \frac{A_i}{\cos\theta - 0.075\sin\theta}. \tag{B.2.13}$$

Physical foreshortening amounts to around 7% of the area in the range $\theta = 70°$ to $80°$. Hotinli's equation can be used to calculate the maximum visibility of a sunspot at the solar limb. A becomes zero if $\cos\theta = 0.075$ at $\theta = 85°43'$. Physical foreshortening prevents observation of a sunspot near the solar limb.

On the other hand, the observation of maximum visibility at the limb can be used to determine the factor in Hotinli's equation and its possible relationship with the size of the spot. If there is practically no relationship between the physical foreshortening and the size of the spot, as stated by Archenhold (1940), then this factor should decrease with size. Waldmeier

(1978b) observed an H spot with a diameter of approx 40,000 km up to an angular distance of $88°22'$ from the center of the solar disk, or $0.''4$ from the limb. From this location the physical foreshortening is only $0.028 \sin \theta$. The physical foreshortening and its interpretation therefore has to be seen as a problem of further investigations for amateur observers.

The uncertainty in the correction of perspective effects on the sun moved Waldmeier (1978a) *not* to correct the sunspot area and to use the area sum (in millionths of the area of the solar *disc*) as a measure for solar activity:

$$A^* = \sum_i A_i \frac{1,000,000}{\pi r_o^2}. \qquad (B.2.14)$$

The sum of the area A^* is much easier to determine than A as the angle θ does not have to be measured. No perspective correction means that the solar activity towards the earth has greater weighting as with the Wolf number (see B.2.4.3). To investigate solar-terrestrial relationships, A^* is preferred to A.

A^*, like A, is almost linearly related to the Wolf number R_z if the annual means are used (Waldmeier 1978a). The quotient A_g^*/R_Z between 1874 and 1959 was around 20 for R_Z less than 60 and around 22 for R_Z greater than 60. During this period the quotient showed no systematic change with time; the scale values of the Zürich Wolf numbers have remained constant for almost a century. The quotient A_g^*/A_g was 1.34 over this period. The uncorrected area sum is larger than the corrected one as the former is related to the solar disc, whereas the latter is related to the solar hemisphere, which is twice as large.

Determining the area number A or A^* is a worthwhile observation program for amateurs offering a number of evaluation possibilities. Area measurements are easiest to undertake on the projection screen with the image on millimeter graph paper (Hedewig 1978b). The same method was used in Zürich and Locarno to determine A^*. Prerequisites for precise area measurement are stable mounting and guiding and a stable projection screen, if possible built into a black box which one can look into from above (see Section A.2.1). A vibrating projection screen prevents any kind of area measurement. The objective lens diameter should not be too small, as a bright solar image should still be visible on the relatively dark graph paper. "Indirect" area measurement, e.g., drawing the boundaries of the spots on white paper and then superimposing transparent graph paper, is not worthwhile as the errors in drawing are too large. One major problem is the poor visibility of small spots on the graph paper. The Zürich area sums are on average 1.7 times lower than the values determined photographically in Greenwich (Waldmeier 1978a). Waldmeier explains this

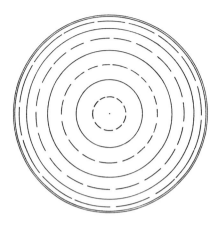

Fig. B.2.26. *Template for determining angle θ.*

finding as "smudging" of the spots by atmospheric disturbances when being photographed. At least part of this effect is caused by the lack of small spots during measurement on the projection screen. (Using the same measuring method, the systematic deviation is only 15%.) Another problem occurs in all measurements on the projection screen. The image of the sun produced by the eyepiece is *distorted,* (i.e., the scale of the image varies from the center to the edge of the eyepiece field of view) and is different for different eyepiece types and focal lengths. Distortion can be measured and corrected if the solar image is always exactly in the center of the eyepiece field (Bendel 1978b; see B.3.2.3).

All of the above problems in area measurement are avoided by the second method in which projection of the solar image is carried out by a negative in a darkroom. Practically distortion-free solar photographs with adequate resolution can be obtained in the primary focus of a 3-inch refractor. The time and material cost is low, as prints from negatives are not required (unless for other purposes). The focal length of the enlarger's lens should not be too short to keep distortion at a minimum (for solar photography see Section A.5).

If the focal length of the telescope is so small that small spots disappear in the film grain, using eyepiece projection will increase the scale. In still air the large granules can be photographed using a 2-inch refractor if their area is on average about $A = 1MH$. Area A of a sunspot is then the approximate result of division of the measured area by that of a granulation cell without the radius of the overall solar image having to be known. Even correction of perspective foreshortening is unnecessary as the areas of the granules are also subject to foreshortening.

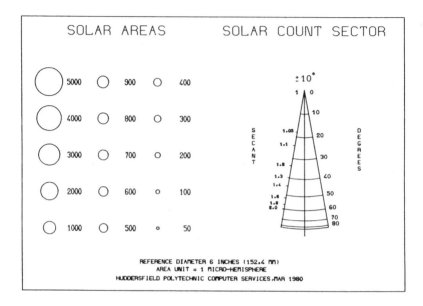

Fig. B.2.27. *B.A.A. sheet for measuring sunspot areas.*

If the area number A of the image of the entire sun is to be determined, the angular distance θ of each sunspot group from the center of the solar disk has to be measured. For this calculation the solar image is projected onto a system of concentric circles (see Fig. B.2.26), the radii of which are calculated as follows:

$$r = r_o \sin \theta \qquad\qquad (B.2.15)$$

with r the radius of the image. An interval between the circles of $\theta = 10°$ is enough to be able to measure θ of the spots to 1° to 2°.

However, measurements for θ of more than 70° are difficult as the concentric circles get progressively closer towards the edge of the solar image. Unfortunately, a small error in measuring θ at the solar limb can have a great effect on area A. Perspective correction is carried out using factor $1/\cos\theta$, which increases beyond all bounds towards the solar limb. The measurement of the area of a sunspot group can thus lead to fantastic values being obtained. In such cases it is better to extrapolate the area measurements of the days preceding or following the observation day.

A third method of interest to amateurs, which was developed by the solar group of the British Astronomical Association (Dougherty 1980), involves comparing the sunspot areas with circles of a known area. The smallest circle which just surrounds the spot and the largest which still fits into the spot are found. The sunspot area is then the average of the two circles. The B.A.A. provides a sheet on which fifteen such circles are shown (see Fig. B.2.27). The 20° section on the right of the template serves to measure angular distance θ. It is a section from the template of concentric circles (see above). At the right hand edge of the section the θ values are given, and on the left the corresponding values $(1/\cos\theta)$, i.e., the correction factor for perspective foreshortening.

Comparative circles for area measurement can be established for any radius r_o of the solar image. If the circle is to have area A or A^* (in millionths of the hemisphere or solar disk), then its radius is r:

$$r = 0.001 r_o \sqrt{2A} \qquad\qquad (B.2.16)$$

or

$$r = 0.001 r_o \sqrt{A^*}. \qquad\qquad (B.2.17)$$

The radius of circle $A = 5000$ is exactly 10% of the radius of the solar image while $A = 50$ is only 1%.

In addition to the comparison circles, *ellipses* can also be developed for larger spots, the smaller axis of which has been shortened by a factor of $\cos\theta$ with regard to the longer axis; i.e., they automatically take perspective foreshortening into account.

The method developed by the B.A.A. is practical for the area measurement of large, regular sunspots. It is more difficult to measure large open F groups in which each of the individual spots has to be measured. The method becomes largely unusable in complex sunspot groups with an irregular shape. In this situation, photographic measurement is vital for precision.

Unfortunately, there have been no investigations as yet into the accuracy of the different methods of measuring area or systematic differences. According to Waldmeier (1978a), the area determined using the photographic method is systematically larger than that measured using projection. The reason for this disparity is presumably atmospheric disturbance (see above). Studies by amateurs could be of use in resolving this discrepancy.

Following is a concluding summary of the advantages of the area number over the Wolf number as a measure of sunspot activity on the sun:

1. The k-factor of the area number, i.e., the quotient of mean values of the standard observer's and the observer's area numbers, should vary much less between observers than the k-factor of the Wolf number. Atmospheric disturbance and the quality of the optical systems, above all, affect the visibility of small spots (see B.2.4.6) which play a small role in the area number. Different ways of allocating the spots to groups are not important as far as the area number is concerned. According to Waldmeier (1978a), the random error of an area measurement is around 5%, with systematic

differences between various observers only reaching 15%. In contrast, the Wolf number k-factor varies by 50% and more.

2. The relationship between the k-factor of the Wolf number and sunspot activity, which originates in the equal evaluation of all groups, does *not* occur for the area number.

3. The area number is of greater physical significance than the Wolf number as the sunspot area is linked with the magnetic field strength in the spot (but not with flare activity. See also B.2.3.1).

Amateur observers should not, therefore, be satisfied with only determining the Wolf number, but should also carry out area measurements of spots. The evaluation of such measurements covers the following areas:

1. Development of sunspot groups (see B.2.2.3)

2. Classification of sunspot groups (see B.2.3.5)

3. Comparison with other figures relating to solar activity (Wolf number, new area number (see B.2.4.8), radio flux)

4. Temporal changes in solar activity (see B.2.5)

For observation programs 3 and 4 all that is required is to determine area number A^*, whereas for 1 and 2 the area number A, corrected for perspective foreshortening, is necessary.

B.2.4.8   The New Area Number According to Beck

Despite its indisputable advantages, finding the area number is not popular in amateur circles, presumably because of the greater amount of time required compared with determining the Wolf number. Ideas, such as how to link the advantages of area number with the easier method of counting used for the Wolf number, led to the definition of the "new area number" R^* (Beck 1977, 1978c).

The table in Section B.2.3.5 gives the quotients of the mean values of area A and sunspot number f for different Waldmeier class sunspot groups. These quotients A/f can be used for estimating the area of a group if the sunspot number and Waldmeier classes are known. The areas of all the groups are added and the *new area number R^** is obtained by the following formula:

$$R^* = \sum_i G_i f_i. \tag{B.2.18}$$

The weighting factors G_i depend on the Waldmeier classes and are identical to the quotients A/f:

Waldmeier class	A	B	C	D	E	F	G	H	J
Weighting factor G_i	4	4	8	18	25	36	50	44	37

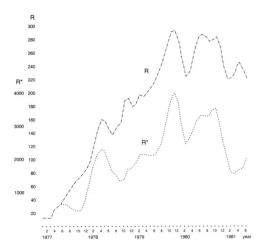

Fig. B.2.28. *Comparison of "old" Wolf (R) and "new" area (R*) numbers (averaged over 5 months).*

The highest weighting factors are those in the late Waldmeier classes G, H, and J when the sunspot number has fallen, but the area of the principal spots is still large.

The relatively rough allocation of groups into area classes leads to the new area number R^* for individual group and individual observation days deviating from the area number A. The new area number (like the "old" Wolf number) as a yardstick for sunspot activity is only significant as a mean over more than one rotation period.

As the sunspot number f depends on the observation conditions (atmosphere, quality of the optical system), the new area numbers R^* vary for different observers. The introduction of a k-factor is also necessary for R^* to reduce the data to those of the standard observer. It is to be expected that the k-factors of different observers will vary as they do in the case of the "old" Wolf number. Advantage 1) of the area number A (see the end of Section B.4.7) therefore does *not* apply to the new area number R^* while advantages 2) and 3) apply in the case of both A and R^*.

Since the beginning of 1977 several observers have been determining both the "old" and the new numbers. Gerland (1978, 1981) showed that both numbers are correlated, although the relationship is not *linear*. Figure B.2.28 shows the variations in the monthly mean of R and R^* between 1977 and 1981 (Gerland 1981). The curves were smoothed by averaging over five months.

The following table gives the mean relationship R^*/R of two observers (see Reil 1980):

Year	1979	1980	1981	1982	1983
R^*/R	3.2	4.5	5.4	5.8	3.9

The relationship between R^*/R therefore continued to increase after the maximum of the twenty-first sunspot cycle (end of 1979). In fact, the highest values for R^* were not observed until March 1982, July 1982, and June 1983 when large sunspot groups appeared.

The original definition of R^* contained a correction for perspective foreshortening, but this was dropped (Beck 1978c) after criticism from observers (Hedewig 1978a) due to R^* values being important only as rotation means (see above). Moreover, the definition of R^* already contains one correction of perspective foreshortening: sunspots in Waldmeier classes A, B, D, E, and F are rarer in the vicinity of the solar limb (Krüger 1980). Whereas A and B groups are invisible there; D, E, and F groups are erroneously classified as G, H, or J as only the large sunspots are visible. This effect is compensated for in the new area number by the large weighting factor for G, H, and J groups.

The question of whether the new area number R^* will become widely used can only be answered once comprehensive material is available to allow comparison with the "old" Wolf number, and above all, with the area number (to which R^* should be proportional).

B.2.4.9   The Paderborn Sunspot Number

Since 1976 the observer network of the Paderborn Astronomical Association has been using its own sunspot number, the "Paderborn sunspot number S_{PB}" which is defined as

$$S_{PB} = Gr + Grfp + Grf + Efp + Ef. \qquad (B.2.19)$$

Where Gr (groups) is the number of structures with at least two umbrae, there is also one penumbra with two umbrae, but not individual sunspots. $Grfp$ is the total number of all sunspots with penumbrae within the groups; Grf is the total number of all spots without penumbrae in the groups. Epf is the number of individual spots with a penumbra and only one umbra; Ef is the number of individual spots without a penumbra (Wiechoczek 1977).

Initial results show that $Grfp$ and Grf are the decisive components (Grf dominating almost without exception) in the overall activity and that they vary fairly asynchronously with the Zürich Wolf number. The course of Gr is more even, as there is no multiplication by 10, and Efp and Ef, as stated above, do not count as groups. Efp and Ef only assume values of between 0 and 3 and seem to play a subjugated role in overall activity.

Evaluation of the data from the observer network is carried out using two weighting factors: the instrument factor F_G and the condition factor F_B. The standard instrument is the 60 mm refractor. F_G is obtained from the division of the aperture of the observation instrument by 60 mm. F_B is determined through the atmospheric quality G (see Section B.1.3) in accordance with the following table:

$$G: \quad 1 \quad 2 \quad 3 \quad 4 \quad 5$$
$$F_B: \quad 2 \quad 1.5 \quad 1 \quad 0.5 \quad 0.1$$

Both factors are arbitrary. The product of F_G and F_B is the overall weighting factor with which the observer's data are entered into the statistics. The sum of all observations on one day must then be divided by the sum of all the weighting factors. The higher this sum, the more reliable the S_{PB} value for that day. Fluctuations caused by varying participation by observers are reduced in importance if more people are involved. The main problem with S_{PB} is obtaining reliable observers. Many years of experience are necessary to be able to decide on the usability of a new sunspot number.

B.2.4.10   The Pettis Sunspot Number

Pettis (1978) introduced a further sunspot number which takes into account the formation of penumbrae as a sign of high solar activity:

$$SN = 10p + s \qquad \text{(B.2.20)}$$

where p is the number of sunspots with penumbrae, and s is the number of sunspots without penumbrae. A spot with a penumbra and several umbrae is counted as $p = 1$. Experiences with SN were published by Götz (1984, 1985).

B.2.4.11   The Activity Area Number

To answer the question of how solar activity can be described reliably yet simply, Fracastoro and Marocchi (1978) developed an "activity area number" (n). The number of 5° bands in heliographic latitude in which at least one spot has been observed in the month being studied is given by n. The number and size of the spots are not considered, only the distribution of the spots in heliographic latitudes. If the period of one solar rotation is studied rather than a period of one month, n can be read directly from the synoptic charts (see Section B.3.3.1).

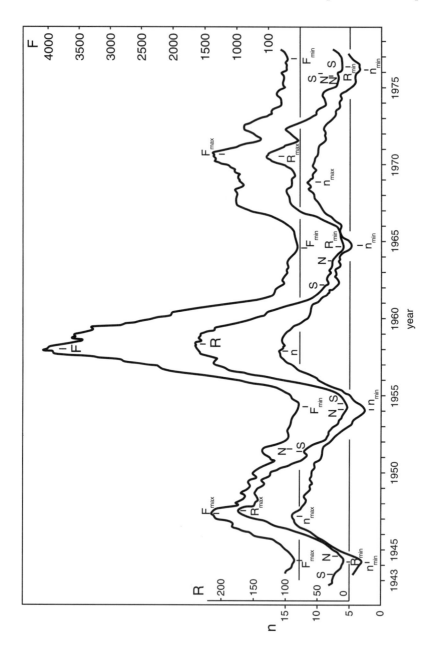

Fig. B.2.29. *Comparison of Wolf number R, and activity area number n.*

| SUNSPOT NUMBERS IN MONTH | | | | | | | | | | | | | | | 19 |

Observer (Name, Address):

geogr. Longitude: Latitude:

Instrument/Method:
O Refractor   Ø= _____ mm, f= _____ mm
O Reflector   Magnification: _____ x
O Binocular: _____ x _____ mm
O visual;   O Projection, Ø: ____ mm;   O photogr.

Day	Time UT hh:m	Motion M 1-5	Sharpn S 1-5	Quality Q	North g_n	f_n	South g_s	f_s	total g g_n+g_s	f f_n+f_s	Re ·10g+f	Beck index R_B	Pettis number p	s	SN ·10p+s	Classif. value CV	naked eye A	
1																		
2																		
3																		
4																		
5																		
6																		
7																		
8																		
9																		
10																		
11																		
12																		
13																		
14																		
15																		
16																		
17																		
18																		
19																		
20																		
21																		
22																		
23																		
24																		
25																		
26																		
27																		
28																		
29																		
30																		
31																		
Sum:																		
Number:																		
Mean:																		

Quality: 1-E (xcellent), 2-G(ood), 3-F(air), 4-P(oor), 5-W(orthless); Motion, Scharpness: modified Kiepenheuer scale, values: 1 (no image motion), 2, 3, 4 or 5 (motion· 6)

Fig. B.2.30a. *Sonne network solar activity sheet. Sunspot Numbers in Month.*

Key to Figure B.2.30a

In Month 19	: Month and year of observation.
Observer:	Name and address of observer and geographical coordinates of observing place.
Instrument/Method:	Type of instrument used for observing (Refractor, Reflector or Binocular) and optical details (effective aperture ø, focal length f in mm, and magnification used for sunspot counting, or magnification and aperture in mm for binocular user), method of observation (visual, projection [in the latter case please also specify the diameter of the projected solar disk in mm], or photographic). Please use an extra sheet for each instrument and method. Changes of the instrument or modifications of the method of observations should be avoided. Please notify of any such modifications.
Day:	Date (day) of observation.
UT:	Universal time of observation.
M, S, Q :	M(otion), S(harpness) of solar image on the modified Kiepenheuer scale, and Q(uality) of the observation (judging see B.1.2.3).
g_n, f_n:	Number of sunspot groups/individual spots on the *Northern* hemisphere of the sun (please fill in these and the following two columns only if positions of sunspot groups were measured).
g_s, f_s:	Number of sunspot groups/individual spots on the *Southern* hemisphere of the sun.
g:	Total number of sunspot groups ($g = g_n + g_s$).
f:	Total number of spots ($f = f_n + f_s$).
Re:	Wolf number ($Re = 10g + f$).
R_B:	New area number according to Beck.
p:	Number of penumbrae.
s:	Number of spots without penumbra.
SN:	Sunspot number ($SN = 10p + s$) according to Pettis.
CV:	Classification value according to Malde.
A:	Number of sunspots visible by naked eye according to Keller.
Sum:	Sum of the daily numbers noted in each column. Readings in this line are used as a check sum for data entered into the computer. Please calculate and fill in these numbers carefully. This will help to avoid errors during evaluation of your data.
Number:	Number of observation days that month of each column.
Mean:	Arithmetic mean of each column.

On the reverse there are nine columns for classifying the sunspot groups (see Fig. B.2.30b). These can be used to note the individual group types (according to Waldmeier scale, see Fig. B.2.15) and the number of individual spots in the groups each day. The forms can be obtained from:

Arbeitsgruppe Sonne der Wilhelm-Foerster Sternwarte

Munsterdamm 90

D-12169 Berlin

Germany

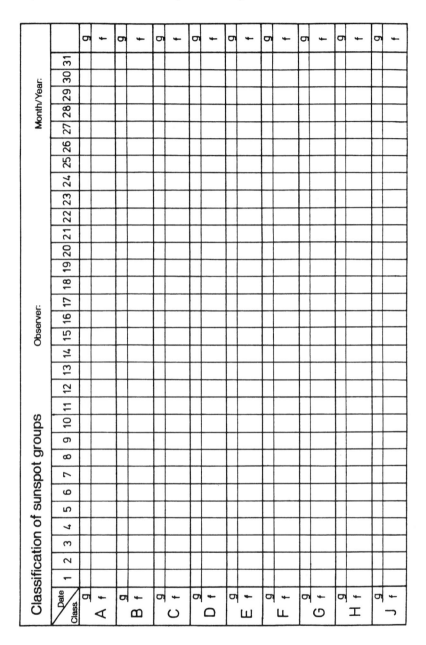

Fig. B.2.30b. *Sonne* network solar activity sheet. *Reverse of Sunspot Numbers in Month sheet (Fig. B.2.30a).*

Figure B.2.29 shows the temporal change in the Wolf number R, area number A, and the activity area number n between 1943 and 1977 (Fracastoro and Marocchi 1978). For smoothing the curves, means over ten months were used. The dashes show maxima and minima of the curves. The number n is particularly suited to determining the maximum and minimum of a sunspot cycle (see also B.2.5.3) as changes with the cycle phase are much more regular than the Wolf number or area number curves. At the period of maximum activity the number of activity areas in the northern and southern hemispheres is roughly equal.

B.2.5   Temporal Changes in Sunspot Activity

The sun is a highly variable astronomical object. Its appearance changes from day to day, and it seems as if sunspots appear and then disappear again quite spontaneously. Only years and even decades of observation will reveal any patterns which could bring us closer to understanding the sunspot phenomenon. Studying the known and finding new patterns provide a fascinating task for amateurs who observe the sun on a regular basis over many years.

B.2.5.1   Wolf Number Observer Networks

The most frequently used measure among amateurs is the *Wolf number* (see B.2.4.1). Continuous determination of the Wolf number is often not possible for a single observer due to unfavorable weather conditions. Also, individual observers are subject to considerable outside influences (see B.2.4.6). It is therefore recommended that the Wolf numbers of many observers are brought together.

In Germany a Wolf number observer network was founded in 1977 in Berlin along with the magazine *Sonne*. In 1993 this network had more than 120 participants (Reinsch 1992, for information about the solar activity sheet see Fig. B.2.30a). The oldest amateur network is the American AAVSO (Taylor 1991), whose results are published monthly in the *Solar Bulletin* and in *Sky and Telescope*. There are other Wolf number networks in Belgium (*Corona*), Bolivia, Brazil (*Nicolini* 1981), Czechoslovakia (*Bulletin o pozorovani slnecnej fotosfery*, Finland (*URSA*), France (Larguier 1980, *Ciel et Espace*), Great Britain (BAA Solar Section), Japan (*The Heavens*), Norway (*Helios*), Poland (*Szymanski* 1981; *Komunikat*), Sweden (*Solbladet*), Switzerland (*Orion*), Spain (*Aster*) and Hungary (*Meteor*).

The various observer networks use different methods of evaluating their data. Some groups rely on experienced "principal observers" and only see "secondary observers" as fulfilling the function of plugging gaps; others treat all the observers as equal (e.g., the *Sonne* network). Only observers using a standard 63/840 mm instrument are permitted to join the Polish network.

No observer can ever determine the "true Wolf number," for this depends on a number of factors (see B.2.4.6) as does every other physical measure. Some of these influences change from day to day, are "coincidental" and can be reduced only by bringing in many observations. Other influences are more or less constant for the same observer (e.g., the optical system). These influences are therefore systematic and can be eliminated using the k-factor with one reference observer being necessary for comparison.

In the *Sonne* network the k-factor of each observer is calculated every quarter as a comparison to the "provisional network Wolf number" of the principal observers (see B.2.4.5) (Principal observers are those with many years of experience whose k-factors show only small variations and can therefore be fixed for a year). The daily Wolf numbers of each observer are "reduced" (multiplied) with a *mean* k-factor. The *Sonne* network Wolf number for one day is obtained from the mean value of the reduced Wolf numbers. The network Wolf numbers are therefore generally in a constant relationship with the "official" numbers from Uccle. This relationship can vary, however, as both the *Sonne* network and the "official" network cannot completely eliminate the influences on determining the Wolf number. Also, the k-factors from *Sonne* and Uccle are related to the level of solar activity (see B.2.4.6). The *Sonne* report form is shown in Fig. B.2.30a/b. The AAVSO form can be found in Taylor (1991, p. 92). The AAVSO observers began "democratically" in 1948, but soon realized that their k-factor was slowly changing with regard to the one from Zürich, and therefore "principal observers" were introduced in 1951 as in Zürich. Despite this adjustment there were deviations between the AAVSO and Zürich figures (Ruf 1977). Presently, the AAVSO applies weighting factors to its observers (Taylor 1991, p. 136).

B.2.5.2   Averaging of Sunspot Numbers with Time

The information value contained within the daily sunspot number (Wolf number, area number, etc) is slight as it depends on the observation conditions. Also, it describes only solar activity facing the earth ignoring the far side of the sun. For this reason the sunspot numbers of an observer network are traditionally averaged out over each month, even though the sun's period of rotation varies between 26.8 days (synodic) in the region of the equator and 29.1 days at a heliographic latitude of $\pm 40°$. An active sunspot group can be observed both at the beginning and end of a month.

The *monthly mean* does not, therefore, truly reflect average solar activity. It is better to use a *rotation mean* over twenty-seven days (period of rotation of the main sunspot zone), although even then sunspot groups can be recorded twice.

Even the monthly or rotation means of sunspot numbers do not show a regular increase or decrease, but vary considerably. Each sunspot cycle has several secondary maxima and minima of similar levels which make it more difficult to determine the time of highest and lowest solar activity. Further smoothing of the curve is therefore unavoidable, e.g., by sliding monthly means of five monthly averages (Schulze 1978b).

In Zürich (and since 1981 in Uccle) the monthly means of the "official" Wolf number are averaged over thirteen months with the first and thirteenth month receiving only half their weighting. This smoothed monthly "R13 mean" is calculated as follows (e.g., for month 7):

$$
\overline{R}_7 \;=\; (R_1 + 2R_2 + 2R_3 + 2R_4 + 2R_5 + 2R_6 + 2R_7 + 2R_8 \\
+ 2R_9 + 2R_{10} + 2R_{11} + 2R_{12} + R_{13})/24 \tag{B.2.21}
$$

or in short:

$$
\overline{R}_7 = \frac{\sum_{i=1}^{12} R_i + \sum_{i=2}^{13} R_i}{24}. \tag{B.2.22}
$$

This form of averaging, which was introduced by Wolf, can be carried out quickly using a pocket calculator. The averaging period of thirteen months guarantees that the curves of the compensated monthly means and of the annual means are similar; otherwise it is chosen at random. An averaging period is better which provides an integer multiple of the synodic rotation of a sunspot zone, e.g., 9 months (10 rotations) or 17 months (19 rotations). However, the differences in determining the maxima and minima of a sunspot cycle are slight (Müller 1966).

The purpose of smoothing the Wolf number curve is to compensate for short-term variations to show up the medium-term trends. From a mathematical point of view, the Zürich method of smoothed monthly means, with its sharp-edged weighting function, is not suited to this task as certain variations lasting less than thirteen months are "let through." Weighting functions such as polynomials, Gauss curves, etc., are better, for they give the month in the middle of the averaging period the highest, and the adjacent months a regularly decreasing weighting. Meeus (1958) proposed distributing the weights for the thirteen months as follows:

1/3/5/7/9/10/11/10/9/7/5/3/1.

The deviations from the traditional thirteen month average are a maximum of 1.2 years for the maximum of the fourteenth sunspot cycle (Meeus 1977).

Karkoschka (1979) investigated various weighting functions and proposed the "P17 Mean" as a result. In this procedure, the Wolf number monthly means are smoothed out over a period of 17 months (19 rotations) by a sixth-order polynomial of the form $(1 - x^2)^3$. Figure B.2.31 shows the Zürich monthly means together with the values for the twenty-first solar activity cycle calculated according to P17 (full curve) and the Zürich R13 method (dotted line). The P17 curve is smoother (fewer turning points) and better because it takes into account short-term variations of the monthly means better than the Zürich curve. The various methods for smoothing the Wolf numbers are interesting from a mathematical rather than a physical point of view as there is great uncertainty in the data.

B.2.5.3   The 11 Year Solar Activity Cycle

In 1843, after 20 years of observing sunspots, the amateur astronomer H. Schwabe discovered that solar activity varies in cycles of approximately ten years. Wolf (1853) improved this value to 11.1 years. The Zürich monthly means between 1749 and 1986 distinctly show twenty-two cycles. (see Fig. B.2.33). The numbering of the cycles starts at zero—with this cycle having attained its maximum in 1750 and its increase not having been fully recorded. The cycle which began in 1986 is number 22 (see also Taylor 1991, p. 19).

Figure B.2.32 shows the running annual mean of the Wolf number and area number (northern hemisphere, thick curve; southern hemisphere, thin curve) between 1874 and 1971 (White and Trotter 1977).

The following table contains periods of minima and maxima and the level of all sunspot cycles observed so far, as determined by using the Zürich method of smoothed Wolf numbers (R13), Wolf numbers using P17, and Greenwich area numbers calculated using the Zürich method (F13). In addition, the time of rise T to maximum (in years) and the total duration D of the cycle (in years) are shown, related to the R13 period in column 3.

Cycle	R13 Method			P17 Method			Max(F13)	T	D
	Min.	Max	$\overline{R}_{max}$	Min	Max	$\overline{R}_{max}$			
0	(1745.0)	1750.3	92.5	—	1750.1	90.1	—	5.3	10.2
1	1755.2	1761.5	86.5	1755.3	1761.5	89.0	—	6.3	11.3
2	1766.5	1769.7	115.8	1766.6	1769.8	122.5	—	3.2	9.0
3	1775.5	1778.4	158.5	1775.5	1778.5	160.2	—	2.9	9.2
4	1784.7	1788.1	141.2	1784.5	1787.9	142.2	—	3.4	13.6
5	1798.3	1805.2	49.2	1798.5	1805.0	51.6	—	6.9	12.3
6	1810.6	1816.4	48.7	1810.6	1816.2	50.2	—	5.8	12.7
7	1823.3	1829.9	71.7	1823.2	1829.5	70.6	—	6.6	10.6
8	1833.9	1837.2	146.9	1833.7	1837.1	150.7	—	3.3	9.6
9	1843.5	1848.1	131.6	1843.5	1848.0	129.7	—	4.6	12.5
10	1856.0	1860.1	98.0	1856.1	1860.5	97.4	—	4.1	11.2
11	1867.2	1870.6	140.4	1867.2	1870.5	143.2	—	3.4	11.7
12	1878.9	1883.9	74.8	1878.9	1884.1	77.2	1883.9	5.0	10.7
13	1889.6	1894.1	88.0	1890.1	1893.6	88.3	1894.1	4.5	12.1
14	1901.7	1907.0	64.4	1901.9	1905.8	63.3	1905.5	5.3	11.9
15	1913.6	1917.6	105.4	1913.5	1917.5	110.0	1917.6	4.0	10.0
16	1923.6	1928.3	78.2	1923.3	1928.5	80.9	1926.3	4.7	10.2
17	1933.8	1937.3	119.3	1933.7	1937.4	119.0	1937.4	3.5	10.4
18	1944.2	1947.4	151.8	1944.2	1947.5	158.6	1947.4	3.2	10.1
19	1954.3	1958.2	201.3	1954.3	1957.9	206.5	1957.9	3.9	10.5
20	1964.8	1968.9	110.6	1964.6	1969.1	111.0	1968.3	4.1	11.7
21	1976.5	1979.9	164.5	1976.3	1979.9	165.8	—	3.4	10.2
22	1986.7	1989.6	157.9	1986.7	1989.8	160.9		2.9	

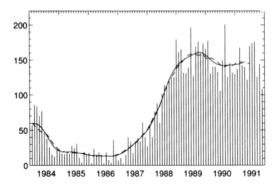

Fig. B.2.31. *Observed and smoothed Wolf numbers monthly means. Vertical bars: observed monthly means; continuous line: P17 smoothed means; dashed line: R13 smoothed means (K. Reinsch).*

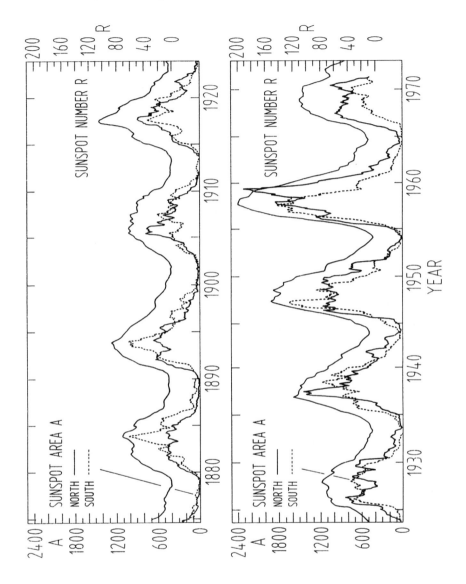

Fig. B.2.32. *Running 12-month means of Wolf sunspot number R for Zürich and area number A for Greenwich (lower curves) for the northern and southern hemispheres separately from 1874 to 1971.*

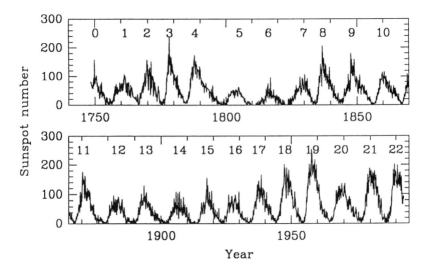

Fig. B.2.33. *Monthly means of the Zürich Wolf number in sunspot cycles 0 to 22 (K. Reinsch).*

The calculations for R13 and P17 are by Staps (see also Bendel and Staps 1980); those for F13 are by Schroeter (1976).

The values based on R13 do not completely correspond to those published by Waldmeier (1955, p. 153) as the latter included other criteria apart from the Wolf number in determining the maximum and minimum periods.

The table shows that determining the maximum and minimum periods depends on which measures and averaging methods were used. The greatest deviations occur in the Wolf number and area number (using the same averaging method). In cycle 16 this is as much as two years! Differences between the R13 and P17 means for the Wolf number are smaller, with 0.5 years for the maximum and 0.3 years for the minimum. The maximum is usually higher with P17 averaging.

A closer look at the maximum periods determined with R13 shows a puzzling effect (Gleissberg 1975). The first six months is clearly overrepresented with fifteen maxima; of these, thirteen are in the months February to May. As the earth can hardly control sunspot activity on the sun, the "error" must lie in the R13 averaging method. In fact, the seasonal effect is much reduced if the periods determined using P17 and F13 are investigated.

Sunspot numbers offer the amateur excellent material for statistical work. Of great importance is a precise study of the effect of the averaging procedure on the minimum and maximum periods and the smoothed curves. A study should also be carried out to determine whether other measures besides the Wolf number and area number are suitable for determining minima and maxima.

Ahnert (1978) proposed the use of the "number of spot-free days" to work out the minimum. The maximum number of spot-free days coincides exactly with the minimum Wolf number except for one month. The number of activity areas on the sun, like the Wolf number and area number, is suitable for describing temporal changes in sunspot activity (see B.2.4.11). Even the number of sunspots visible with the naked eye can be used to determine the sunspot maximum (see B.2.6, Keller 1980, Tarnutzer 1992).

The eleven year sunspot activity cycle was recognized even before the start of regular solar observation (1749) using drawings from telescopic observations since 1610 and from naked eye observations, especially from China. These go back to the fifth century B.C. Wittmann (1978) and Wittmann and Xu (1987) showed that the length of the cycle has not changed systematically in two millennia. He worked out the mean cycle length as

$$T = 11.116 \pm 0.007 \text{ Years.} \tag{B.2.23}$$

The eleven year cycle is therefore considered a fundamental feature of solar activity.

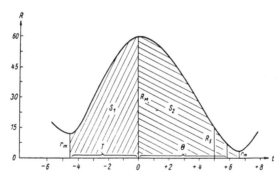

Fig. B.2.34. *Sunspot curve of the eleven-year cycle (schematic); from Gleissberg 1952.*

B.2.5.4 The Waldmeier Laws

Solar activity, which at first glance appears to be random, exhibits a certain regularity if studied over many years, i.e., the eleven-year cycle. The question therefore arises of whether the *sequence* of these cycles follows a regular pattern and whether there are statistical similarities in the *form* of the cycles. Whereas the first question can only be answered with difficulty because of the short period of observation since the introduction of the Wolf number (see also B.2.5.5), the second question has already been looked at in depth.

As can be seen from the table in the previous section, the duration of a cycle varies between 9.0 and 13.6 years, with an average of 11.0 years. There is no recognizable connection between the total duration of the cycle, D and time of rise T or $\overline{R}_{\max}$. The time of rise T varies between 2.9 and 6.9 years (average 4.4 years). The highest cycles (2, 3, 4, 8, 11, 18, 19, 21) show the shortest times of rise. As long ago as 1861, Wolf suspected there was a relationship between the time of rise and the intensity of the cycle, but it was Waldmeier (1935) who first formulated this relationship. Waldmeier found further parameters in the form of the sunspot cycle which depend on its height:

1. The higher the maximum, the shorter the time of rise.

2. The higher the maximum, the longer the time of fall.

3. The higher the maximum, the stronger the sunspot activity five years after the maximum.

4. The higher the maximum, the higher the descent area.

5. The ascent area is almost independent of the intensity of the maximum.

The time of rise T (in years) is the time between the minimum and maximum points of the cycle; time of fall θ is the time between the maximum and the point at which the smoothed monthly means of the Wolf number reach 7.5. S_1 and S_2 are the ascent and descent areas of a cycle, i.e., the sum of the smoothed monthly means between the minimum and maximum and maximum and following minimum.

The "Waldmeier laws" read as follows in mathematical form: For even-numbered cycles

$$\log \overline{R}_{\max} = (2.69 \pm 0.09) - (0.17 \pm 0.02)T, \tag{B.2.24}$$

and for odd-numbered cycles

$$\log \overline{R}_{\max} = (2.48 \pm 0.10) - (0.10 \pm 0.02)T. \tag{B.2.25}$$

These equations were calculated using cycles 1–16. The difference between even- and odd-numbered cycles seemed justified as the polarity of the magnetic field in the sunspots changes from cycle to cycle. However, the inclusion of the following cycles allowed Waldmeier to combine the two formulae into a single equation. If cycles 1–21 are considered, then

$$\log \overline{R}_{\max} = (2.50 \pm 0.10) - (0.11 \pm 0.02)T. \tag{B.2.26}$$

The correlation coefficient r is 0.76, i.e., an assured relation.

Bendel and Staps (1980) found the following for the first Waldmeier law based on P17 averaging (B.2.5.2) for cycles 1–20:

$$\log \overline{R}_{max} = 2.87 - 0.198T. \tag{B.2.27}$$

The correlation coefficient of $r = 0.77$ is similar to the one obtained by traditional averaging.

Waldmeier (1935), cycles 1–16, found the following:

$$\theta = 0.030\overline{R}_{max} + 3.0. \tag{B.2.28}$$

Bendel and Staps (1980), 14 cycles, found that

$$\theta = 0.023\overline{R}_{max} + 3.5. \tag{B.2.29}$$

Six of the twenty cycles did not reach the minimum value $\overline{R}_{min} = 7.5$ and were not considered by Bendel and Staps (1980). The remaining cycles with $r = 0.69$ produce relatively high correlation. However, if instead of the time of fall θ to $\overline{R} = 7.5$, the time of fall to the next minimum is used, no significant correlation is obtained, nor is there a correlation between the overall length of the cycle and its intensity.

Waldmeier (1935); cycles 1–16:

$$R_5 = 0.29\overline{R}_{max} - 11.4. \tag{B.2.30}$$

Bendel and Staps (1980); $r = 0.61$; 21 cycles:

$$R_5 = 0.215\overline{R}_{max} - 2.33. \tag{B.2.31}$$

Waldmeier (1935); cycles 7–16:

$$S_2 = 40.6\overline{R}_{max} - 572. \tag{B.2.32}$$

Bendel and Staps (1980); $r = 0.90$; cycles 1–20:

$$S_2 = 40.1\overline{R}_{max} - 389. \tag{B.2.33}$$

The correlation coefficient r of this relationship is clearly higher than that of the other "laws"; i.e., the descent area and intensity are closely linked.

Waldmeier (1935), cycles 7–16:

$$S_1 = 0.4\overline{R}_{max} + 2538. \tag{B.2.34}$$

Bendel and Staps (1980); $r = 0.57$; cycles 1–20:

$$S_1 = 9.3\overline{R}_{max} + 1484. \tag{B.2.35}$$

In accordance with Waldmeier's assumptions, there is a weak relationship between the ascent area and the intensity, but this is insignificant.

According to Schulze (1978a) only the first and fifth Waldmeier laws were fulfilled in cycle 20, while cycle 21 behaved more "normal" (Schulze 1988). The time of rise of cycle 21 was 3.7 years so that according to various versions of the first Waldmeier law, a value of between 120 and 130 would have been expected for $\overline{R}_{\mathrm{max}}$ whereas $\overline{R}_{\mathrm{max}} = 165$ was in reality observed. The fact that the twenty-first cycle "officially" began in 1976.5 would reduce this difference slightly.

The term "laws" for the relationships discovered by Waldmeier is misleading as they do not involve physical natural laws, but empirical relationships (derived from observation) which are statistically significant. The "constants" in the "laws" have to be readjusted after each new cycle.

The first "Waldmeier law" can be used to forecast sunspot activity. If the average rate of increase $\overline{v}$ (increase of the smoothed monthly means per month) is known, the expected intensity of the maximum can be worked out with the following formula:

$$\overline{v} = \frac{\overline{R}_{\mathrm{max}} - \overline{R}_{\mathrm{min}}}{273 - 109 \log \overline{R}_{\mathrm{max}}}. \tag{B.2.36}$$

For $\overline{R}_{\mathrm{min}} = 10$, the following results are obtained:

$\overline{R}_{\mathrm{max}}$:	50	75	100	125	150	175	200
$\overline{v}$:	0.5	0.9	1.6	2.6	3.9	5.8	8.6

The above equation cannot be solved for $\overline{R}_{\mathrm{max}}$. It is easier to use the "normal curves" published by Waldmeier (1968) (see Fig. B.2.35). The longer the rise of the cycle is observed, the more accurate the forecast of the intensity and time of the maximum. Even with a short initial section of the curve, the sunspot activity for the whole of the current cycle can be predicted. In practice, a curve section from the minimum to 1.5 years is enough; i.e., observation for the first two years of the cycle, as the smoothed monthly means are only known six months later.

If all normal curves are superimposed on each other so that the maxima fall at the same time, they will all intersect around 1.9 years before the maximum at $\overline{R} = 50$. The maximum can therefore be expected 1.9 years after the point at which the smoothed monthly means reach $\overline{R} = 50$. However, this method can only be applied 1.4 years before the maximum as the smoothed monthly means are only known with a delay of six months.

Bendel and Staps (1980) found another simple method of predicting the maximum on the basis of P17 averaging. If the rate of rise, for example, between the seventeenth and eighteenth months after the minimum, is known, then $\overline{R}_{\mathrm{max}}$ is derived from

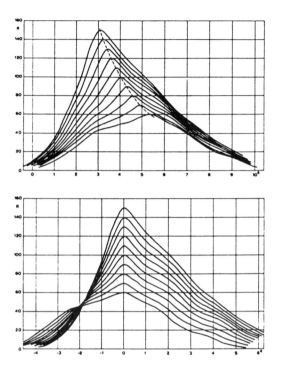

Fig. B.2.35. *Waldmeier "normal curves" for sunspot cycles.*

$$\overline{R}_{\text{max}} = 22.7 v_{18} + 40.9 \qquad (\text{B.2.37})$$

$(r = 0.87; \text{ cycle } 1\text{--}20).$

The prediction becomes even better if the P17 average $\overline{R}_{25}$ is known for the twenty-fifths month after the minimum:

$$\overline{R}_{\text{max}} = 1.39 \, \overline{R}_{25} + 34.0 \qquad (\text{B.2.38})$$

$(r = 0.96; \text{ cycle } 1\text{--}20 \text{ apart from } 9 + 13).$

If the values for the twenty-first cycle are used, then $\overline{R}_{\text{max}} = 161$ and 151, which corresponds well to the observed value of 166. From this, the first Waldmeier law indicates a time of rise of 3.3 years, whereas 3.6 years was observed (see B.2.5.3). The next minimum was expected in 1987; it occurred in 1986.7.

The first "Waldmeier law" is not the only way of mathematically calculating the relationship between the time of rise and the intensity of a cycle. If the observed values of T and $\overline{R}_{\text{max}}$ are on a double logarithmic scale, there is a clear correlation, which is similarly significant to the one found by Waldmeier (cycles 1–21):

$$\log \overline{R}_{\max} = (2.76 \pm 0.15) - (1.20 \pm 0.23) \log T \qquad (B.2.39)$$

$(r = 0.77)$, and

$$\overline{R}_{\max} = (580 \pm 200)T^{-(1.20 \pm 0.23)}. \qquad (B.2.40)$$

Xanthakis (1967) did not use an exponential function for the relationship between T and $\overline{R}_{\max}$, but a parabola:

$$\overline{R}_{\max} = a + b(T - c)^2. \qquad (B.2.41)$$

Using the observed values for cycles 7–18, Xanthakis found the following constants for his function: $a = 55.6$; $b = 13.52$; $c = 5.76$. If cycles 1–21 are taken into consideration, the following are obtained: $a = 59.4$; $b = 5.06$; $c = 7.32$. The correlation coefficient of $r = 0.72$ is slightly less than in the other functions.

Xanthakis' equation (1967) describes the observation of most sunspot cycles very well, apart from abnormally high cycles 9, 19, and 21. If these are not taken into account, the constants become $a = 60.1$; $b = 10.2$; $c = 6.0$. The high correlation coefficient of 0.89 shows that the observed curve has been well approximated—better than with Waldmeier's formula.

Observers who are interested in mathematics will find another area in which to work here, especially as professional astronomers do not have a great interest in questions of solar activity statistics.

All the methods of predicting sunspots described above see the sunspot cycle as a single, independent phenomenon. Ahnert (1978), on the other hand, found a slight correlation between the minimum smoothed monthly mean and the duration of the previous cycle. Schulze (1981) calculated "cycle means" (averages of the annual means for each cycle) and discovered that there is a relationship between them and the interval between adjacent maxima. There is, therefore, a possibility that sunspot cycles influence each other.

B.2.5.5   The Long Sunspot Cycle

Figure B.2.36 shows the annual means of the Zürich Wolf numbers. Observations from the seventeenth century are few and far between, but it appears to have been a period of little sunspot activity, the "Maunder Minimum" (Eddy 1976, 1983). Gleissberg and Damboldt (1979) indicated, however, that the lack of information regarding observed sunspots could be

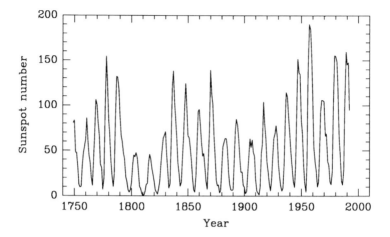

Fig. B.2.36. *Annual mean of the Zürich Wolf numbers.*

the result of inattentiveness on the part of the observers at the time (see also Wallenhorst 1982). Naked-eye observations from China are available (Cullen 1980).

Despite the uncertainty surrounding observations before 1700, it is clear that the intensity of the eleven-year sunspot cycle does not vary randomly, but a series of greater maxima follows a series of lower ones. After the particularly low fourteenth cycle (1901–1913), for example, the intensity of the maxima gradually increased until, during the nineteenth cycle (1954–1964), it reached its highest value since the beginning of regular solar observations. The twentieth cycle (1964–1976) was lower, but the twenty-first cycle (1976–1986) was the second-highest ever. Other phases of low maxima occurred around 1700, 1750, 1810, and 1900. This situation indicates a "long sunspot cycle" lasting around eighty years. Gleissberg (1952) introduced the term "80-year cycle."

The existence of a long cycle becomes even clearer if the annual Wolf number means of the even-numbered cycles are plotted positive and those for the odd-numbered cycles plotted negative in accordance with the magnetic polarity (Hartmann 1971). The curve connecting the maxima on both sides shows a long cycle (see Fig. B.2.37).

The maximum of the long cycle appears to occur earlier in the even-numbered cycles than in the odd-numbered ones. It is, therefore, understandable that the twentieth cycle was relatively low, while the twenty-first as the "magnetic successor" of the extremely high nineteenth cycle, also exhibited very intense sunspot activity. The twenty-second cycle has also developed a high maximum, indicating that the long cycle is rising.

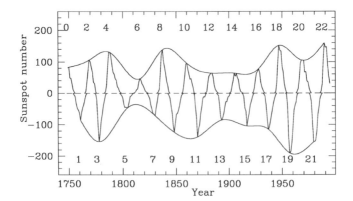

Fig. B.2.37. *Annual mean of the final Wolf numbers plotted positive for even-numbered and negative for odd-numbered cycles.*

Gleissberg (1952, see p. 36 onwards) introduced the "secular averaging" method to determine the minimum and maximum of the long cycle. This method consists of obtaining continuous quadruple means of the minimum and maximum periods of the eleven-year cycles and averaging two successive quadruple means. The same method is used for the intensity of the eleven-year cycle. The long cycle is seen both in the curve for the secular cycle length averages and in the intensities. Gleissberg worked out the length of the long cycle to around eighty years, but a definitive figure will only be possible after a number of long cycles have occurred. A detailed discussion of the features of the eighty-year cycle is given in Schulze (1984).

According to Waldmeier (1957), the long cycle is also seen in the *North-South asymmetry* of sunspot distribution. For this calculation to be appropriate, the Wolf number (or another measure of sunspot activity) has to be worked out separately for the northern and southern hemispheres. Waldmeier (1957) found that in particularly active eleven-year cycles, the southern hemisphere became active and reached its sunspot maximum earlier than the northern hemisphere. The opposite occurred in low cycles. In average active cycles ($\overline{R}_{max}$ = around 100), there is no phase difference between the two hemispheres. This effect can be represented during the course of the long cycle, as in Fig. B.2.38.

Unfortunately, observations during the last three complete eleven-year cycles do not always fit into this picture. In the nineteenth cycle, sunspot activity began in the southern hemisphere but finally dominated in the northern hemisphere. The ratio of sunspot activity between the northern and southern hemisphere was 1.4 (Waldmeier 1966). In the twentieth cycle, activity began a year earlier in the northern hemisphere and dominated

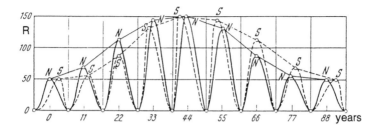

Fig. B.2.38. *Wolf numbers during a long cycle on the northern and southern hemispheres of the sun.*

there throughout the cycle (Schulze 1978). In the twenty-first cycle, activity also began in the north, but since 1983 has dominated in the south so that on the average sunspots were equally frequent in both hemispheres (Reinsch 1985, Schulze 1988). This agrees with Kopecky's (1991) finding that the phase of the long cycle is, at present, shortly after the minimum. The twenty-second cycle started on the northern hemisphere, too.

This scenario shows the difficulties in trying to predict the behavior of solar activity. On the other hand, the unpredictability of the sun is an incentive to work with sunspot statistics in the hope of discovering some regularity after all. The study of north-south asymmetry in particular is a very promising area suitable for amateur work (see Reinsch 1983).

The average lifetime of sunspot groups seems to be of importance with regard to the course of sunspot cycles. According to Kopecky (1967, 1991), the eleven-year cycle is caused by the *frequency* of sunspots while variations in the average *lifetime* of sunspot groups are responsible for the long cycle. As the lifetime is relatively simple to ascertain (see B.2.2.2), this phenomenon offers a further field of activity for groups of observers who can collate material over longer periods of time.

B.2.5.6 Long-Term Sunspot Forecasting

The "Waldmeier laws" (see B.2.5.4) are the basis of medium-term forecasts of sunspot activity. Short-term forecasts of the non-averaged Wolf number monthly means are not possible as these show short random variations of non-specific periods.

Should the eleven-year cycle be a closed, independent phenomenon (an eruption of solar activity), sunspot activity cannot be predicted beyond the current cycle. The existence of a "long cycle" (see B.2.5.5) shows, however, that there is a (weak) link between the eleven-year cycles; i.e., the sun does not "forget" how active it was in previous cycles (e.g., Wilson 1992,

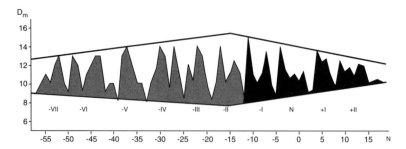

Fig. B.2.39. *The 900-year cycle in variation of the duration of the eleven-year cycles. The numbers indicate the sequence of eleven-year cycles; the Roman numerals, the sequence of the eighty-year cycles.*

Letfus 1994). The difficulties of such forecasts have made many authors think that sunspot activity is determined not by one, but by several long cycles of varying lengths. These cycles can be discovered using the Fourier analysis if the observation material covers a sufficiently long period of time (Wallenhorst 1982). As reliable Wolf numbers have only been available since 1750, naked-eye observations of sunspots, aurorae, and tree rings have all been taken into account to follow sunspot activity back in time. Kuklin (1976) summarized the results of the analyses. Numerous sunspot cycles with periods of between 0.4 and 1800 years were found. It is not possible to check on the significance of all these periods—this will have to be left to observers in the coming millennia. An example is the 900-year cycle discovered by Henkel (1972), which is expressed in the duration of the eleven-year cycle.

Ahnert (1973) derived equations for calculating the maximum and minimum periods:

$$\text{Max} = 1706.0 + 11.0N + 2.2\sin(155°6 + 16°36N) \qquad (\text{B}.2.42)$$

and

$$\text{Min} = 1701.4 + 11.0N + 2.2\sin(144°0 + 16°36N). \qquad (\text{B}.2.43)$$

N is the number of the eleven-year cycle. These equations assume that the length of a cycle is on average 11.0 years and varies with an amplitude of 2.2 years and a period of twenty-two cycles (242 years).

A detailed description of all the methods for predicting sunspot activity is to be found in the book *Solar Activity Forecasting* by Vitinski (1965).

Waldmeier (1981) demonstrated the difficulties of long-term forecasting. Twenty-three groups of authors put the maximum of the twenty-first cycle between 1978 and 1984 with an intensity of between 50 and 200—only four of these forecasts were within the indicated limits of error! In the case of the twenty-second sunspot cycle, it is even more frustrating: none of the long-term forecasts predicted such strong activity as observed in 1989.

Cycle twenty-two will end in 1996/1997. Predictions for cycle twenty-three are quite promising: Even-odd cycle pairs indicate a strong cycle, the sunspot maximum is expected between the years 2000–2002 with $\overline{R}_{\max}$ between 180 and 210 (Wilson 1992, Letfus 1994)! Good reasons to continue solar observation . . . .

B.2.6   Naked-Eye Sunspot Observations[†]

B.2.6.1   Introduction

It is a well known fact nowadays that large sunspots or sunspot-groups can be seen without the aid of any optical instrument except the one we are endowed with by nature—our naked eye. At sunrise or sunset, or if the sun's glare is dimmed enough by fog or haze, we have a direct view of the sun's disk. Under such conditions, spots on the sun were observed by our ancestors 2000 years ago; most of these sightings were made by observers in China. However, only about 200 pre-telescopic recordings (before 1610) are known (Wittmann 1987). It is therefore important to extract as much information from this data as possible. One way to do this is by directly comparing simultaneous sunspot observations by using the unaided eye and then comparing those findings with what is seen at the telescope.

B.2.6.2   Systematic Observations by Unaided Eye

To avoid any damage to the eye, optical filters reducing the sun's glare by a factor of 10^6 must be used for direct vision. Safe filters are arc-welders glasses #12, #13 or #14 (for binocular vision), glass solar filters on telescopes (objective filters for binocular vision and ocular filters for monocular vision), and Solar Skreen[T.M.] (reflective plastic Mylar sheet). Sunspots big enough to be seen by the unaided eye appear through such filters as black points, like small holes in the sun's disk. This observation method certainly is the simplest way to detect sunspots; it is cheap, it doesn't need much time, and observations can be carried out from any place, be it at work, in the streets or on a journey. However, sunspots big enough for naked-eye visibility are a rather rare phenomenon. To detect a spot requires a fair amount of patience, especially during sunspot minimum, when there are seldom any spots visible for weeks or months. At sunspot

---

[†]Written by H.U. Keller

maximum, on the other hand, up to 5 or 6 spots may be seen on the sun's disk at one sighting.

For the purpose of statistical treatment of such observations, *naked-eye sunspot numbers A* were introduced in 1980 (Keller 1980); A being the symbol for *Auge*, the German word for eye. To make a set of observations as complete as possible, a network for naked-eye sun observers called "*A-Netz*" was established in 1984 (Keller 1984). This international network combines about 50 observers and is part of the "Fachgruppe Sonne der VdS." The observers of this network carry out daily sunspot counts through solar filters and report their results quarterly to the coordinator. From these observations, a mean daily naked-eye sunspot number A_{Netz} is evaluated.

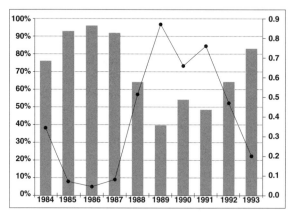

Fig. B.2.40. *Columns: Percentage of days without naked-eye spots (left scale). Dots: Yearly means of naked-eye sunspot numbers (right scale). (Sunspot minimum: 1986; Sunspot maximum: 1989).*

B.2.6.3   The 11-Year Sunspot Cycle Registered by Naked-Eye Observations

Due to the simplicity of this observing method, the scale of the sunspot counts ranges from zero to five or six only. Most of the days the counts are zero or one spot. During a sunspot minimum on more than 90% of the days no spots are visible to the unaided eye, whereas the amount of spotless days decreases to about 40% during sunspot maximum (Fig. B.2.40). For the variation of the sunspot frequency to become apparent, mean values of the daily counts over a longer period must be calculated in the same manner as the Wolf sunspot numbers: In a first step mean monthly values are calculated from the daily counts of each month, and in a second step smoothed

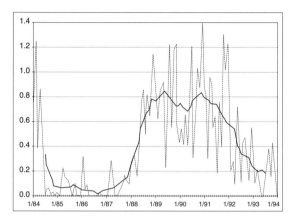

Fig. B.2.41. *Monthly means (fine line) and smoothed monthly means (bold line) of naked-eye sunspot numbers.*

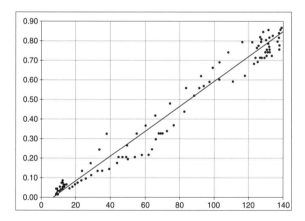

Fig. B.2.42. *Horizontal scale: Sunspot Wolf numbers R. Vertical scale: Naked-eye sunspot numbers A. Dots: Corresponding values of naked-eye sunspot numbers A and sunspot Wolf numbers R (Smoothed monthly means). Line: Linear relation approx. R = 160A + 6.*

monthly means are calculated from 13 consecutive monthly means. Thus it is possible to follow the course of the sunspot cycle as is shown in Fig. B.2.41. The curve of cycle twenty-two reaches it minimum in the autumn of 1986 and its first maximum in the summer of 1989, which corresponds remarkably well to the curve of the sunspot Wolf numbers.

The approximate linear relation between the smoothed monthly means of the naked-eye sunspot numbers A and the sunspot Wolf numbers R is shown in Fig. B.2.42. The straight line obviously doesn't run through the origin of the diagram because during sunspot minimum, when there are no spots visible by naked eye for a long time, the Wolf numbers evaluated by telescopic resolution still are above zero.

With some experience it is quite easy to draw simple sketches of the position of observed spots on the sun's disk (Keller 1991). By comparing the sketches of consecutive days, the rotation of the sun then becomes apparent. Thus it is possible to show that the largest spots can be seen by unaided eye at the utmost for 11 days of the total $13\,1/2$-day east-west passage.

B.2.6.4   Visibility Limit of the Naked-Eye Sunspots

The naked-eye visibility of a sunspot or sunspot group depends on its size, geometry and contrast. Groups of McIntosh type Dkc, Ekc and Fkc with A>500 MH are most likely naked-eye objects. To evaluate a representative average visibility limit, the A proves to be extremely useful because it consists of observers with different acuity, age, and observation experience. The daily A_{Netz} sunspot numbers show if any spots were visible or not, and whether they were recorded by all observers or only by part of them. Of particular interests are those spots which were detected only by a part of the observer group. These spots actually represent a threshold of naked-eye visibility.

To establish the exact sizes of the individual spots, their umbral and penumbral diameters were measured from telescopic sunspot tracings at Zurich Observatory (25 cm diameter projection image of the sun's disk). The analysis was restricted only to solitary, compact spots of an even shape. As shown in Fig. B.2.43, the mean umbral and penumbral diameters D_{MU} and D_{MP} represent the arithmetic means of the largest and smallest extensions of spots, and the angle θ indicates the spots' distance from the center of the disk (center: $\theta = 0°$, limb: $\theta = 90°$). Accordingly, both the mean umbral diameters of 122 spots and the mean penumbral diameters of 117 were separately measured and then plotted in Fig. B.2.44; the penumbral diameters in the upper part and the umbral diameters in the lower part of the diagram. To discern the sunspots which were visible to the unaided eye by the majority of the observer group from those invisible, the former are shown as dots and the latter as open circles. The two curving lines 1 and 2 in Fig. B.2.44 indicate the lower limit of visibility for mean umbral and penumbral diameter. They show that an average observer is able to detect, by naked eye, a sunspot near the center of the sun's disk whose mean umbral and penumbral diameters are at least 15 arcseconds (11,000 km) and 41 arcseconds (30,000) respectively.

For correct interpretation of the visibility limits, it is essential, however, to keep in mind that all observations entered in the diagram are the result of an intentional and concentrated search for sunspots by more or less experienced observers. This fact has to be considered should the result of such an intentional survey serve as reference for the interpretation of ancient pre-telescopic recordings of sunspot sightings by unaided eye; even more so by taking into account that these observations were most likely carried out without the aid of artificial filters.

To gather more information about the frequency and size of sunspots visible without the aid of solar filters, all spot sightings under natural conditions are reported as A^* by the observer group since 1993 (Keller 1993).

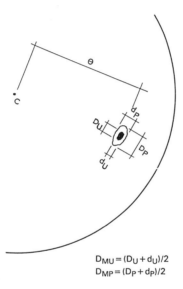

$$D_{MU} = (D_U + d_U)/2$$
$$D_{MP} = (D_P + d_P)/2$$

Fig. B.2.43. *Sunspot position and size: θ: Angular distance between the center of the sun's disk and the center of the spot; if the spot is in the center: $\theta = 0°$, if the spot is on the limb: $\theta = 90°$; D_U, d_U: largest and smallest umbral diameter; D_P, d_P: largest and smallest penumbral diameter; $D_{MU;P}$: mean umbral and penumbral diameter.*

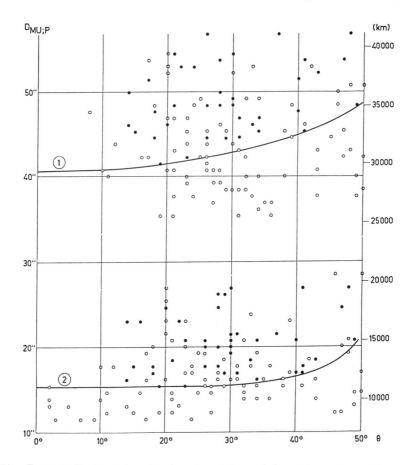

Fig. B.2.44. *Horizontal scale: Angular distance θ from the center of the sun's disk. Vertical scale left: apparent mean umbral and penumbral diameter in arcseconds. Vertical scale right: real mean umbral and penumbral diameter in km. Dots: mean umbral (lower part) and mean penumbral (upper part) extension of spots visible to the naked eye. Circles: mean umbral (lower part) and mean penumbral (upper part) extension of spots not visible to the naked eye. Line 1: lowest limit of mean penumbral diameter for average naked-eye visibility. Line 2: lowest limit of mean umbral diameter for average naked-eye visibility.*

Chapter B.3

Position Determination

B.3.1 Introduction[†]

In addition to purely phenomenological observation of the sun and statistical recording of activity, the measurement of the heliographic positions of sunspots, faculae, filaments, etc., provides essential information about what is occurring on the sun. With a small, equatorial telescope and a projection screen, position measurements accurate to a few degrees can be obtained and the distribution of sunspots investigated. A very stable and precisely oriented instrument allows an accuracy in measurement of $0°5$ and when particular care is taken it can be $0°1$, enabling the study of sunspot and sunspot group movements.

Furthermore, heliographic position determination is an essential aid to many other areas of investigation (such as sunspot development (see B.2.2), latitude movement of sunspot zones (B.3.3.2), inherent motion in sunspot groups (B.3.3.5), and rotation studies (see B.3.3.6)). Knowing a sunspot's position makes it possible to identify the sunspot the next day or in the following rotation. Measuring proper motions of sunspots is important for flare predictions. Section B.3.2 will describe in detail the methods for determining positions on the sun. Section B.3.3 is devoted to some examples of evaluating sunspot positions. Of course, these methods can also be used to determine the positions of other structures (e.g., faculae, filaments, etc.). Other useful position-determination information can also be found at the beginning of this book in the section entitled "For the Beginner."

[†]Written by Klaus Reinsch and Elmar Junker

B.3.2   Observation Methods[†]

B.3.2.1   Heliographic Coordinates

In this and the following sections the terms location and position are defined as follows: The *location* of a sunspot is where it is aligned on the solar image while its *position* is where it is situated on the sun itself. The location is given in plane—either in Cartesian (x, y) or polar (r, θ)—coordinates (Fig. B.3.1) while the position is in spherical coordinates (Fig. B.3.2).

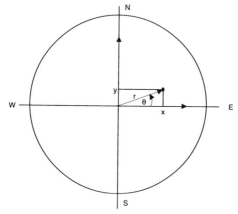

Fig. B.3.1. *Plane coordinate system for location measurement.*

The following conversions exist between the two systems. Cartesian coordinates into polar coordinates:

$$r = (x^2 + y^2)^{\frac{1}{2}}, \quad \theta = \arctan \frac{y}{x}; \tag{B.3.1}$$

polar coordinates into Cartesian coordinates:

$$x = r \cos \theta, \quad y = r \sin \theta. \tag{B.3.2}$$

The use of polar coordinates for determining positions may appear involved, but it has been proved to be very useful when taking into account effects which will be dealt with in more detail at a later stage (distortion in particular).

The position of a sunspot is given in the heliographic coordinate system. In accordance with the geographical coordinate system consisting of

---

[†]Written by Klaus Reinsch

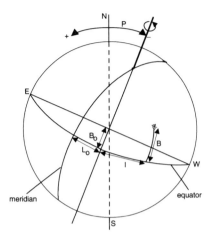

Fig. B.3.2. *Heliographic coordinate system.*

geographic latitude and longitude, the heliographic longitude L and heliographic latitude B are used to describe a position on the sun (see Fig. B.3.2).

The heliographic latitude is measured from $0°$ to $+90°$ from the solar equator to the north and from $0°$ to $-90°$ to the south. The northern solar hemisphere is the one which points towards the northern sky as defined by the Earth's axis.

As there is no invariable reference marking for longitudes on the sun, the heliographic longitude is measured as the angle between the solar meridian passing through the spot and the poles and Carrington's zero meridian towards the west from $0°$ to $360°$. On 1 January, 1854 at 12h universal time, this zero meridian passed through the ascending node of the solar equator projected on to the ecliptic.

Distance l of a spot from the central meridian is distinguished from the heliographic longitude and is measured positively to the west and negatively to the east from $0°$ to $\pm 90°$. As a result of the rotation of the sun, the orientation of its axis, and the annual movement of the earth around the sun, the positions of the solar equator and zero meridian are subject to temporal variations for the earth-bound observer (see Fig. B.3.3).

The rotation of the sun, which is made particularly clear by the east-west transit of sunspots across the solar disc, takes 27.2753 days (synodic solar rotation in the mean heliographic latitudes of the sunspt zone: $B = \pm 16°$) as seen from earth. Since the sun's rotational direction is the same as the earth's, solar rotations are longer than a sidereal rotation

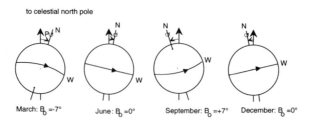

Fig. B.3.3. *Annual variations of the position of the solar axis and equator.*

(25.380 days) which is based on a fixed direction relative to the stars: The sun must catch up with with the earth, which moved ahead due its orbital motion.

The solar equator is inclined at an angle of $i = 7.25°$ to the ecliptic, i.e., the plane of the orbit of the earth. Sunspots, therefore, do not appear to move in straight lines but in semi-elliptical paths, because of this tilt. During the course of the year the northern and southern hemispheres are alternately more strongly inclined towards us affecting the curvature of the paths followed. The heliographic latitude B_o of the center of the solar disc varies between $+7.25°$ and $-7.25°$.

Also variable with time is the position angle P between the solar axis and the north-south direction in the sky (see Fig. B.3.3). This angle is determined by spatial superimposing of the inclination of the earth's equator vis-á-vis the ecliptic of $23.43°$ and that of the solar equator of $7.25°$. It therefore varies in a year between $\pm 26.37°$ whereby $(+)$ is the solar axis inclined towards the east and $(-)$ an inclination towards the west.

The change in the position of the zero meridian is expressed by the heliographic longitude L_o of the apparent center of the sun, which falls periodically from $360°$ to $0°$. The points of time at which $L_o = 0°$ characterize the beginning of the continuously counted synodic solar rotations according to Carrington (beginning of rotation no. 1 on 9.11.1853). These times, as well as the daily values of B_o, P, and L_o, are to be found in an astronomical almanac. A different counting method is used in geophysics where solar rotation is considered as twenty-seven days (Bartels rotation). The period of rotation introduced above only describes the rotation of the sun accurately in the mean heliographic latitudes of the sunspot zone ($B = \pm 16°$).

Numerous detailed investigations in which the axial rotation of the sun has been determined from continuous observations of sunspots, faculae, and prominences, or from the Doppler Shift of the Fraunhofer lines at the solar limb, have shown that the sun does not rotate about its axis like a rigid object, but rotates at varying speeds which decrease from the equator towards the poles. This is known as differential rotation. Its effect is that

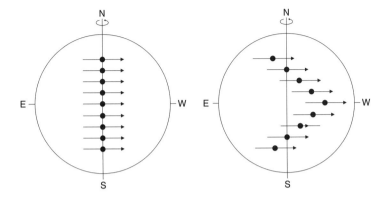

Fig. B.3.4. *Differential rotation of the sun.*

the equatorial zones require around five hours less for one rotation than the central sunspot zones while the rotation time at $B = \pm 60°$ is around four days longer. This means that if on day x a number of sunspots start at the central meridian, one solar rotation later they would not arrive at the central meridian at the same time, the equatorial spots having hurried ahead (Fig. B.3.4). The following table shows the duration of the synodic rotation T_{syn} for several heliographic latitudes:

$B(°)$	0	10	20	30	40	50	60
$T_{\mathrm{Syn}}(d)$	26.8	27.1	27.5	28.2	29.3	30.3	31.5

Because of solar rotation, a sunspot group is visible for a maximum of fourteen days (see B.2.2.3). Its apparent daily movement (synodic angle of rotation) is approximately 13.2°. The mechanisms for the development and maintenance of differential rotation are still largely unknown. Empirical descriptions of the latitude dependence of solar rotation as well as methods of determining the rotation patterns of the sun are given in Section B.3.3.6.

B.3.2.2 Visual Methods of Determining Positions

B.3.2.2.1. Direct Marking.[†] The usual method for determining the positions of sunspots in amateur circles is "direct marking." The sun is projected onto a screen using a telescope, and the positions of the sunspots are marked on a paper overlay. To produce accurate results the projection screen has to be perpendicular to the telescope's optical axis. It is a good idea to attach the screen holder to the eyepiece as otherwise the size of

---

[†]Written by Ulrich Bendel

the image will change during focusing. An overlay made of white paper or cardstock with a circle drawn on it is attached to the screen so that it appears in the center of the projected image. It is much easier to adjust the solar image onto the overlay if instead of a full circle, the circular line is broken in several places. Centering the image is much quicker if a second circle is drawn concentrically around the overlay circle with a radius corresponding to approximately half the projected image. Should the edge of the field of vision just be visible on the projection screen, its position can be determined by moving the telescope so that the solar image wanders out of the field of vision in various directions.

With smaller instruments (2- to 4-inch refractors) the projected solar image should have a diameter of between 10 and 15 cm. With longer focal length optics even larger diameters can be selected if the instrument is mechanically stable. Lightly touching the projection screen should not cause it to wobble.

If an azimuthally mounted telescope is being used, it is almost impossible to obtain relatively reliable measurements due to the lack of precise tracking and the rapidly changing orientation of the image during the day. The instrument should therefore have an equatorial mount. Automatic tracking is helpful so one can concentrate fully on the markings with only an occasional need for adjustments in declination or hour angle. With portable instruments great emphasis must be placed on the accuracy in orienting the equatorial mounting; otherwise rotating images are produced.

As most commercially available instruments are equipped with a non-rotatable projection screen, the following steps are taken in the very important procedure for determining the N–S and E–W orientation of the solar image, which is carried out before and after marking of the spots. With the tracking system switched off, the motion of the solar image on the projection screen (from east to west) caused by the rotation of the earth is observed. The image is therefore allowed to wander out of the overlay circle. With the tracking system switched on again, two points of intersection of the solar limb with the circle are marked which when connected together indicate the geocentric N–S orientation of the solar image (not the solar axis!). This procedure is repeated several times to ensure accuracy. It is recommended that the movement of a sunspot, which has to pass through the center of the overlay or field of vision (to avoid distortion) is recorded with a drawing. The corresponding compensating line for E–W orientation should then be perpendicular to the lines showing N–S orientation (Fig. B.3.5)

If a rotatable projection screen or corresponding overlay template device is available (there are no limits to amateur construction skills), the sun can be projected onto an overlay template centered in the field of vision, which

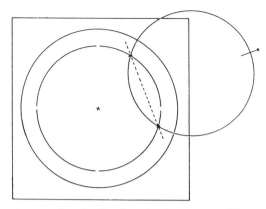

Fig. B.3.5. *Overlay template for fixed projection screen with moving solar image and markings to determine the orientation of the solar image.*

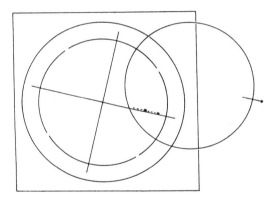

Fig. B.3.6. *Overlay template for rotatable projection screens with moving solar image and sunspot to determine the solar image orientation.*

consists of a circle with drawn-in axis cross (x = E–W axis, y = N–S axis). The x-axis is very carefully oriented in an E–W direction using a sunspot running along it (Fig. B.3.6).

To distinguish the northern and southern points of the solar disk, the telescope is moved in declination. If, for example, movement is made towards higher declination, the northern point of the sun disappears last from the field of vision. With the tracking system switched on, the location of the individual sunspot is marked using a soft, sharp pencil. With a little practice it will be possible to do the marking without touching the projection screen with the hands. Detailed drawings of sunspot groups are necessary for identification and comparison purposes. To make these drawings a second overlay template can be used, or the structures may be drawn, at higher magnifications, on another card.

To make small and poorly contrasting spots clearer, observation can be carried out under a dark cloth or from a dark room at the same temperature as outside. If only the main points of the sunspot groups are to be determined, the customary coordinate grids can be used (Bendel 1979). (See B.3.2.5.1.) On the other hand, if the intention is to determine the position of individual spots within a group, the overlay template can be measured and converted into heliographic coordinates (Roth 1981). For the greatest degree of accuracy, the distortions of the projected image (Fritz et al. 1975; Bendel 1977), image rotation (Vogt 1977), etc., can all be taken into account. The conversion of coordinates into positions will be described in B.3.2.5.

B.3.2.2.2. Transit Method.[†]   Because the *transit method* only requires a stable equatorially mounted telescope but no automatic tracking system, it is a practical method for the amateur. We assume here that the observation is by projection using a refractor. (For other methods and procedures, see Fritz et al. 1975.)

The principle of the transit method is simple. A measuring grid consisting of an x-axis (E–W direction), a y-axis (N–S direction), and two diagonals is centered on the field of view and arranged carefully on the projection screen in E–W direction. With the telescope not tracking, the image of the sun is allowed to pass across the field of view and time T_w is measured between the transit of the western limb of the sun (first contact, solar limb S_1, sunspot F_1 in Fig. B.3.7) and the sunspot (S_2, F_2 in Fig. B.3.7) through the y-axis. In addition, the southern limb, for example, can be allowed to pass along the x-axis, and time T_s is measured between the transit of the sunspot through, for example, diagonal $y = x$ (S_1, F_1 in Fig. B.3.8) and the diagonal $y = -x$ (S_2, F_2 in Fig. B.3.8).

The spot is then located at

$$x = T_w - R_t \ \text{ and } \ y = T_s - R_t \qquad\qquad (B.3.3)$$

where $R_t = \rho/15 \cos \delta$ indicates the radius of the sun in timescale, ρ its angular radius and δ its declination. Also, T_e towards the eastern limb and T_n from the northern limb can be determined, and it is ideal to measure T_w, T_e, T_n, and T_s repeatedly. The advantage of a sharply reduced observation time is offered by using a fine measuring grid (Fig. B.3.9 and B.3.10).

There are many combinations of parallels and diagonals between which transit times can be measured. Two examples will illustrate this. First,

---

[†]Written by Otto Vogt

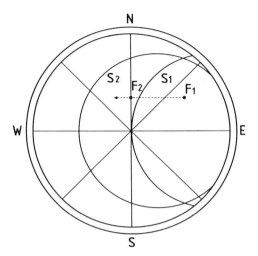

Fig. B.3.7. *Transit method, measuring T_w.*

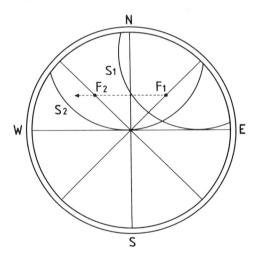

Fig. B.3.8. *Transit method, measuring T_s.*

where D is the grid interval, time t_w is measured between the transit of the western limb through line $x = -D$ (S_1, F_1 in Fig. B.3.9) and of the sunspot through the y-axis (S_2, F_2 in Fig. B.3.9), or, second, the northern limb is allowed to travel along line $y = D$, and time t_n is measured between the transits of the spot through diagonal $y = x - D$ (S_1, F_1 in Fig. B.3.10) and the diagonal $y = -x - D$ (S_2, F_2, in Fig. B.3.10)

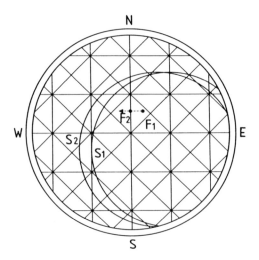

Fig. B.3.9. *Subdivided measuring grid for the transit method.*

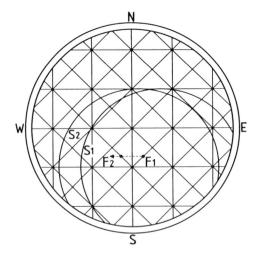

Fig. B.3.10. *Subdivided measuring grid for the transit method.*

It follows that

$$T_w = D + t_w \text{ and } T_n = 2D - t_n. \tag{B.3.4}$$

In general $T_w = m_w D + t_w$, $T_n = m_n D + t_n$, $m = 0, 1, 2, \ldots$). The same applies for the measurement towards either the eastern limb or the southern limb. Depending on circumstances t is either positive or negative. D has to be determined daily. It can be measured either directly or calculated subsequently, e.g.,

$$D = (2R_t - (t_w + t_e))/(m_w + m_e). \qquad (B.3.5)$$

The transit method provides the spot location numerically rather than as a drawing. To be able to measure positions in the usual way using grid overlay templates, a drawing has to be made. It is easier and quicker, however, to calculate positions. (See B.3.2.5 for determining the position of spots from location coordinates.) A drawing should also be made but it does not need to be to scale.

B.3.2.2.3. Micrometer Plate.[†]   A problem encountered during the reduction of sunspot positions which cannot be ignored is accounting for errors caused by the optical system. Distortion has to be corrected, particularly in the case of the direct marking and transit methods. This distortion will probably be caused by an eyepiece which should be observationally checked and replaced, if necessary, until one is found that is distortion free. On the other hand, the image of the sun in the focal plane (primary focus) of a good quality, small aperture refractor will probably show little distortion.

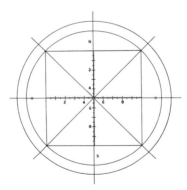

Fig. B.3.11. *Eyepiece micrometer for the transit method.*

This situation suggested the idea of placing an appropriate measuring grid, in the form of a micrometer plate, in the focal plane of the eyepiece (at the eyepiece diaphragm, which must be in front of the field lens—Huygens eyepieces are therefore not suitable). Here the image of the sun is affected in the same way as the measuring grid by the errors resulting from the

[†]Written by Ulrich Bendel

eyepiece, and the results obtained are therefore free of distortion. The filter device for reducing the light must, of course, lie in the path of the rays in front of the focal plane (e.g., objective lens filter). An essential advantage of this method of observation is that, for many amateurs, the often unsolvable problem of an incorrectly adjusted projection screen is avoided. For this purpose an appropriate model (see Fig. B.3.11) is photographically reduced and transferred to litho-film in the required size, which is then cut so as to allow the micrometer plate to be centered in the appropriate eyepiece.

Measuring grids etched or ruled on glass are of course better, in that smaller sunspots are often scarcely visible on film because they are hidden by the film's grain. Micrometer plates made of glass or a similar material for position determination will, however, be expensive. If a micrometer plate is used for the transit method, the procedure is the same as for the transit method with a simple grid. Slightly less accurate is sunspot position determination using the scales on the N–S and E–W axes (slightly modified Ahnert method). To go into more detail on this method would be too involved (Ahnert 1952, 1974, 1978).

Other useful micrometers can also be produced as described above (e.g. a subdivided measuring grid for the transit method). The observer who has the appropriate photographic equipment should make an attempt at this procedure (see also Fig. B.2.27).

B.3.2.3   Distortion[†]

Using projection for the direct marking or the transit methods for accurate sunspot position determination involves taking into consideration distortion which is largely caused by the projection eyepiece.

Since the effect of solar heat can damage cemented eyepieces, simple Huygens, Mittenzwey, or Ramsden eyepieces are generally used. These eyepieces are, however, optimized for other purposes. A Huygens eyepiece, for example, has a very convex field whereas a Ramsden eyepiece has only a slightly convex field toward the eye or the projection screen, respectively. Telescope objective lenses with a short focal length can also contribute to distortion of the projected image. To make the necessary corrections, one needs to measure the distortion with an equatorially-mounted telescope. To make this measurement, make a measuring overlay template consisting of a circle with a system of two coordinates drawn within it (Fig. B.3.12), and fix it to the projection screen. The field of vision (not the solar image!) is adjusted so that it completely fills the circle (diameter of field of vision = diameter of overlay template = D_o). One of the two axes, which

---

[†]Written by Ulrich Bendel

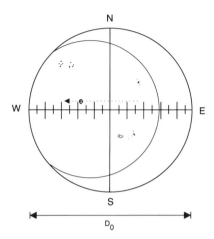

Fig. B.3.12. *Measuring overlay template for distortion.*

is also calibrated, is carefully oriented in E–W direction. This orientation can be successfully carried out if the movement of a prominent sunspot is followed. The overlay template is then turned until the spot moves along the appropriate line.

The radius vectors r_i originating from the center of the overlay template and corresponding to the tick marks i are measured on the projection screen. With the transit method, the corresponding times t_i have to be determined and converted to $\delta = 0°$ ($t_{o,i} = t_i \cos \delta$; δ = declination of the sun at the time of measurement). For each radius vector r_i, t_i should be determined at least five times.

Finally, if $t_{o,i}$ is plotted against r_i, straight lines should result under ideal conditions (similar distances are traversed in identical times everywhere in the field of vision). As Fig. B.3.13 shows, however, a study by the author found a non-linear relationship (distortion!) where $r = F(t)$ or $t = G(r)$. Empirically found formulae (regression analysis) only apply for the selected field of vision diameter D_o and the eyepiece-telescope combination used. Direct marking, on the other hand, operates with a constant solar radius of R, i.e., with a variable field of vision. Assuming that distortion is radially symmetrical, it is possible, however, to calculate approximately R' of the solar image with a field of vision diameter D_o; i.e., $R' = F(T)$ with $T(\sec) = \rho(")/15$ (ρ = angular radius of the sun on the day of observation).

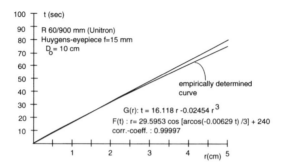

Fig. B.3.13. *Distortion effect.*

For each sunspot n the radius vector r_n obtained from observation is converted according to $r'_n = r_n R'/R$; r_n can now be corrected using $t_n = G(r'_n)$. Finally a conversion is made back to the required solar image radius R: $r_{n,\text{corr}} = t_n R/T$ (Fritz et al. 1975). Correction of distortion can only take place as described if the sunspot position is determined through Cartesian coordinates converted into polar coordinates or directly through polar coordinates (r_n, θ). The correction only relates to radius vector r_n values. For example from a projection of the solar image $(R = 5\text{cm})$, the following polar coordinates have been seen for a sunspot:

$$r = 2.69 \text{ cm} \quad \text{and} \quad \theta = 157°1.$$

The radius of the sun $\rho = 15'48''9 = 949''9$ for the day of observation is obtained from an almanac. Using the above equations the author's instrument produces the following results:

$$
\begin{aligned}
T &= 949''9/15 = 63.327 \text{ sec}, \\
R' &= 29.5953 \cos[\arccos(-0.00629T)/3 + 240] = 4.029 \text{ cm}, \\
r' &= 2.168 \text{ cm}, \\
t &= 16.118r' - 0.02454r^3 = 34.688 \text{ sec, and} \\
r_{n,\text{corr}} &= 2.74 \text{ cm}.
\end{aligned}
$$

With $r_{n,\text{corr}}$ and the invariable value θ, further calculations can be made (see Section B.3.2.5).

Using the normal coordinate grids, one should take into account distortion through the deformation of the grids. It must be remembered, however, that the overlay templates for each eyepiece-telescope combination have to be calculated anew. If the transit method is used in conjunction with a projection screen, producing the subdivided grid in a deformed state is

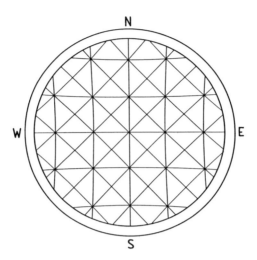

Fig. B.3.14. *Measuring overlay template with curved lines for the transit method.*

worthwhile. Vogt (1977) has described this procedure. The straight line, regular interval grid is considered as being given in a time scale (corresponding to the undistorted image) and it is distorted point by point by changing the values to the measured distortion in the radius vector belonging to the selected points but keeping the direction. This procedure produces a grid with curved lines and irregular intervals (Fig. B.3.14) which can be used as described (see B.3.2.2.2).

B.3.2.4   Photographic Observation[†]

B.3.2.4.1. Position Photography. The main points relating to solar photography are set out elsewhere (see Section A.5) so that only those points specific to position determination are given here. For photographic position determination, two pictures of the sun (double exposure) are required to determine the E–W direction. It is not necessary, even though it may be desirable, for these two pictures to be of the entire sun. One, however, should be. Overlapping of the pictures does not interfere with evaluation, but may cause smaller sunspots to be missed in the overlap area. The refractor is the most suitable instrument for the photographic method. It must have a small aperture and a long focal length so that the primary image of the sun—which is the only one considered in position determination—is not too small.

[†]Written by Ulrich Fritz, Heinrich Treutner, and Cord-Hinrich Jahn

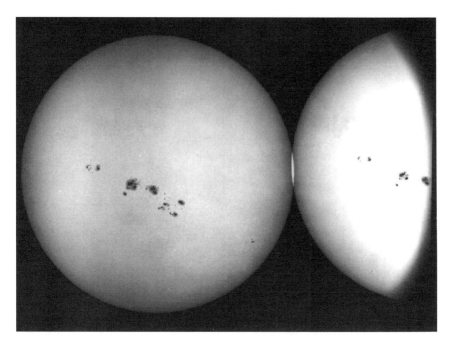

Fig. B.3.15. *Example of a position photograph taken on April 28, 1984 at 10:50 UT (Courtesy H. Treutner).*

A study of inherent motions is also conceivable using a Barlow lens or eyepiece projection. However, the eyepiece must be checked for distortion. The position of the eyepiece and camera must also be fixed so that mathematical correction of distortion is possible (see B.3.2.3).

Special care should be taken to ensure that the SLR camera body is rigidly coupled to the eyepiece because the shutter has to be cocked between the first and second exposures. When cocking the camera the optical alignment can easily be lost with a loose coupling. There are very high stability requirements when using this technique. If any of the mechanical parts give between the two photographs, the picture is distorted and the smallest deviations between one picture of the sun and another will result in an incorrect position, mainly with respect to latitude. A motor drive system facilitates this work greatly. If necessary, manual guiding or clock drive and equatorial mounting can be omitted if the telescope's focal length is smaller than 1.3 m and an exposure time of $1/1000$ second is used.

Fine-grain emulsions such as Agfaortho 25 or Ilford ortho are recommended. Due to differing air transparency, each exposure is separately developed as the degree of development can be specifically targeted.

The exposure technique itself is simple. Once the sun has been focused on the screen, the camera shutter is released using an automatic or remote release mechanism and the time is noted for picture 1. A stopwatch is started and the guide system switched off. The shutter is set—the solar image travels further on—and at the appropriate time, about two minutes later, the telescope drive is switched on again and the shutter released for the second picture. There must be *no* film movement between the two pictures. (When using a 35-mm camera with a long focal length telescope, movement of the film is nearly unavoidable. It has, however, been shown that this movement is usually harmless if the movement is quantified and then taken into consideration during reduction.)

If the two solar images do not completely fit into the film frame, an attempt should be made to adjust them so that picture one is complete and picture two is the one cut off if there are more sunspots on the eastern half of the sun, and vice-versa. As an aid to adjustment, a rough grid is drawn in pencil on the screen against which the position of the sun can be better judged.

Evaluation of the negatives is easiest with properly exposed and developed images. Normal to slight underexposure should be aimed for, particularly if the time-saving "rapid evaluation" method (described in B.3.2.4.2) is to be used. The development of the negative now becomes very important as incorrect exposure can be compensated for by watching the development process in dim light in the darkroom. The developer "Rodinal" has proved to be particularly suited to this method. D-19, HC110, and Dokumol are other suitable developers. Their use depends on the required γ-value (see A.5.1).

It is clear that the time required for observation using the photographic method is *very brief* (around two minutes), which can be a great advantage if the atmospheric conditions are unfavorable, as even gaps in clouds are sufficient to obtain material. To be able to record the solar surface as continuously as possible, observations should be carried out on a daily basis, which can, however, be a considerable commitment for individual observers. Coordination among several observers would be required to obtain gap-free information.

B.3.2.4.2. Evaluation of the Position Photographs. The position photograph is suitable for determining highly accurate positions if a measuring microscope is used and the data reduced mathematically. This procedure is explained later in this section. First of all, we will describe a "rapid method" which can be carried out without measuring microscope and mathematics, which produces good results by using transparent grids (Fig. B.3.17).

The negative is correctly oriented in an enlarger film holder between two glass plates to keep it flat. The image of the sun is then projected onto tracing paper on which a circle of appropriate diameter has been drawn. The edge of the solar disc is made to cover this circle and then focused. The sunspots are then drawn in. The marks for the E–W direction have to be included because they are the basis of subsequent position determination. For this purpose both north and south limbs of the sun are connected by a line, and several sunspots, which appear on *both* pictures, are marked in. The intersection points of the two pictures are also marked.

Once the date, time of observation, angular position of the solar axis, latitude, and longitude of the apparent center of the sun (from an astronomical almanac) have been recorded, the E–W direction is checked using a "T" square and right triangle on the same sunspots in both photographs which have been marked on the sheet. The N–S direction is given by the intersection points of both solar images; it should be perpendicular to the E–W axis. The N–S line need be drawn only through the center of the solar image (hole made by the compass). The position angle of the solar axis is then determined using an angular set square, and this axis is also drawn through the center of the solar image. This is the *central meridian* of the sun, which is required to adjust the grid overlay template (see Section 3.2.5).

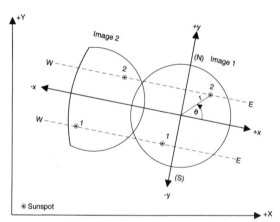

Fig. B.3.16. *Reducing the position coordinates to heliographic coordinates.*

During arithmetic reduction, the locations of the sunspots are first determined using a Cartesian coordinate system (Fig. B.3.16). These coordinates are then converted into polar coordinates, the pole of which coincides with the center of the solar image and from which heliographic coordinates can finally be derived (see Section 3.2.5). When using the photographic method, both pictures are reduced and the results averaged. If, however,

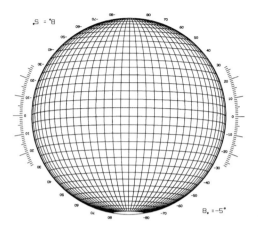

Fig. B.3.17. *Grid for $B_o = 5°$.*

one of the pictures is incomplete, it is better not use it since determining the center point coordinates in the primary system are then uncertain. The incomplete picture is only used for determining the E–W direction.

B.3.2.5 Reducing the Position Coordinates to Heliographic Coordinates

Heliographic coordinates can be determined from the position coordinates using grid overlay templates or by calculation.

B.3.2.5.1. Grid Overlay Templates.[†] To quickly determine the position of solar structures, coordinate grids of the correct size and orientation are placed on position drawings or photographs and the sunspot's or facula area's heliographic latitude B and longitudinal difference l from the central meridian are read off. This coordinate grid is produced by projecting the coordinate system conceived as being on the sun from an infinitely distant point onto a plane perpendicular to the direction of projection. The only variable in this orthogonal projection is the inclination of the solar axis of $90° \pm B_o$ vis-á-vis the direction of projection which is identical to the direction earth-sun (B_o is the heliographic latitude of the center point of the sun). Because of the small size of the earth in comparison with the distance of the sun, the straight line towards the observer can be replaced with a straight line passing through the center of the earth so that B_o can be assumed to be independent of the place of observation.

Due to the small range within which B_o varies, eight grids are sufficient (constructed for values $B_o = 0, 1, \ldots 7$) for a required accuracy of $1/2°$. For

---

[†]Written by Ulrich Bendel

negative values of B_o the positive grids are turned by 180°. Such grids have
been produced by a number of astronomical institutes. In the Anglo-Saxon
world those from the Stonyhurst Observatory are best known. The eight
Stonyhurst discs are calibrated right up to the poles in increments of 10° of
latitude and longitude. Zurich grids, which are more finely calibrated than
the Stonyhurst discs, only cover ±50° in latitude. The Stonyhurst discs
and Zurich grids are available on glass or on transparent film.

The production of the grids is complicated and time-consuming, especially if a high degree of accuracy is sought. The method is briefly described
here. If the origin of a Cartesian coordinates system (with x and y axes)
is placed in the geometric center of an absolute circle, then the following
equations apply:

$$x = R \cos B \sin l \qquad (B.3.6)$$

and

$$y = R(\sin B \cos B_o - \cos B \sin B_o \cos l), \qquad (B.3.7)$$

where R is the radius of the overlay template circle. R should not be too
small. The original Zurich grids have a diameter of 60 cm, and can be
reduced photographically to any required diameter. Copies of the Zurich
grids have been supplied to other institutes, but these are not generally
available to amateurs. Only paper overlay templates with a printed, and
often distorted coordinate grid, have come into the possession of amateur
astronomers. However, amateur astronomers have produced transparent
overlay template sets (Peter and Bendel 1975; Treutner 1977) with Treutner's grids which meet the highest requirements. Transparent overlay templates in the standard national solar observers/NOAA-SESC diameter of
18 cm are available from the ALPO Solar Section.

Working with transparent grids or paper overlay templates is, in principle, the same. To read a sunspot's position off directly, the grid is placed on
our position drawing with its valid B_o such that the middle line is inclined
to the N–S line (Bendel 1977, Fritz 1977) by position angle P of the solar
axis. With paper overlay templates this procedure only works if projection
drawings and overlay template can be placed on a glass plate and illuminated from below. One should not use the coordinate grids printed on the
paper or card directly at the projection screen as the lines interfere with
the projected image and can obscure smaller spots.

While position photographs enable measurements within ±0.1°, most
amateurs, for reasons of time, use the less accurate transparent coordinate
grids to reduce the prints or negative projections (Treutner 1977). If a

complete set of grids is too expensive, a single grid, $B_o = 0°$, may be sufficient (Peter and Bendel 1977). If this grid is placed on the solar projection drawing so that its central meridian is turned by position angle P against the N–S line, approximate heliographic coordinates B' and l' can be read off. To convert these approximate coordinates into precise coordinates B and l, the following equations are used:

$$\sin B = \cos B_o \sin B' + \sin B_o \cos B' \cos l' \qquad (B.3.8)$$

and

$$\cot l = \frac{\cos B_o}{\tan l'} - \frac{\sin B_o \tan B'}{\sin l'}. \qquad (B.3.9)$$

M. Waldmeier's (1950) *Tables for Heliographic Position determination* are also very useful.

B.3.2.5.2. Mathematical Reduction.[†]   The mathematical determination of the heliographic coordinates B, L is based on position coordinates r, θ (polar coordinates); r and θ can be determined from Cartesian coordinates x, y (see B.3.2.1) or from a drawing or photograph.

The angular distance ρ of spot F from the center of the solar disc is determined to an adequate degree of accuracy from the equation

$$\sin \rho = \frac{r}{R} \qquad (B.3.10)$$

where R is the radius of the projected solar image. To calculate the heliographic latitude B and longitudinal difference l vis-á-vis the central meridian, the following equations are used:

$$\sin B = \cos \rho \sin B_o + \sin \rho \cos B_o \sin \theta \qquad (B.3.11)$$

and

$$\sin l = \frac{\cos \theta \sin \rho}{\cos B}. \qquad (B.3.12)$$

B_o is taken from the physical ephemeris of the sun.

The calculation and reading off of the coordinates may directly provide heliographic latitude B, but not heliographic longitude L, and only the longitudinal difference l vis-á-vis the central meridian (see B.3.2.1). To work out the heliographic longitude L from longitudinal difference l, the heliographic longitude L_o of the central meridian is required. As L_o in the physical ephemeris of the sun is usually given as 0h UT, L_o has to be determined with interpolation of the tabular values for the time of observation.

[†]Written by Ulrich Bendel and Klaus Reinsch

Internationally, it is the custom that L_o begins at 360°, falling daily by the mean rotation angle 13.2° and ending with 0°.

From l and L_o, heliographic longitude L is obtained by

$$L = L_o + l. \tag{B.3.13}$$

It is important to notice the prefix of l (see B.3.2.1).

Normally Eq. (B.3.13) will provide an L value of between 0° and 360°. However, two special cases (see Fig. B.3.18) can arise because the beginning of a new synodic rotation is defined as the passage of the zero meridian through the central meridian (see also B.3.2.1):

1. The resulting longitude L is less than 0°; this occurs during the week before the beginning of a new rotation if the sunspot is to the east of the zero meridian and consequently is already counted as belonging to the following rotation. In the example shown in Fig. B.3.18 a), longitudes $L = 0° \ldots 110°$ of the old rotation (no. 1774) and longitudes $L = 290° \ldots 360°$ of the new rotation can be seen.

2. L is greater than 360°. Here the spot is located to the west of the zero meridian, and this in turn is to the west of the central meridian, a situation which can occur during the week after the beginning of a new rotation. The sunspot still belongs to the old rotation. In Fig. B.3.18 b) longitudes 250–360° of the new rotation (1775) are already visible while sunspots in the old rotation (1774) at longitudes 0–70° are gradually disappearing at the western limb.

In both cases a heliographic longitude lying between 0° and 360° is obtained by adding or subtracting 360°, from L. Thus sunspots belonging to a new rotation are recognized by their high values for longitude (180° $\ldots 360°$) while sunspots belonging to the old rotation have low values (0° to 180°).

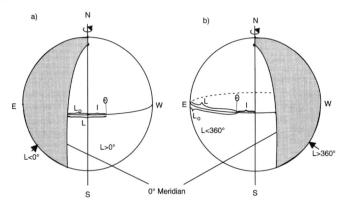

Fig. B.3.18. *Calculation of heliographic longitude L from l and L_o: a) at the beginning of a solar rotation (left) and b) at the end of a new rotation (right).*

B.3.2.6 Applied Position determination, Calculation Example[†]

This section contains a calculation example suitable for observers determining positions using either drawings or double exposure photographs. A measuring device is not absolutely necessary. The enlarger can be used to evaluate photographs, but to a lesser degree of accuracy (see B.3.2.4.2).
B.3.2.6.1. Sunspot Drawing. The determination of the east-west direction should be carried out conscientiously as the required accuracy of the individual positions is heavily dependent on this orientation. An error in orientation causes rotation as does an error in P.

The person making the drawing should also ensure that the image of the sun fits exactly into the circle on the overlay template because errors in the image radius greatly affect accuracy. (Using sunspot a in this example with $R = 5$ cm, an error of 3 mm causes a deviation in B of $0°7$ and $1°7$ in L.)
B.3.2.6.2. Photography. Two pictures of the sun are made on one film frame (double exposure, see B.3.2.4.1). The advantages of this process are manifold:

1. Photography reproduces the solar image exactly (Deviations caused by distortion, refraction, etc. are not taken into account here.)

2. The appearance and position of the sunspots are not altered by the observer.

3. The solar limb is firmly defined.

4. The method saves time during the observation phase.

There are, however, also certain disadvantages:

1. Any atmospheric disturbance is recorded.

2. Focusing and exposure errors are only discovered after developing.

3. Processing is costly.

B.3.2.6.3. Example of Observation. The following example shows a position picture of 27.4.1984, 11.34 UT. The drawing (Fig. B.3.19) was produced at the enlarger, and orientation is indicated by the individual spots. If the E–W orientation is already contained in the drawing, it still has to be determined in the photograph (see B.3.2.4.2). The E–W direction is shown as $R - R$ in the drawing. Further evaluation requires the values of P, B_o, and L_o from the solar ephemeris. These can be found in an almanac and interpolated to observation time T. To avoid errors in drawing in P, it is useful to measure the Cartesian coordinates in the original system $(R\text{-}R)$, convert them to polar coordinates, and add

---

[†]Written by Cord-Hinrich Jahn

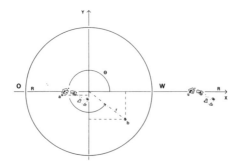

Fig. B.3.19. *The sun, 27.4.1984—example of evaluation.*

them to the appropriate direction angle P. The direct determining of the polar coordinates is not recommended as direction angle θ cannot be measured accurately without a measuring device. (The geometric set square is inadequate.) The heliographic coordinates are calculated using the known formulae (B.3.2.5.2).

Determining the Cartesian coordinates should be carried out with great care as an error of 1 mm in X and Y in this example results in an error of around $0°6$ in latitude and $1°2$ in longitude. For checking purposes the photograph was measured by the author using a comparator, and the positions were calculated using a computer program. For spot a, the coordinates $B = -16°81$ and $L = 331°10$ were obtained. Finally, it should be noted that illustrator should also calculate a correction for field of vision distortion (see B.3.2.3). An example of the calculation for 27 April 1984 follows.

Radius of drawing ($R = 5$ cm):

Ephemerides From the Astronomical Almanac

Date	R'	P	B_o	L_o	
	$'$ $''$	$°$	$°$	$°$	$\Delta R' = 0.3''$
					$\Delta P = -0.16°$
27.4	15 54.8	−24.80	−4.52	359.75	$\Delta B_o = -0.10°$
28.4	15 54.5	−24.64	−4.42	346.54	$\Delta L_o = 13.21°$

Time of observation:
$$T = 11.34 UT$$

Interpolation factor:

$$n = T/24h = 0.4819$$

Ephemeris at time of observation: $\Delta R'$, ΔP, ΔB_o, ΔL_o. n + value on 27.4 where

$$R' = 0°15'54.7'' = 0°26519$$

$$P = -24.72°$$

$$B_o = -4.47°$$

$$L_o = 353.38°$$

Cartesian coordinates in X, Y system. Quadrant selection:

Sunspot	X	Y	y +	+	−	−
a	−2.12	−0.29	x +	−	−	+
b	2.89	−2.18	θ 0	+180	+180	+360

Polar coordinates from Cartesian coordinates:

$$r = \sqrt{X^2 + Y^2} \ , \ \theta = \arctan \frac{Y}{X}$$

Spot a:

$$r_a = 2.140\text{cm}, \ \theta'_a = 7.789° + 180° = 187.789°, \ \theta_a = \theta'_a - P = 212.509°$$

Spot b:

$$r_b = 6.620\text{cm}, \theta'_b = -37.028° + 360° = 322.972°, \theta_b = \theta'_b - P = 347.692°$$

Spot a:

$$\rho' = \text{atn} \left(\tan R' \frac{r}{R} \right) = 0.1135$$

$$\rho = \text{asn} \frac{\sin \rho'}{\sin R'} - \rho' = 25.2274$$

$$B = \text{asn}(\cos \rho \sin B_o + \sin \rho \cos B_o \sin \theta) = -17.39°$$

$$L = L_o + \text{asn} \frac{\cos \theta \sin \rho}{\cos B} = 331.25°$$

Spot b:

$$\rho' = 0.1920$$

$$\rho = 46.1940$$

$$B = -11.97°$$

$$L = 399.50° - 360° = 39.50°$$

B.3.3   Suggestions for Evaluation

B.3.3.1   Mapping the Sun[†]

In addition to the difficulties encountered in reproducing a curved surface on a flat one, further problems arise in solar cartography because of
the rapid temporal changes in the observed structures, differential rotation
(see also B.3.3.6), and the gaseous structure of the sun, which is penetrated
to various depths by the different methods of observation. Solar maps are
therefore only valid for a certain period of time and usually only reproduce
one layer of the solar atmosphere. They are mainly used for instruction. Of
course, every daily drawing and every photograph of the sun constitute a
solar chart, but here only two kinds of chart will be dealt with: the synoptic
chart and the position diagram.

A synoptic chart covers the entire solar surface observed during the
course of one rotation. It includes the heliographic latitude ($-90°$ to $+90°$)
plotted against the heliographic longitude (from 0 to $360°$) for the mean
positions of all observed structures (e.g., sunspots, faculae, filaments) (see
Fig. B.3.20). If the chart includes a timescale which starts at the beginning
of synodic solar rotation according to Carrington and has an interval of
$13.2°$ between two successive days (corresponding to the mean daily synodic
angle of rotation), the structures can be included, using the times of their
passage through the central meridian.

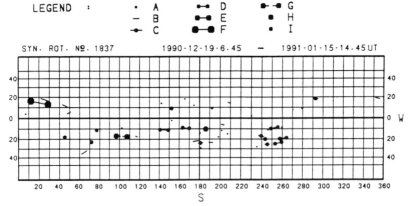

Fig. B.3.20. Synoptic chart of the sun (Carrington rotation No. 1837, Dahmen,
et al. 1991).

[†]Written by Klaus Reinsch

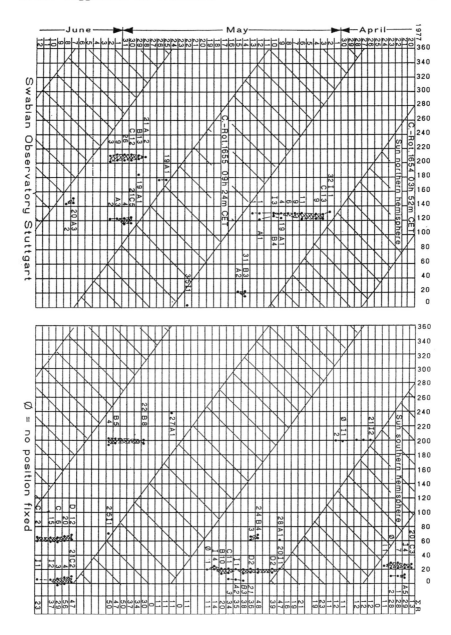

Fig. B.3.21. *Position diagram (rot. no. 1654/1655, Fritz 1977).*

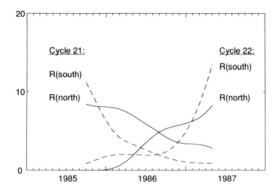

Fig. B.3.22. *Smoothed sunspot numbers for the northern and southern solar hemispheres separated by low-latitude groups (declining cycle 21) and high-latitude groups (beginning cycle 22).   Measurements by Dieter Brauckhoff, Plauen, Germany.*

The synoptic chart gives an overview of the structures observed during the course of a synodic solar rotation, without taking into account its temporal course; the position diagram reproduces the temporal development of the sunspot groups. In the position diagram a spatial coordinate (heliographic longitude or latitude) is plotted against the time axis. The sunspots are then noted in accordance with their observation time and position in the diagram. If the points belonging to the same groups but different observation days are connected, the movement of the sunspots across the sun can be seen (see Fig. B.3.21) (Fritz 1977 to 1979).

In conclusion, synoptic charts can be very helpful in the study of sunspot distribution whereas position diagrams are more suitable for studying movements. Neither of these charts, however, can replace quantitative evaluation, and they should only be used for information purposes, for example, to recognize spots with particular inherent motion and to carry out specific evaluation of observations.

B.3.3.2   Sunspot Distribution[†]

A quick glance is enough to reveal that sunspots are not evenly distributed over the sun, but they occur in certain patterns. Using position determination, it is possible to investigate this phenomenon. Sunspots occur in two zones symmetrical to the solar equator. The heliographic latitude of these zones varies with the phase of the sunspot cycle, a phenomenon known as Spoerer's law. Shortly before the sunspot minimum, sunspot

---

[†]Written by Klaus Reinsch and Elmar Junker

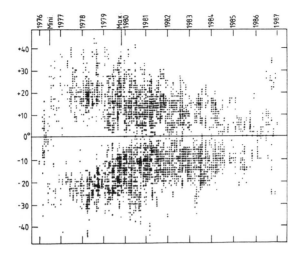

Fig. B.3.23. *Butterfly diagram for cycle no. 21 (drawn up from 6701 individual positions; Hammerschmidt 1987).*

groups appear at high heliographic latitudes ($\pm 30° - 40°$). During the cycle these zones move towards the equator until just after the next minimum when they disappear in its vicinity. The latitude distribution of spots is therefore a valuable indicator in determining the sunspot minimum. In the period around the minimum, the heliographic latitude can be used to separate spots belonging to the old cycle (spots near to the solar equator) from those already belonging to the new cycle (high heliographic latitudes). The sunspots in Fig. B.3.22 have been distinguished in this way (Reinsch et al. 1990).

Particularly easily seen is the zone movement of sunspots in the so-called "butterfly diagram" (see Fig. B.3.23, and Yallop, Hohenkerk 1980). Here the heliographic latitudes of the observed sunspots are plotted against time. If such a diagram is drawn up over several sunspot cycles, the sunspot distribution for each cycle takes on a butterfly-shape, hence the name of the diagram.

A mathematical description of the zone movement is found in Waldmeier (1939). According to this, the mean distance from the equator ϕ_M of the sunspots during the maximum is

$$\phi_M = 8.19° + 0.0699° R_M \qquad (B.3.14)$$

where R_M is the maximum smoothed monthly mean of the relative numbers (see Section B.2.5.2).

It is also interesting to study the longitudinal distribution of sunspots. Although there are no patterns which are as clear as in latitude distribution, it can nevertheless be seen that the longitudinal distribution is not at all random. Some amateur observers of the sun will surely have noticed that spots often appear again and again for months at the same heliographic longitude. It would be of interest for the amateur to try to find a pattern here. A detailed study of heliographic longitude of sunspots was carried out by Hazel M. Losh (1938). The main results of this study follow:

1. Active and inactive longitudinal areas which are approximately 180° apart can be distinguished on the sun.

2. No latitude-determined drift of activity areas, such as is known in sunspots, could be detected. It is therefore assumed that the deeper lying sources of activity centers belong to a possibly rigidly rotating core.

An assumption similar to Losh's was made by Waldmeier (1941/49), i.e., that a group often appears at a heliographic longitude of 180° from a sunspot group and also in the latitudes which are symmetrical to the equator. Losh's second result could not be confirmed by a later study (Becker 1955). From around 12,000 sunspot groups in cycles 12–17, Becker derived a rotation law for the activity areas. These rotate from 2° to 3° faster per rotation than sunspots and, like sunspot groups, exhibit differential rotation. Reference is also made to an east-west asymmetry in sunspot distribution discovered by Maunder (1907), who found that the total number of observed sunspots on the eastern half of the sun is greater than on the western half. This apparent effect can be explained by the sunspot axis being inclined to the west. It is not confirmed by a study carried out by Bruzek (1954).

To determine the distribution of sunspots on the sun, the solar surface is divided into areas extending, for example, 10° in longitudes and latitudes, and the sunspot groups found in the separate zones are counted. The different activity of the groups can be taken into account using appropriate weighting. A simple method is weighting the groups in accordance with their maximum stage of development (Waldmeier classification, see B.2.3.1), as shown in the example in Figure B.3.24. Weighting the sunspot groups with respect to their lifespan and sunspot number is also possible due to the introduction of a relative activity number A (Reinsch 1976). The following equation defines the area below the development curve of a group (see Section B.2.2).

$$A = F = \int_{to}^{tn} f(t)dt \approx 0.5 \sum_{k=1}^{n} ((t_k - t_k, 1)(f_k + f_k, 1) \qquad \text{(B.3.15)}$$

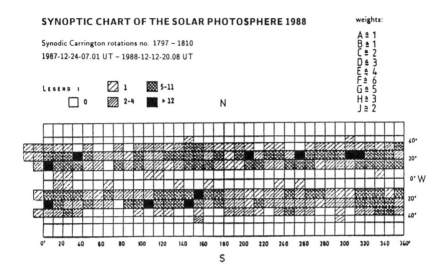

Fig. B.3.24. *Distribution of activity areas observed in 1988 (Dahmen et al. 1989. Idea by Reinsch (1975)).*

where

$f(t) =$ number of individual sunspots in dependence on time t,

$t_o =$ appearance time,

$t_n =$ disintegration time (or last visibility) of the group, and

$t_k, f_k =$ individual observations between t_o and t_n.

The theoretical curve is determined by the integral calculation in practice by the sum approximating the integral. A number of measuring points (best of all data from several observers) produces an accurate result. The N–S asymmetry visible in Figure B.3.24 in the distribution of sunspot groups becomes even clearer by showing the percentage sunspot distribution as in Figure B.3.25. As the activity of the northern and southern hemispheres is often different, both in terms of latitude and phase of the 11-year cycle, long-term observation of the N–S distribution of sunspots is useful and can be carried out with the simplest means. Cooperation between many observers is necessary to obtain enough data so that conclusions drawn from the data are statistically valid.

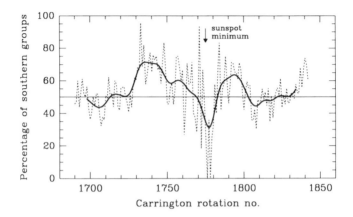

Fig. B.3.25. *Percentage of sunspot groups on the southern hemisphere, Carrington rotations No. 1690 (December 1979) to 1842 (May 1991). Dashed line: observed values; continuous line: smoothed values (P17 means).*

B.3.3.3   Extension Measurement of Sunspot Groups[†]

B.3.3.3.1. Coordinate Grid. If a positive or negative image of the sun is projected onto a coordinate grid, the extension of a sunspot group can be read off (cf., for example, Thiele 1980). The real extent of a group is, however, only correct in the equatorial region as the distance between two longitude circles on the surface of a sphere decreases with the cosine of latitude. The extent of a group, therefore, has to be broken down into a N–S component (ΔB) and an E–W component (ΔL). The E–W component ΔL is then multiplied by factor $\cos B$ (B = mean heliographic latitude). The total extent (in heliographic degrees) then follows through the use of the Pythagorean theorem. For conversion to kilometers the following equation is used:

$$1 \text{ Heliographic Degree} = 12148 \text{ km.} \tag{B.3.17}$$

The following equation is used for calculating length s:

$$s(\text{km}) = 12148\sqrt{(\Delta L \cos B)^2 + \Delta B^2} \tag{B.3.18}$$

where ΔL, ΔB, and B are measured in heliocentric degrees.

Spherical trigonometry equations provide greater accuracy (Zerm 1982). For these computations a programmable calculator is recommended.

B.3.3.3.2. Stopwatch (see also Section A.2.3.1). In this method the time T (in seconds) it takes a group to transit across a marked line on the

---

[†]Written by Rainer Beck

projection screen is measured (with the tracking system switched off). The E–W extent *in the sky* is

$$s(\text{arc sec}) = 15\ T(\text{sec}) \cos \delta. \tag{B.3.19}$$

where δ is the declination of the sun at the time of observation. To determine the extent s' on the sun, the following values have to be known:

r: the angular radius of the sun in the sky at the time of observation (in arc seconds),

α: the angle between the E–W direction in the sky and the main axis of the sunspot group, and

θ: the angular distance between the main part of the group and the center of the solar disc ($\sin \theta = r'/r$ if r' is the distance from the center of the solar disc in arc seconds).

Length s' of the group is then calculated as follows:

$$s'(\text{km}) = 696000\ (15\ T(\text{sec}) \cos \delta)/(r \cos \alpha \cos \theta). \tag{B.3.20}$$

Even this rather cumbersome equation is still not exact, as correction of perspective foreshortening (factor $1/\cos \theta$) assumes that the main part of the group is radial towards the solar limb. In all other cases correction is less than the factor given above (see B.3.3.3.3). The stopwatch has proved to be impractical for daily use. Only the diameters of larger individual spots can be measured. $\cos \alpha = 1$ can be set. If the spot is in the center of the solar disc, perspective foreshortening can be ignored ($\cos \theta = 1$) so that the equation is simplified to

$$s'(\text{km}) = 696000\ (15/r)T(\text{sec}) \cos \delta. \tag{B.3.21}$$

At perihelion (end of December or beginning of January)

$$s'(\text{km}) = 9800\ T(\text{sec}). \tag{B.3.22}$$

The quotient s'/T (km per second transit time) rises to 10800 at the end of March, falls back to 10100 at the end of July, climbs to 10900 at the end of September, and then falls again to 9800.

B.3.3.3.3. Micrometer Plate (see Section A.2.3.2). Much easier than the stopwatch method is measuring the axial extent of a sunspot group using a micrometer plate in the focal plane of the eyepiece. The distance between the lines has to be small (e.g., 50 lines/mm) to be able to measure the smallest angles. If the distance between two lines is known in arc seconds, length s can be measured immediately and converted into kilometers as shown below:

$$s \text{ (km)} = 696000 \ s \ ('')/r. \qquad\qquad (B.3.23)$$

Here, too, correction of perspective foreshortening is necessary. For this calculation s has to be broken down into a radial (i.e., along the appropriate radius of the solar disc) and a tangential component (perpendicular to the radius), for example, using an overlay template of concentric circles (Fig. B.3.26). If β is the angle between the principal axis of the group and the concentric circle, then the following applies:
Radial component:

$$s_r = s \sin \beta. \qquad\qquad (B.3.24)$$

Tangential component:

$$s_t = s \cos \beta \qquad\qquad (B.3.25)$$

$$(\tan \beta = s_r/s_t).$$

With angle θ (see B.3.3.3.2) the actual length of s' becomes

$$s' \text{(km)} = \sqrt{s_t^2 + (s_r/\cos\theta)^2}. \qquad\qquad (B.3.26)$$

B.3.3.3.4. Overlay Template with Concentric Circles. If great accuracy is not required, there is a simple method which requires little time to accomplish. The sun is projected onto an overlay template (see Fig. B.3.26). The radius of a circle r' at angular distance θ from the center of the solar disc (radius r) is

$$r' = r \sin \theta. \qquad\qquad (B.3.27)$$

The overlay template allows direct measurement of the length of a group in heliocentric degrees or in kilometers ($1° = 12148$ km) if the principal axis is radial, i.e., perpendicular to the circles. The length is equal to the angular difference $\theta_2 - \theta_1$ between the beginning and end of the group. If the overlay template has a diameter of at least 15 cm, the length can be read off to an accuracy of $1°$. If angle β between the circle and main axis of the group is less than $90°$, then the length is less perspectively foreshortened, and measurement has to take place between circles lying further in. The angular interval of the sought circle from the center is θ'. For this angle the following applies:

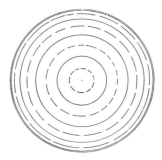

Fig. B.3.26. *Overlay template with concentric circles corrected for distortion.*

$$\cos \theta' = s/s' \qquad\qquad (\text{B.3.28})$$

where s is the apparent, and s' the actual length. Using equations (B.3.24) to (B.3.26),

$$\cos \theta' = \cos \theta \sqrt{\frac{\tan^2 \beta + 1}{\tan^2 \beta + \cos^2 \theta}}$$

$$= \frac{1}{\left(\sqrt{\frac{\cos^2 \beta + \sin^2 \beta}{\cos^2 \theta}}\right)} . \qquad\qquad (\text{B.3.29})$$

For the pair of values β and θ, the following table gives the corresponding value of θ', based on full $10°$, as the concentric circles are at intervals of $10°$.

β	θ 10°	20°	30°	40°	50°	60°	70°	80°
10°		0°	0°	10°	10°	10°	20°	30°	40°
20°			0°	10°	10°	20°	20°	30°	40°	60°
30°		10°	10°	20°	20°	30°	40°	50°	70°
40°		10°	10°	20°	30°	40°	50°	60°	70°
50°		10°	20°	20°	30°	40°	50°	60°	80°
60° to −90°	10°	20°	30°	40°	50°	60°	70°	80°

This table indicates onto which circle θ' the sunspot group is to be set by moving the telescope with its main axis perpendicular to this circle. In this position the length (in degrees) can be read off directly (without further correction).

θ is measured by projecting the solar image directly onto the overlay template. Angle β has to be estimated, but with a small angle β (group parallel to the circle), an accuracy of $10°$ is required. If β is more than $40°$,

θ' is hardly distinguishable from θ, and no displacement of the solar image is required. The accuracy of the method for measuring lengths described here is, of course, limited due to the coarse overlay template. The mean error increases from 2% at $\theta = 10°$ to 5% at $\theta = 30°$ and reaches 10% at $\theta = 50°$. For larger angular intervals from the center of the solar disk, the error increases rapidly. At the same time the reading error increases to over $1°$ because of perspective foreshortening, so that measurements in the region where θ is greater than $50°$ are less useful. The following table shows the error (in degrees) from a reading error of 1 mm with an overlay template diameter of 15 cm.

θ	10°	20°	30°	40°	50°	60°	70°	80°
s	0.8°	0.8°	0.9°	1.0°	1.2°	1.5°	2.2°	4.4°

To keep the reading error low, the projected solar image should be as large as possible. A stable projection screens and accurate tracking are further prerequisites for good longitude measurements. Manual tracking requires a great deal of patience.

A third possible error in longitude measurement is distortion of the image caused by the projection eyepiece (see B.3.2.3). Distortion is different for each eyepiece type, but can be determined using a measuring overlay template. Correcting this error requires only a small change to the radii of the concentric circles (equation B.3.27). During projection it should be ensured that the solar image is exactly in the middle of the eyepiece field of view.

B.3.3.4   Axis Inclination of Bipolar Sunspot Groups (see also B.2.2.5)[†]

In bipolar sunspot groups an axis passing through both principal spots can be determined; generally the axis is inclined against the lines of constant latitude. The value of this inclination α is calculated from latitude difference ΔB and longitude difference ΔL of the principal spots and the mean heliographic latitude B of the sunspot group using the following formula:

$$\tan \alpha = \Delta b / \Delta L \cos B. \qquad (B.3.30)$$

Positive and negative axis inclinations are distinguished. A positive axis inclination is understood to mean the front, in terms of the solar rotation, or western p-spot is closer to the equator than the following f-spot. Negative is vice-versa. If the axis inclinations are to be instigated, it is

---

[†]Written by Ulrich Bendel

important to be familiar with the development stage of the sunspot groups in question. As there is a strong divergence in longitude, particularly at the beginning of development of the sunspot group, the mean axis inclination is less than at the initial stages. Hale (1919), Brunner (1930), and Pfister (1975) have studied the relationship between the axis inclination and the heliographic latitude. The authors are almost in agreement as to the result that for $B > 5°$ the axis inclination increases approximately linearly with distance from the equator by around 0.4° per degree of heliographic latitude. For $B < 5°$ Hale claimed that α increases towards the equator. Brunner believed it decreases; to Pfister it appeared to be constant. Because of these contradictions it would be worthwhile to evaluate existing observation material to reach a valid conclusion.

In all latitude zones there are a greater number of positive inclinations than negative ones so that the means for α are always positive. The average axis inclination of bipolar sunspot groups is 10° to 15° in higher heliographic latitudes and 0° to 5° in lower latitudes. According to Pfister, the proportion of sunspot groups with a negative axis inclination is around one-third for equatorial groups and only one-tenth in groups more than 25° from the equator.

After having studied α with respect to heliographic latitude— irrespective of the activity cycle phase—we will now look at the time variation of α without regard to heliographic latitude. A statistical analysis by Pfister (1975) shows that α generally decreases during the course of a solar cycle. This decrease is to be expected as activity areas occur closer to the equator because of zone wandering, and closer proximity to the equator means smaller α values. However, during the sunspot maximum, this tendency is interrupted by a marked α minimum (proven for cycles 19 and 20). Whether this aberration will apply to future cycles remains to be seen. These observational results can only be explained qualitatively by Babcock's theory (1961), in which the direction of the sunspot axis is identified with that of the magnetic field "tubes." The calculated angles of inclination (around 1°) are around one order of magnitude smaller than the observed angles.

B.3.3.5   Inherent Motion in Sunspot Groups[†]

A worthwhile task for the amateur is observing the different types of inherent motion in individual spots within a group. These are generally related to the development of the group. However, such investigations require a high degree of accuracy in position determination, for the observed move-

---

[†]Written by Klaus Reinsch

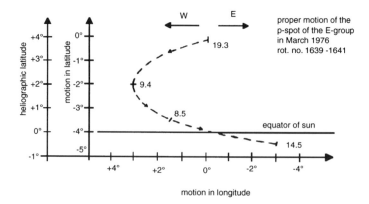

Fig. B.3.27. *Inherent motion of a sunspot (Bendel 1976).*

ments have values in the region of tenths of a degree per day and only rarely reach values of 1° per day. With some care in position determination, the required degree of accuracy can be achieved by the amateur as can be seen from a number of examples (Bendel 1976; Fritz, Treutner, Vogt 1976) (see Figs. B.3.27 and B.3.28).

Pfister (1975) provides a systematic means of classifying inherent motion in sunspot groups. He distinguishes among nine different types of motion:

1. Inherent motion in sunspot division. The line of connection through both umbrae created by sunspot division rotates in a characteristic manner. In the northern hemisphere, it is a clockwise motion; in the southern hemisphere, counterclockwise.

2. Longitudinal motion of a component of the p-spot. If the p-spot consists of a group of several components, displacement between these components can frequently be observed.

3. Longitudinal motion of a middle section of a sunspot group.

4. Tangential motion. In type H and J groups a reactivation often occurs in which parts of the principal spot break off and move away at a tangent.

5. Strong diverging motion. During the development of a bipolar sunspot group, a westward movement of the p-spot and an opposite f-spot movement are observed. This motion stops during the maximum development period of the group and is reversed during the group's decline (see Fig. B.3.29).

6. Convergence of spots. Well-developed spots of identical polarity usually converge only up to a certain distance, dependent on the strength of the magnetic field (and sunspot surface).

7. Penetration. Because of inherent motion, the penetration of neighboring sunspot groups may occasionally occur without there being any reciprocal influence being exerted on the groups (see Fig. B.3.30)

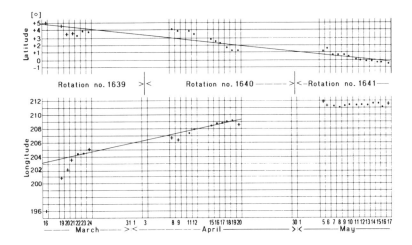

Fig. B.3.28. *Inherent motion of a sunspot (Fritz et al. 1976).*

8. Latitude motion. Spöerer (1895) observed that sunspots at latitudes of $B > 16°$ move towards the pole and at $B < 16°$ towards the equator. Pfister (1975), on the other hand, discusses latitude movement of the p-spots in the direction of the equator and movement of the f-spots towards the pole in even-numbered cycles and vice-versa in odd-numbered cycles (see B.3.3.4).

9. Longitude motion. This includes various movements of groups and individual spots in terms of heliographic longitude.

B.3.3.6 Differential Rotation[†]

The sun's differential rotation can be measured with position determination (see B.3.2.1). While latitude-dependent rotation period can be determined by simple means (see for example Junker 1980), precise evaluation of the rotation laws requires a number of position measurements on different spots (a good opportunity of working together with other observers). The measurements must be taken very accurately (Vogt 1977). Nevertheless, it is worth trying to find a rotation law for the different latitude zones on the sun (e.g., Zerm 1980, Joppich 1991).

The phenomenon of differential solar rotation was described by Scheiner (1630). There are two ways of determining differential rotation:

1. Evaluating the Doppler shift in spectral lines

2. Determining the position of structures on the sun, such as sunspots, but over several days

---

[†]Written by Klaus Reinsch

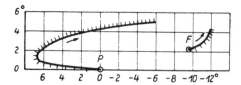

Fig. B.3.29. *Inherent longitudinal and latitudinal motion of the main spots of a bipolar group (Waldmeier 1955).*

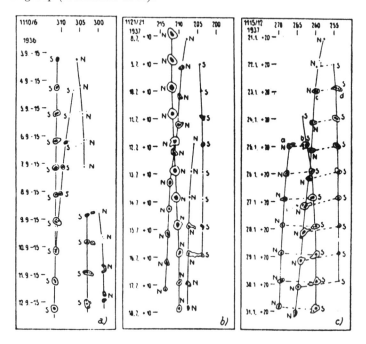

Fig. B.3.30. *Penetration of sunspot groups caused by inherent motion (Waldmeier 1955).*

Of these methods, only the latter will be used by the amateur. He will also concentrate mainly on measuring sunspots. In selecting the sunspots suitable for evaluation, the following should be taken into account:

1. To obtain as many measurements as possible of the same spot over a longer period of time, only stable and therefore generally long-lasting spots should be considered.

2. The spots should only exhibit slight inherent motion (see B.3.3.5).

3. The selected spots should cover as many latitude zones as possible.

From 1 and 2 above it follows that for measurements of differential rotation, only Waldmeier class H and J spots can be considered as they are frequently stable throughout several rotations. With respect to latitude selection, the main difficulty is that spots occur at heliographic latitudes of over 40° only in exceptional cases. The relationship between the angular velocity ω of the sun and the heliographic latitude B is expressed in the following way:

$$\omega(B) = a - b\sin^2 B \qquad (B.3.31)$$

where parameter a is the angular velocity of the sun at the equator, and b describes the change in the angular velocity with latitude.

For parameters a and b quite different values are given in the literature. Given here are Waldmeier's (1955) values, i.e., $a = 14.37°/d$ and $b = -2.60°/d$, and those of Balthasar and Wöhl (1980) for sunspot groups between 1940 and 1968, i.e., $a = (14.525\pm0.009)°/d$ and $b = -(2.83\pm0.08)°/d$.

Different rotation patterns are also obtained if faculae or filaments instead of sunspots are investigated. Wöhl (1980) discusses different rotation laws for the northern and southern hemispheres as well as periodic changes of the coefficients a and b with the phase of the eleven-year activity cycle on the sun. It has still not been explained how differential rotation is maintained since frictional forces should lead to a fixed rotation within a short period of time. Wöhl (1977, 1980) suspects that meridional flows, which are driven by solar convection, transport angular momentum to the equatorial zone thus constantly accelerating this area.

Chapter B.4

Wilson Effect

B.4.1 Historical Background[†]

For much of the seventeenth and eighteenth centuries there were a number of theories about sunspots, some of which seem rather strange now. For example, in 1769 Alexander Wilson, and shortly afterwards Christoph Schülen, discovered that sunspots which are symmetrical while located at the center of the solar disc become asymmetrical during their transit towards the limb and that the part of the penumbra located towards the center of the solar disc becomes narrower and narrower before finally disappearing altogether, while the other half of the penumbra more or less keeps its shape (see Fig. B.4.1). Wilson, after whom this effect was named, assumed that sunspots were a conical depression in the sun's surface and that the phenomenon was therefore one of perspective (see Fig. B.4.2). His calculations of the depth of sunspots produced values of several thousand kilometers. The astronomer Angelo Secchi further developed the theory of the "depression" by including the appearance of faculae. Secchi describes his observations as follows:

> The surrounds of a sunspot semi-shadow are generally formed by a real facula, i.e., a ring which is brighter than the rest of the photosphere. ... A type of glowing crown can be seen from which irregular branches project. These branches have the appearance of true protrusions and together form a clearly visible mound. ... The sunspot thus looks rather like a lunar crater, for which reason this type of round sunspot can be called a crater without connecting the concept of volcanic eruptions with it. (Secchi 1872)

[†]Written by Andreas Seeck

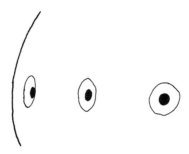

Fig. B.4.1. *Stages in the development of the Wilson effect.*

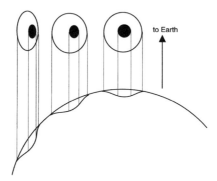

Fig. B.4.2. *Wilson's explanation of the Wilson effect.*

Fig. B.4.3. *Secchi's illustration of a sunspot with faculae.*

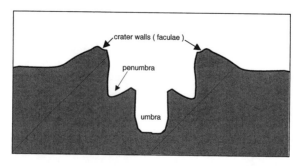

Fig. B.4.4. *Secchi's "crater model."*

B.4.2   Present-day Problems[†]

Work carried out by subsequent observers clearly confirmed the existence of the Wilson effect. However, with the use of more modern techniques, its observed strength diminished. The differences between the results obtained by earlier observers are being explained by the small number of observations carried out and the limited performance of their optical equipment. Furthermore, many observers failed to report on asymmetrical sunspots, which, if asymmetrical enough, can distort the Wilson effect or even give the impression of an opposite effect. For example, the sunspot shown in Fig. B.4.5 cancels the Wilson effect because of its shape—the Wilson effect is not recorded at the solar limb. To avoid such errors, sunspots are now measured both at the limb and near the center of the solar disc.

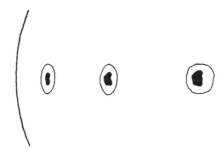

Fig. B.4.5. *Wilson's effect in an asymmetrical sunspot.*

Small regular sunspots photographed, if possible, on every day of their transit are preferred. For some time now brightness profiles have also been drawn up to allow more detailed studies to be carried out (see Fig. B.4.6).

Today's models are very similar to Wilson's. However, as the sun does not have a fixed surface but a density which steadily decreases away from its center, this simple model had to be modified. It is assumed that the umbra is more transparent than the penumbra at the same geometric level (height) and that the latter is in turn more transparent than the photosphere, with the result that light from the umbra originates from lower levels than in the penumbra and photosphere (see Fig. B.4.7). If a line of equal optical depth[1] is drawn for a sunspot, a picture very similar to that of the crater model is obtained (see Fig. B.4.8).

[†]Written by Andreas Seeck

[1]The optical depth (or density) characterizes the light permeability of a layer of material of a certain thickness. For example, a 10 m thick glass plate has the same optical density as a 0.1 mm thick metal sheet since both transmit the same proportion of light.

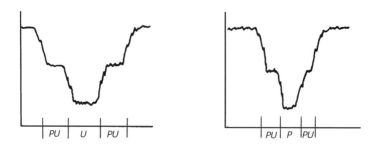

Fig. B.4.6. *Brightness profiles of a sunspot, left; center of solar disc, right; eastern limb (U = umbra; PU = penumbra, based on P.R. Wilson and P.S. McIntosh).*

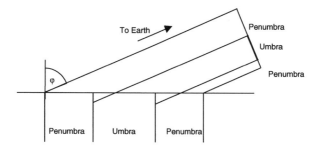

Fig. B.4.7. *Simple illustration of the sunspot model according to Loughhead and Bray (1958).*

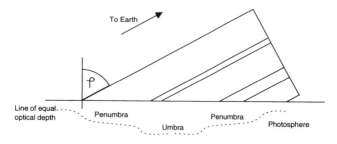

Fig. B.4.8. *Sunspot model according to P.R. Wilson and P.S. McIntosh.*

For this reason the frustum model is still widely used as an approximation. The "depths" obtained today are usually between 500 km and 1500 km. The model shown in Fig. B.4.8 also explains a further phenomenon which occurs in sunspots close to the solar limb when the umbra-penumbra boundary on the side directed towards the center of the solar disc appears much more indistinct than on the side directed towards the limb.

Studies have shown that the depth of sunspots increases with their size (Chystiakov 1962; Prokakis 1974). However, the apparent variation in depth with heliocentric angle θ of the sunspots observed by the Russian astronomer Chystiakov is disputed. According to his studies the depth appears to decrease with θ. Extensive investigations into the relationship of depth and θ which might provide key information about the structure of sunspots still have to be carried out. There is also doubt about the east-west asymmetry of the Wilson effect established in 1974 by the Greek astronomer Prokakis. According to Prokakis, the Wilson effect is on average stronger at the eastern limb of the sun than at the western limb. The same theory was proposed by the amateur astronomer W. Sanders as early as 1960 on the basis of his admittedly imprecise, but nevertheless extensive observations (over 6000 sunspots!). However, he suspected a systematic error in his observations.

B.4.3 Observation Programs for the Amateur[†]

Amateur and professional astronomers can contribute towards explaining the Wilson effect. A method is described below by which the amateur can obtain quantitative information about the characteristic dimensions of a sunspot (Jaedicke and Seeck 1975). For reasons of simplicity, it is assumed that the spot to be studied is symmetrical, with Waldmeier class H and J spots being principally observed. For a method of studying asymmetrical sunspots, see Seeck (1977).

B.4.3.1 Measure of Strength of the Wilson Effect

To study the Wilson effect it is necessary to establish as accurate a measure as possible of its strength. A scale of -1 to 3 is not sufficient here. A much more precise and informative figure is the relationship between the apparent penumbra widths $f = P_L/P_C$ (see Fig. B.4.9). P_L and P_C are sections of a straight line from the center of the solar disc to the center of the sunspot, i.e., the strongest geometric foreshortening of the spot. P_L is always the section directed towards the limb; P_C is the section directed towards the center.

The figure f, however, does not take into account the perspective foreshortening of P_L and P_C (see B.4.4.3).

[†]Written by Jost Jahn and Klaus Reinsch

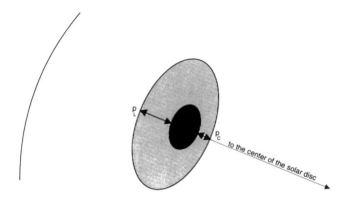

Fig. B.4.9. *Definition of the P_L/P_C ratio as a measure of the strength of the Wilson effect.*

B.4.3.2   Visual Observation of the Wilson Effect

The following measurements are taken from the projected image of the sun. First of all, the entire image is slightly enlarged and distance c of the spot being studied from the apparent center of the sun is determined, as is radius r of the solar image. The heliocentric angle θ of the sunspot can later be calculated from these numbers (see B.4.4). Then, with further enlargement, axis P of the penumbra perpendicular to the line between the center of the sun and the spot is measured and radius R of the projected solar image noted.

From this point on, only the relationship between distances needs to be determined or estimated during high magnification observations (see Fig. B.4.10): i.e., the ratio U/P of the larger umbra axis to the larger penumbra axis (on the perpendicular to the sunspot-center line), the ratio P/p of the larger to the smaller penumbra axis and the relationship P_L/P_C of the penumbra widths directed towards the limb and center.

B.4.3.3   Photographic Measurement of the Wilson Effect

Photographs are a more accurate method of measuring the Wilson effect, but one which undoubtedly involves more work. With fine grain film, several spots can be measured on one photograph. In this way one can work even through gaps in cloud cover. In contrast to working directly at the telescope, photography allows the measurement of distances rather than the relationship between distances (see Fig. B.4.10). The measuring error must be determined and included with the data. In both the visual and photographic methods, it is important to measure the spot at both the limb

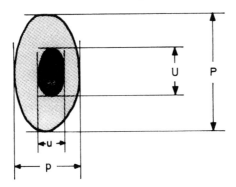

Fig. B.4.10. *Sections necessary for measuring the Wilson effect.*

and near the center of the disc to pick out any possible asymmetry which would preclude the use of the evaluation method described in Section B.4.4.

B.4.4 Evaluating Wilson Effect Observations[†]

These are the dimensions based on the measuring methods described in B.4.3 (see Fig. B.4.10):

$$
\begin{aligned}
c &= \text{Distance of the sunspot from the center of the sun} \\
r &= \text{Radius of the solar image for measuring } c \\
P &= \text{Large penumbra axis} \\
R &= \text{Radius of the solar image used for measuring } P \\
U/P &= \text{Relationship of large umbra axis to large penumbra axis} \\
P/p &= \text{Relationship of large to small penumbra axes} \\
P_L/P_C &= \text{Relationship of penumbra widths}
\end{aligned}
$$

Note that all sections of a line between the sunspot and the center of the sun are subject to perspective foreshortening. Only U and P are undistorted. A close approximation of the heliocentric angle θ of the sunspot (see Fig. B.4.11) is obtained from c and r by using

$$
\sin \theta = \frac{c}{r}. \tag{B.4.1}
$$

[†]Written by Jost Jahn and Klaus Reinsch

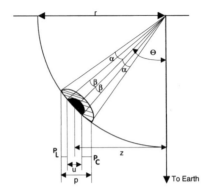

Fig. B.4.11. *The angles at the sunspot.*

B.4.4.1   Extent of the Umbra and Penumbra

The angular extent of the penumbra is calculated by

$$\sin \alpha = \frac{P}{2R} \tag{B.4.2}$$

(see Fig. B.4.11). As a small angle is involved the approximation

$$\alpha(\text{rad}) = \frac{P}{2R} \tag{B.4.3}$$

is quite adequate. Conversion of angular measurements into degrees is through

$$\alpha \ (\text{degree}) = \alpha \ (\text{rad}) \frac{180}{\pi}.$$

Similarly, a good approximation of the angular extent β of the umbra is obtained by

$$\sin \beta = \frac{U}{2R} \tag{B.4.4}$$

and

$$\beta(\text{rad}) = \frac{U}{P}\alpha. \tag{B.4.5}$$

Using conversions

$$a(\text{km}) = 696000 \ \alpha \ (\text{rad})$$

and

$$b(\text{km}) = 696000 \ \beta \ (\text{rad}), \tag{B.4.6}$$

the actual extent of the umbra and penumbra on the sun can be determined.

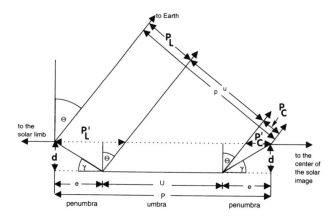

Fig. B.4.12. *Nomenclature for calculating "depth" d and "gradient" γ.*

B.4.4.2   Evaluating the "Crater Mound"

Using the simplified crater model for the Wilson effect (see B.4.2) the depth d and gradient γ of the crater mound can be calculated (see Fig. B.4.12).

The relationship between γ and d is

$$\tan\gamma = \frac{d}{e}. \tag{B.4.7}$$

In addition,

$$\tan\theta = \frac{p'_L - e}{d} = \frac{e - p'_C}{d} \tag{B.4.8}$$

where p'_L and p'_C are the perspectively corrected lines p_L and p_C (see B.4.4.3). Equation (B.4.8) is solved in accordance with p'_L and p'_C and quotient p'_L/p'_C is formed which is abbreviated as x for the *perspectively corrected* measure of the Wilson effect ($x = p'_L/p'_C$). Solving d results in:

$$d = \frac{e(x-1)}{\tan\theta(x+1)}. \tag{B.4.9}$$

Finally, equations (B.4.7) and (B.4.9) produce

$$\tan\gamma = \frac{(x-1)}{\tan\theta(x+1)}. \tag{B.4.10}$$

e, which is required to calculate d, can be obtained in two ways:

$$e = \frac{P - U}{2} \tag{B.4.11}$$

and

$$e = \frac{p - u}{2 \cos \theta}. \tag{B.4.12}$$

(B.4.12) includes perspective distortion and can only be applied with the photographic method. Otherwise only the relationship between p and u would be known.

Using the hypothesis of a "circular spot," one should average both values. Otherwise a difference in the two values can be considered to be a sign of asymmetry.

With (B.4.7.) and (B.4.11) or (B.4.12), depth d is finally calculated as

$$d = e \tan \gamma = \frac{P - U}{2} \tan \gamma. \tag{B.4.13}$$

Conversion into kilometers is through

$$d'(\text{km}) = \frac{d\, 696000 \text{ km}}{R}. \tag{B.4.14}$$

B.4.4.3   Perspective Correction

The above corrections to the perspective foreshortening of P_L and P_C are obtained by multiplying the distances by the foreshortening factor $1/\cos \theta$, where θ is the heliocentric angle of the distances. From Fig. B.4.11 the heliocentric angles for P_L and P_C can be read off:

$$\theta + \frac{\alpha + \beta}{2}$$

or

$$\theta - \frac{\alpha + \beta}{2}$$

Thus, the perspectively corrected distances P'_L and P'_C are

$$P'_L = \frac{P_L}{\cos\left(\theta + \frac{\alpha+\beta}{2}\right)} \tag{B.4.15}$$

$$P'_C = \frac{P_C}{\cos\left(\theta - \frac{\alpha+\beta}{2}\right)} \tag{B.4.16}$$

and the perspectively corrected measure of the Wilson effect is

$$x = \frac{P'_L}{P'_C} \tag{B.4.17}$$

$$x = \frac{P_L}{P_C} \frac{\cos\left(\theta + \frac{\alpha+\beta}{2}\right)}{\cos\left(\theta - \frac{\alpha+\beta}{2}\right)}.$$

Example: Evaluation of the Wilson effect

Assume the following measurements have been obtained:

c	r	R	P	U/P	P/p	P_L/P_C
46 mm	50 mm	123 mm	3.5 mm	0.40	0.30	1.8

Then using the formulae given above will lead to the following results:

(B.4.1):	$\theta = 67°$
(B.4.3):	$\alpha = 0.0142$ rad $= 0.82°$
(B.4.5):	$\beta = 0.0057$ rad $= 0.33°$
(B.4.6):	$a = 9900$ km
	$b = 4400$ km
(B.4.17):	$x = 1.7$
(B.4.10):	$\gamma = 6.3°$
(B.4.13):	$d = 0.12$ mm
(B.4.14):	$d' = 650$ km

B.4.4.4   Conclusion

Despite the amount of time-consuming calculations the observation and evaluation of the Wilson effect is a worthwhile field of activity for the amateur. Using simple instruments one can obtain important information about the phenomenon of sunspots. A small computer simplifies evaluation, particularly if there is a great deal of data. It would be gratifying if observing the Wilson effect—an activity which has previously been largely neglected by amateurs—were to become more widespread, not least because a number of important questions (see B.4.2) in this field can still be investigated by the amateur.

Chapter B.5

Light Bridges

B.5.1 Introduction[†]

This chapter begins by describing particular types of light bridges, then describes their development and next introduces two different classification schemes. The observation of physical parameters which until now have received only scant coverage will be summarized in the third section. Finally, suggestions are made where amateur research into light bridges might be appropriate.

B.5.2 General Features

In addition to umbrae and penumbrae, small telescopes (lower limit = 60 mm clear aperture) are capable of seeing within sunspots, bright areas or light bridges, which usually cross individual spots in the form of bright bands. Three main types can be distinguished.

1. "Classic Light Bridges": Bright intrusions into the sunspot with a structure similar to the photosphere. There is "normal" granulation, and brightness is similar to that of faculae and the outer bright ring. They can last from one day to several weeks.

2. "Islands": These are situated in the penumbra and have no direct link with the photosphere, appearing as brighter areas between the dark penumbra filaments. In the regions where islands are present, the penumbra appears ragged and irregular, and its radial orientation (i.e., away from the center of the sunspot) is affected. Islands can last from between a few hours to several days.

3. "Streamers": These most difficult to observe light bridges (width $1''$–$5''$) are found particularly frequently in sunspot groups. They often divide

---

[†]Written by Heinz Hilbrecht

into a short-lived network within the umbra, where they usually connect
opposite parts of the inner penumbra. Very high resolution photographs
(0.3″–0.5″) show that these are extensions of individual bright penumbra
filaments from which granules with a diameter of 1″–2″ break off. Again
they last from several hours to several days.

All three types are typical stages in the development of light bridges, and
it is possible for them to run from one to another. Common to all of
them is the fact that they are composed of granules and are able to affect
the apparently normal umbra/penumbra composition of sunspots (in the
case of islands, the penumbra, and in the case of streamers, the umbra).
Differences between them evidently lie in the behavior of the granulation.
The lifespan and appearance of granulation cells in classic light bridges are
similar to conditions in the photosphere (lifespan around 10 to 20 minutes,
although precise information of this type is not yet available). As in the
case of the bright outer ring, the granulation cells in classic light bridges
appear to be smaller than in the photosphere (see Sections B.2.1 and B.7).

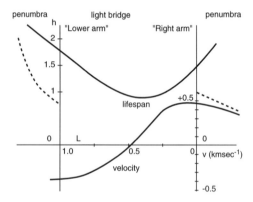

Fig. B.5.1. *Radial velocity (right-hand scale) and lifespan of granulation in a
streamer (Muller 1979).*

Observations of streamers (Muller 1979) have shown properties similar
to those of penumbrae. Figure B.5.1 shows that the lifespan (in hours [h])
of granulation decreases by a factor of 2 as it moves towards the center of
the umbra while at the same time the radial velocity (in km/sec) decreases.
Thus some of the penumbra filaments project into the umbra, and granules
break off to wander through the umbra towards a point on the inner penumbra which is usually directly opposite. The closer they approach the center
of the umbra, the more they are slowed down and their stability reduced.
Granules in a streamer have a lifespan of 50 to 100 minutes and a speed of
less than 0.5 km/sec and are similar to those of penumbra filaments.

Changes that take place over periods of seconds (*L'Astronomie,* 1957) are most likely due to the effects of atmospheric turbulence. After all, the observation of light bridges is made all the more difficult by their small size, which makes them very susceptible to the seeing conditions. The apparent changes in position, shape, and brightness due to atmospheric turbulence, all seriously affect observation and measurement. Attentive observers will notice that the brightness of classic light bridges appears to diminish in the vicinity of umbrae. This is caused by the "scattering" of light into the umbra because of atmospheric turbulence. Structures such as granulation, which have been "robbed" of brightness by scattering light, receive very little scattered light in return from the neighboring umbra and therefore appear darker. Such effects are virtually uncontrollable, and particular attention must be paid to them when determining brightness (and temperature using the Boltzmann equation as in Section B.2.1). These problems also help to explain why there is relatively little observation material available.

B.5.3   The Development of Light Bridges

The development of light bridges is closely related to the development of the entire sunspot group. However the appearance of light bridges is not, as is often assumed, an indication of imminent decay. Rather light bridges constantly accompany every group of sunspots, regardless of age and activity. Most light bridges occur following maximum activity of a group and before its stabilization as a *J*-spot with a diameter of approximately 30,000 km (Bumba 1965a). At this point the sunspot group is no longer developing and is entering an unstable phase. Light bridges preferentially form across projections, i.e., where there is deviation from the circular form of the sunspot. During the course of their development, sunspots take on an increasingly rounded shape with projecting parts (penumbra, or umbra together with the surrounding penumbrae) being cut off by light bridges, the fragments decaying in a matter of hours or days, depending on their size. There are exceptions in very large sunspots where fragments may remain for several days or even weeks.

Even in pores with a diameter of only 6″–7″, there are indentations which are reminiscent of light bridges (Secchi 1872; Danielson 1961), even though they have little in common with traditional concepts of light bridges, and no studies of these "proto light bridges" have as yet been carried out. The first genuine light bridges form as soon as a penumbra has developed around the sunspot (Type C, according to Waldmeier). Individual light bridges project from the photosphere, and individual streamers can be observed. Then, as the activity of the sunspot group increases, the number of light bridges stagnates and actually diminishes in proportion to the area of the sunspot (Hilbrecht 1977b). Only when peak sunspot activity has been passed do light bridges begin to increasingly appear, and smaller streamers develop into bright bridges. In the f-spot particularly, a great variety of light bridges is formed until the sunspot eventually decays. If, finally, only the p-spot remains, it becomes rounded in the above manner until it attains a diameter of approximately 30,000 km (the diameter of a supergranule in the chromosphere). At this point the sunspot does not decay as rapidly as after its period of maximum activity, and light bridge activity enters another phase. More and more islands form in the penumbra, and during the course of a few days, streamers become increasingly widespread until eventually the sunspot is divided again. Once a "stabilized" J-spot has become divided, it usually quickly disappears.

According to preliminary studies by Hilbrecht (1977b, 1982), light bridges occur in the various Waldmeier sunspot group types as follows:[1]

Group	common light bridge types	particularly common light bridge type
C	g, h, j, l, m	g, l, m
D	d, h	h
E	d	d
F	a, g, j, k	a, g
G	b, h, k	b
H	a, l, m	l, m
J	a, d, l, m	l, m

Hilbrecht (1977b) also published the first data on the relationship between the light bridge number (LB_N) in a group, its area (A_i), and individual sunspot number (N_i):

Group	D	E	F	G	H	J
LB_N/A_i	0.004	0.004	0.001	0.001	0.003	0.010
LB_N/N_i	0.62	0.09	0.03	0.05	0.11	0.37

The reduction in the proportion of light bridges in active groups (E, F, G) can be clearly seen. The high LB_N/N_i value in the D groups is explained by the low individual spot number. Area is far more suited to this type of study as it provides more information.

It does not, therefore, appear that light bridges split sunspots. Rather they seem to be visible indications of changes in the magnetic field of the sunspot, a view which conforms to Abdussamatov's theory (1970) that light bridges are embedded in the "magnetic rope" which is considered to be the source of the sunspot's magnetic field (see B.2.2.1).

---

[1] Hilbrecht's light bridge classification system is given in Section B.5.4 (Fig. B.5.3).

Having looked at the development of the entire group in general terms, the development of individual light bridges will now be dealt with in more detail. Basically there are six phases, which are shown in Fig. B.5.2.

1. There are no light bridges in the sunspot.

2. Individual bright penumbra filaments project from the inner penumbra into the umbra. Very often the filaments grow towards each other from opposite sides of the umbra.

3. Granules break off from the bright penumbra filaments and travel into the umbra.

4. If a complete streamer is formed the penumbra begins to join up.

5. The sunspot has been divided, but there are still remnants of dark penumbra filaments in the light bridge.

6. A "classic" light bridge divides the remaining areas of the sunspot. It often consists of only two rows of individual granules, but it is much brighter than a streamer.

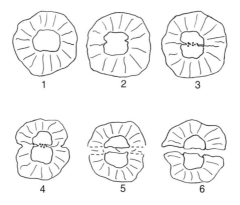

Fig. B.5.2. *Development of light bridges in a sunspot.*

Each of these stages of development can also be a final stage. For as yet inexplicable reasons, many "successful" light bridges recede. The interaction between increasing activity and decay in the sunspot does not appear to be a progressive process. Abdussamatov coined the phrase "re-establishment of photospheric-like conditions" to describe the development of light bridges. This dynamic property of light bridges makes it difficult to define the individual stages of development. The "rules" according to which light bridges develop still have to be set out.

B.5.4   The Classification of Light Bridges

With the aid of visual observations and photographs, the author has devised a classification system (Hilbrecht 1978b) suitable for use in the study of light bridge development. This system is shown in Figure B.5.3. It should be used in conjunction with good-quality photographs (penumbra filaments visible) or a large number of visual observations (for statistical evaluation).

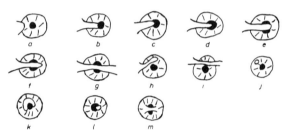

Fig. B.5.3. *Hilbrecht's system of classifying light bridges. For definitions see the main text. Type n, island-type light bridges in the umbra, was proposed by Seebörger-Weichselbaum (1984) but can only be observed infrequently and in very good seeing conditions.*

The form shown in Figure B.5.4 can be used to record the observations. For physical studies a different type of classification system is more suitable but requires Hα observations. For example, Korobova distinguishes between three types in her studies:

   I. Bridges related to sunspot decay (low level)

  II. Bridges representing facula chains penetrating into the sunspot (medium level)

 III. Arch bridges which appear to surround filaments in the vicinity of sunspots (high level)

This classification will be referred to again in Section B.5.5. Parfinenko (1982) restricts light bridges to formations which consist of filaments of an anomalous penumbra with separate bright granules. These bridges are located along the neutral line of the magnetic field. However, this definition is too narrow as it ignores bright bridges in unipolar H and J groups, and regarding the development of light bridges can at best be used for special stages only. Delimiting causes problems. Investigations should be made to determine whether Hilbrecht's classification (Fig. B.5.3) can be extended through indices which take greater account of the stages of development. In direct observation with a larger telescope, the following abbreviations should be used: g for granules, f for filaments, and gf if both are present in a light bridge. In Fig. B.5.2, number 5 would be a $g(gf)$ light bridge, while number 6 would be classified as type $g(g)$. A precondition of this kind of observation is good seeing quality and the classification $g(\mathrm{nd})$ for "not determined" should be noted.

LIGHT BRIDGES IN MONTH

Name :
Address :

Instrument :						Magnification :				
f= mm						Eyepiece: mm				
d= mm										

Date	UT	M	S	Type	Np	Nf	N	LBp	LBf	Notes

Fig. B.5.4. *Form for recording light bridge observations As in any other time series observation, changes in instrumentation should be avoided.*

Subject of the form	Light bridges
Light bridges in month	Enter month and year (e.g., 8/1995)
Name	Name and full postal address
Address	
Instrument: f = mm, d = mm	Focal length (f) and object lens diameter (d) in millimeters
Magnification	Eyepiece magnification during observation, diameter of the projected image
Date	Date of observation
U.T.	Universal time (U.T.)
M and S	Image motion and image sharpness according to the Kiepenheuer scale (see B.1.2)
Type	Sunspot group type according to Waldmeier $(A, B, C, \ldots J)$
N_p and N_f	Number of individual preceding (p-) spots and following (f-) spots of a bipolar group with respect to the rotation of the sun
N	Total number of sunspots in a group ($N_p + N_f = N$)
LB_f and LB_p	Light bridges in the f- and p-spots
Notes	Notes

Please fill in for *every group of sunspots* (even if there are no light bridges).

B.5.5   Physical Parameters

All investigations into physical parameters are affected by atmospheric turbulence. Even with the best available telescopes (e.g., Beckers and Schröter [1969], who used the Sacramento Peak telescope for their observations), the possibilities are limited. The greatest hopes for research into light bridges lie with solar space telescopes.

a) Intensities/Temperatures. Korobova (1966) studied the intensities of light bridges, found that type I was 1.10 times brighter than the photosphere ($I_{LB} = 1.10 I_{\text{phot}}$) and from this discovery determined the excess heat of 140 K compared with the undisturbed photosphere. For type II she gives (1968a) an electron temperature of more than 7000 K.

Figure B.5.5 shows typical contrast and limb darkening curves (Korobova 1966). As a rule, types I and II are brighter than the photosphere ($I(\theta)/I_{\text{phot}}(\theta) > 1.0$). While it is within 50° of the center of the solar disc, type III scarcely changes in brightness, but after that point its brightness rapidly decreases. Korobova interprets this curve as evidence of the arched nature of type III bridges and concludes that there is no reduction in temperature with altitude (temperature gradient). The contrast function of type III is also quite different from that of types I and II and the faculae.

b) Movement/Velocities. The presence of granulation in light bridges indicates convection. Beckers and Schröter (1969) observed a weak flow directed towards the observer which could be interpreted in this way. Abdussamatov (1970) determined upper limits for the flow velocity, finding for type I that $v \leq 0.7$ km/sec and for type II that $v \leq 2$ km/sec. In contrast, the flow velocity in photospheric granulation is approximately 0.2 to 1.0 km/sec.

Kneer (1973) gives an upper limit of $\Delta\lambda \leq \pm 10$ $m\text{\AA}$, corresponding to 0.5 km/sec, for the Doppler shift of the spectral lines in a light bridge which has not fully developed. For turbulence velocity (measured in the ionized calcium line (Ca-II-K)), Korobova (1968) gives 30 km/sec.

The movements of material appear to be related to other flows within the sunspot. Kneer (1973) found that the negative radial velocity (components of the flow directed towards the observer) increases in the penumbra, the nearer to the light bridge measurements are taken (B.9.4.9).

c) Magnetic Field. Magnetic field strengths in light bridges appear to be around 200–800 Gauss lower than in neighboring umbrae (Abdussamatov 1967; Beckers and Schröter 1969; Kneer 1973). Abdussamatov (1970) compares the field strength of a type II bridge with that of a facula field.

There is clearly contradictory evidence about the position of light bridges in the magnetic field. It has not been clarified whether or not light bridges separate areas of different polarities (Abdussamatov 1970; Korobova 1968b). Preliminary studies by the author show that light bridges lie

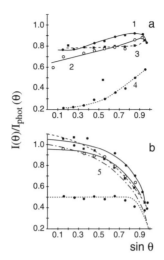

Fig. B.5.5. *Contrast curves (a) and limb darkening curves (b) for 1) faculae, 2) type II light bridges, 3) type I light bridges, 4) type III light bridges, and 5) the photosphere (Korobova 1966).*

both on the dividing line between polarities (as in filaments/prominences) and "in the middle" of the magnetic field of one polarity. The development of several light bridges shows that they prefer to form in unstable areas of the sunspot, including the dividing line between polarities if the different poles are connected in a joint penumbra. This so-called δ configuration (see B.8) is recognized as being unstable.

Certain scientists believe that the preferred orientation of type II bridges in a north-south direction (Minasjants, Obashev, Minasjants 1971) is also connected with the sunspot's magnetic field. They see this as an indication of embedding in the "magnetic rope" (Abdussamatov 1970). In contrast, type III bridges have no preferred direction of orientation (Korobova 1968b), but it will be possible to assess the implications of this fact only when more observation material relating to type III is available.

B.5.6 Suggestions for Research

B.5.6.1 Studying Visual Observations

In addition to a number of other solar observers' groups, there is also a light bridge group which sends its observations to the author for the purposes of compilation and evaluation. For classification of the light bridges, the group uses the system in Figure B.5.3, and to facilitate observation it uses the form illustrated in Figure B.5.4. So far the results have been

encouraging, particularly as regards the relatively minor deviations in frequency of the light bridge types observed in particular types of sunspot
groups. The following table shows the problems and the advantages of
using this classification system (Hilbrecht 1982). Shown are differences in
the frequency with which particular light bridges were observed during the
same period.

Greatest Difference (3 Observers)	Light Bridge Types
0% to 5%	c, h, i
6% to 10%	d, f, j, k, m
11% to 15%	b, g, l
16% to 20%	a

Considering that the classification used leaves plenty of scope for the observer's own subjective perception, the differences are tolerably small for
eight out of thirteen types. Types b, g, and l are relatively difficult to
observe, for they often cannot be distinguished from irregularities in the
sunspot (b) or easily seen with small telescopes in unfavorable atmospheric
conditions (g, l). Irregularities at the edge of a sunspot can be recognized
only as type a once they have developed into a larger light bridge. Furthermore, types a, b, and l develop rapidly, and agreement between observers
can be expected only after longer periods of observation. Discrepancies
between observers will become the subject of important study in the future. On one hand these studies will play the same role as, for example,
factor k does in sunspot number observations; on the other hand they can
be used to determine the accuracy of classification systems. Observation of
light bridges cannot, therefore, be carried out by an amateur working by
himself. It is important to know the quality of one's own observations by
comparing them with others so as to avoid any accusation of "subjectivity."

B.5.6.2   Distribution Statistics

In addition to observing short-term effects which affect only small areas
of sunspots, the amateur can also observe the long-term "behavior" of light
bridges—and this is the area on which the amateur observer of light bridges
should concentrate his efforts. All the necessary equipment for working on
such problems is available to the amateur. Through observations similar
to those for determining the sunspot number (the classification into types
of the light bridges occurring in sunspots), a number of questions can be
addressed:

1. How are particular types of light bridges related to the sunspot group types;
   i.e., what part do light bridges actually play in the "life" of a sunspot?

2. What is their connection with the development of the number and area of sunspots; i.e., what part do light bridges play in the development of sunspot activity?

The table shown in Section B.5.3 shows trends in the answers to these questions, although such results are still not too reliable since they are based on limited observations. Professional astronomers who have studied light bridges consider them to be just as important as the more familiar penumbra and umbra, belonging to the most important features of a sunspot and without which a description of a sunspot would be woefully lacking.

B.5.6.3 Position in the Magnetic Field

Using the methods described in the section "Amateur Magnetic Field Observation" (B.8) or using notes from professional institutes (NOAA, Solnechnye Dannye), one can determine the position of light bridges in the magnetic field. It is best to use photography or video as small light bridges can easily be overlooked.

B.5.6.4 Light Bridge Granulation

To study light bridge granulation requires very high resolution photographs (around $0\rlap{.}''3$), which even professional institutes can obtain only under excellent observation conditions. It is noteworthy that apart from Muller's study (1979) there has been no other research into light bridge granulation and there is virtually no information on lifespan and size. The difficulty in determining lifespan is increased by the requirement for high resolution photographs taken over several hours. One possible solution here would be photographs taken from balloon-borne telescopes (Danielson 1961).

Diameter distribution has to cover several hundred granules. In a study of the dimensions of granulation in bright rings around sunspots, Macris (1979) measured around 2000 granules in forty photographs. He also described a practicable method for the amateur with the appropriate means. Within a defined area the granulation cells are counted and the relationship between "normal" photospheric granulation and the diameter of the granules being studied is determined. He found that in the case of ring granules (B.2.1.9–10), the size depends on the strength of the magnetic field, which can also apply in the case of light bridge granules.

Due to the special difficulties they pose, light bridges present an interesting challenge to the amateur observer, who, if he is going to study them, should be patient and prepared to undertake long-term work. It is extremely important to become a member of a group of observers as the large quantity of data thus generated will significantly improve the prospects of obtaining meaningful results.

Chapter B.6

Photospheric Faculae[†]

B.6.1 Appearance of Faculae

Almost every day bright veins of light or bright patches known as *photospheric faculae* can be observed towards the solar limb. Photospheric faculae consist of formations in the upper photosphere which, despite covering the entire surface of the sun, are only visible in the vicinity of the limb because of limb darkening (see A.5.4). However, by using narrow band monochromatic filters in calcium K or hydrogen alpha light, it is possible to observe faculae at the center of the solar disk. These are *chromospheric faculae* (see Section B.9.6) which are a continuation of photospheric faculae in the chromosphere, but they differ considerably from the latter in shape and area. This section will deal with photospheric faculae, although the observation and evaluation methods can also be used for chromospheric faculae. Faculae consist of "aligned mottles" between 5,000 and 10,000 km wide and up to 50,000 km in length which are composed of round or oval "coarse mottles" with a diameter of approximately 5,000 km. Coarse mottles consist of facula granules approximately 1,000 km in size. Faculae always mark an area of increased activity in which sunspots can form or have disappeared. Almost every sunspot group has an area of faculae, but not all areas of faculae produce sunspots. Faculae form in advance of sunspots and usually survive them by several weeks. Their area is substantially larger than that of the corresponding sunspot group, and their average lifetime is ninety days. The temperature of faculae is several hundred degrees Kelvin higher than that of the undisturbed photosphere, the contrast in luminosity at $\sin\theta = 0.95$ being around 10% (where θ is the heliocentric angle, see Eq. B.6.7). Magnetic induction in the brighter faculae is between 0.001 and $0.01T$, and between granules, up to $0.1T$ ($1T = 1$ Tesla $= 10^4$ Gauss).

[†]Written by Michael Delfs and Volker Gericke

B.6.2   Instruments

Telescopes with a 30 mm or larger objective can be used to observe faculae. If the objective is small, a objective filter is recommended since faculae are difficult to distinguish and the full resolving power of the instrument is best maintained with a full aperture objective filter. Visual measurements dictate a stable projection screen. If filters are used, a small amount of enlargement usually shows more detail in the faculae areas than very large enlargement. Finally, a clock driven telescope considerably facilitates area and position measurements.

B.6.3   Observation

While photospheric faculae offer the amateur observer a great deal of scope, a particular facula area can only be seen at the solar limb for three or four days, although in rare cases very bright areas can be observed almost at the center of the solar disk.

B.6.3.1   Facula Activity

B.6.3.1.1. Counting of Facula Areas. Like sunspots, faculae are signs of solar activity. A proven method of determining solar activity is counting the facula areas daily, designating areas with sunspots (F_w), and areas without sunspots (F_{wo}). The sum is the total of each facula group counted in one day (F_t):

$$F_t = F_w + F_{wo}. \tag{B.6.1}$$

F_t, F_w, and F_{wo} should always be noted, never just F_t on its own. F_t provides a rough indication of facula activity over a period of time. Another interesting possibility is studying the relationship F_w/F_{wo} with regard to time or as a function of total activity F_t. An example of evaluation can be seen in Fig. B.6.1 with facula activity F_t compared to the number of sunspot groups g between 1978 and 1980. These values were obtained from observations carried out by the *Sonne* network of observers.

B.6.3.1.2. Facula Relative Number. Facula activity can be represented like sunspot activity by using a relative number, known here as the facula relative number R_{FA}:

$$R_{FA} = 10F_t + F_I. \tag{B.6.2}$$

As with the sunspot Wolf number (B.2.4.1), the number of facula areas F_t is multiplied by 10 and the number of individual facula appearances F_I is added. "Individual facula appearances" means the number of individual

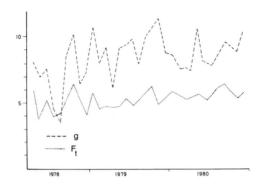

Fig. B.6.1. *Comparison between facula and sunspot activities between April 1978 and December 1980.*

facula veins, sections, segments, etc., in the facula areas. Details of the facula relative number are given by Völker:

> The facula relative number was conceived in February 1971 by W. Wichmann and P. Völker of the Wilhelm-Foerster Observatory in Berlin. After many years of observing faculae, it was decided to keep amateur records of faculae. Numerous ideas eventually resulted in the facula relative number being defined as $R_{FA} = 10F_t + F_I$.

B.6.3.1.3. Discussion. The number of individual sunspots which can be seen depends on the size of the instrument, and the same is true for individual faculae. Photospheric faculae fields can only be observed near the solar limb; sunspots, only on the side of the sun directed towards us and subject to strong perspective foreshortening towards the limb, etc. In other words, the facula relative number possesses all the difficulties and problems of the sunspot Wolf number (see B.2.4). The small degree of contrast between the faculae and the photosphere also creates observation difficulties. This and the ever present atmospheric turbulence result in a very patchy picture of facula activity. However, one aspect of this observation is encouraging. During sunspot minima there are also few extended faculae, whereas there are many during a maximum. If the cycle can be proved by counting the faculae, R_{FA} would be suitable for amateurs without requiring too much observation time. The only condition is that R_{FA} must always be determined directly during observation with an instrument (or from photographic enlargements with the same diameter) and observation must always be carried out with the same instrument. We selected a 6-inch refractor with a projection of 15 cm diameter. A few precautions are recommended if small instruments are used for observing faculae (due to the lesser degree of contrast than with sunspots). The projection screen should be screened off (black box; black cloth over the head; projection into a dark room), or direct observation should be carried out using objective and/or eyepiece filters.

B.6.3.1.4. Checking the Facula Relative Number. Professional astronomers also kept statistics on photospheric faculae based on the faculae area. They used as a unit an area extending over 5° in length or width on the heliographic maps. Until it was discontinued in 1979, Waldmeier published the figures for every rotation of the sun in the *The Solar Activity of the Year* ... issued by the ETH Zürich Observatory. The graph of the facula relative number worked out by the Wilhelm-Foerster Observatory (WFS) is compared with the facula activity graph prepared by professional astronomers to arrive at the value R_{FA}. A graphic evaluation by R. Rothe indicated that it would be worthwhile studying the values in more detail using data processing, which was done by J. Dreyhsig. Dreyhsig's results are found in Figures B.6.2 and B.6.3 (in cooperation with V. Gericke and J. Jahn). Shown are sliding 9 rotation means (see also B.2.5.2). The curve "WFS-Zurich" (Fig.B.6.2) shows a correlation coefficient of 0.806 and although the WFS observations (around 1,500) have gaps due to the local observing conditions, the Zurich figures were not distorted by adverse weather conditions.

A further result of the observations is given in Fig. B.6.3. Here the two WFS facula observers R. Böhlendorf and P. Völker are compared. P. Völker has been determining the facula relative number since 1971, and R. Böhlendorf, since 1973. The correlation between them is 0.918. However, the facula relative numbers of later observers differ quite markedly, and even show a contrary temporal behavior. There are problems in observing small dot-shaped faculae whose number depends to a great extent on the size of the instrument, the seeing conditions, and the attentiveness of the observer. Dot-shaped faculae have still not yet been adequately studied (see also B.6.3.6 and B.6.3.7). Single large faculae sometimes blur if atmospheric conditions are unstable and can only be counted with difficulty.

B.6.3.2   Types and Classification of Faculae

Since the end of 1977, a classification system has been used (V. Gericke, U. Korte, A. Cadenbach) to describe the structure of a facula area. Five different types can be distinguished and are indicated with a small Roman letter:

1. a = veined, network-like structure
2. b = extended, continuous
3. c = extended, fragmented
4. d = dot-shaped faculae
5. e = collection of dot-shaped faculae

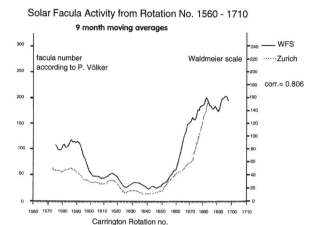

Fig. B.6.2. *Comparison of the facula number determined at WFS with the Zurich facula areas.*

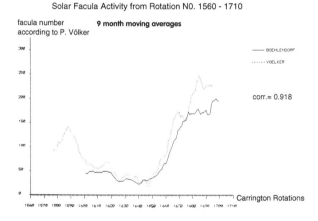

Fig. B.6.3. *Facula numbers obtained by two observers at WFS.*

The surface of an area of faculae must be at least 80% continuous to belong to type *b*. Type *d* includes a maximum of two dot-shaped faculae each extending over less than 2°. If there are more than two dot-shaped faculae, the classification becomes type *e*. The classification of a facula group is not always straightforward—in the same way as there are often difficulties in classifying sunspots according to the Waldmeier system. Some schematic examples are shown in Figure B.6.4. The system attempts to categorize the multiplicity of facula structures. It should, however, be noted that the

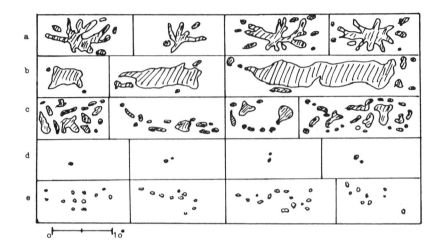

Fig. B.6.4. *Classification scheme for facula areas.*

order of the five types does *not* represent the chronological development of a facula group!

B.6.3.2.1. Results of Facula Classification to Date. Initial investigations have shown that *c*-type faculae are most common (approximately 50%), followed by *a*-type (25%) and *b*-type (12%). Types *d* and *e* are the least common, and to date type *e* has only been observed without sunspots. However, these are not yet definitive facts. Rather it should be assumed that the relative frequency of the various types changes during the course of a sunspot cycle. It is still to be determined whether particular types of sunspots occur more often with particular types of faculae. The temporal development of a facula group has still not been investigated in detail. Hydrogen alpha observers could look into whether the classification system can also be used for chromospheric faculae and whether there is a difference in their structures. There are, therefore, a number of interesting possibilities in the field of facula classification.

B.6.3.3 Latitudinal Distribution and Position Measurement

The latitudinal distribution of faculae is similar to that of sunspots, although the two facula zones parallel to the solar equator are about 10° broader, extending to heliographic latitudes of about 55°. Outside these zones, polar faculae occur. A separate Section (B.6.3.7) is devoted to these. Methods for determining position are dealt with elsewhere in this book, which in addition to being used for sunspots, can also be used for faculae (see B.3). When measured, a facula area should be noted as either the remainder or the forerunner of a center of sunspot activity. Zone wandering can be established and a butterfly diagram worked out.

B.6.3.4 Area

B.6.3.4.1. Estimating Method. Methods for estimating the surface area of faculae were established by K.O. Kiepenheuer. Surface area of faculae is given in terms of a 10-point scale:

Stage	0	1	2	3	4	5	6	7	8	9
Area (degrees square)	0–1	2–3	4–6	7–12	13–20	21–30	31–45	46–60	61–75	>75

(Table taken from *Astronomer's Handbook*, Roth 1981). Estimation is facilitated by using a coordinate grid onto which comparative areas are added and the sun projected.

B.6.3.4.2. Measurement. Precise measurements of facula areas requires a photograph or accurate projection drawings of the sun. Such a drawing can be made only with a stable projection screen, intensive light, and a solidly mounted clock-driven instrument. The actual measurements are not carried out at the telescope but at a desk. Transparent millimeter graph paper is placed on the drawing or photograph, and the counting is best carried out with the aid of a magnifying glass. First to be counted are all the millimeter squares which partially or totally correspond to the facula area (see Fig. B.6.5). In this way a slightly oversized area, or upper limit UL, is obtained. Next to be counted are all the squares which fully correspond to the facula area. This number provides a lower limit LL for the facula area. From the UL and LL a mean value M is obtained:

$$M = \frac{UL + LL}{2}. \tag{B.6.3}$$

As the area of a facula group is to be calculated as a fraction of the surface area of the visible solar hemisphere, it has to be divided by this area. The surface area SA of a solar hemisphere is

$$SA = 2\pi R^2. \tag{B.6.4}$$

where R is the radius of the projected image or photograph. Therefore, for unreduced area A'

$$A' = \frac{UL + LL}{4\pi R^2} \tag{B.6.5}$$

As the sun is a sphere, the limb area of the visible disk and, therefore, the facula area, appears badly distorted. This foreshortening has to be taken

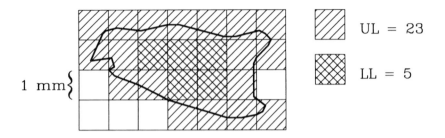

Fig. B.6.5. *Example for the measurement of facula areas.*

into account when calculating the surface area. Final area A is obtained
by the following equation:

$$A = \frac{A'}{\cos \theta} = \frac{UL + LL}{4\pi r^2 \cos \theta},\qquad \text{(B.6.6)}$$

θ is the heliocentric angle. A good approximation of it is calculated by
using the following equation:

$$\sin \theta = r/R \qquad \text{(B.6.7)}$$

where R is again the solar radius on the photograph or drawing; and r is the
distance of the focus of the facula area from the center of the solar image
(R and r in mm). The heliocentric angle is also suitable for investigating
the visibility of facula areas as a function of their distance from the limb.
This method of calculating area can, of course, also be used for sunspots
(see B.2.4.7). An alternative to this method is calculating the area using
image processing (see A.7).

The temporal development of the area of a facula zone can be followed
and compared with the development of the accompanying sunspot group.
It is interesting to study the change in the relationship between sunspots
and facula areas over a longer period of time, for example, over an eleven-
year cycle. Comparing facula areas and types also allows characteristic
surface areas of the five facula types to be worked out. These evaluations
are worthwhile if carried out over several years.

B.6.3.5   Brightness

Even a cursory glance will reveal that faculae vary in brightness, but
precise measurements of luminosity can be carried out only with a great
deal of expenditure on equipment (photometric process).

An alternative although very subjective method is to estimate the
brightness of a facula group according to three levels—bright, normal, less

bright. The brightness of the five types of facula can be investigated, and developments in the luminosity of a group over a period of time can be registered using this method, but estimates of brightness and measurements thereof are distorted by scattered light and the seeing conditions.

B.6.3.6 Lifetime of Dot-Shaped Faculae

Types d and e faculae are not only exceptional because of their small size, but they are also visible on the sun at all times and are particularly frequent during a sunspot minimum. Their lifetime is also of interest as it appears to be quite different from that of flat area faculae and to depend on the size, brightness, and vicinity of similar types of facula. In addition, it is presumed that their lifetime changes in accordance with the phase of the eleven-year cycle, a fact which probably also applies to polar faculae which occupy a special position among dot-shaped faculae as they occur at the polar regions of the sun.

B.6.3.7 Polar Faculae

B.6.3.7.1. Introduction. Faculae which occur at heliographic latitudes of more than $\pm 55°$ are called polar faculae in accordance with Waldmeier's description (1955), although more modern observations (1986) show they occur down to at least $\pm 50°$. All the results have been obtained from white light observations, although polar faculae can also be seen in the chromosphere, for example, in hydrogen alpha light. A correlation between polar faculae and the coronal radiation of a minimum corona is suspected (Waldmeier 1955).

B.6.3.7.2. Size, Brightness, and Fine Structure. The apparent size of polar faculae is $3''$, and their average diameter is 2300 km. Larger polar faculae can attain a diameter of approximately 5000 km. In brightness they vary as much as other faculae. Small polar faculae are round; larger ones have fine structures and are sometimes joined so that branches similar to very large area faculae can be seen. Occasionally two polar faculae occur very close to each other, and on very rare occasions there may be three or more. These appear to be more stable than individual faculae and therefore last longer.

B.6.3.7.3. Lifetime. Waldmeier (1955) studied the lifespan of polar faculae during the years 1953 and 1954. He distinguishes between faculae with a short and a long lifetime—their average lifetime varying as follows in each year:

	1953	1954
Short lifetime	6.3 mins	17.5 mins
Long lifetime	238 mins	159 mins

In reality, however, all periods of time ranging from a few minutes to up to fifty hours occur. Waldmeier suspected a relationship between lifetime and size, which is confirmed by Cortesi (1978). Cortesi makes the following distinctions:

Size	Average Lifetime (mins)
Small	16
Average	39
Large	143

According to Waldmeier, the temporal decay of polar faculae is exponential and theory is based on the equation

$$N(t) = A \exp(-at) + B \exp(-bt), \tag{B.6.8}$$

where $N(t)$ is the number of originally observed polar faculae still present at time t. One addend describes the decay of short polar faculae, and the other describes that of long-lasting polar faculae. A and B show the initial distribution; a and b are decay constants. Time t is in minutes. This law was determined on the basis of observations carried out in 1953/54, with Waldmeier establishing the following values (standardized to an initial figure of 100 faculae):

	Short Lifetime		Long Lifetime	
	A	a/min	B	b/min
1953	72	0.160	28	0.0042
1954	60	0.057	40	0.0063

According to these data, large and bright polar faculae usually have a long lifetime, whereas small, weaker ones last for a shorter period of time. At any one time one may observe approximately 2/3 short lifetime and 1/3 long lifetime polar faculae.

Figure B.6.6 shows the theoretical decay of polar faculae in 1954. At time 0 there were 100 polar faculae of which approximately 20 could still be observed after 120 minutes. Determining lifetimes causes great problems because of atmospheric turbulence which can affect the quality of images to such an extent that polar faculae either appear or disappear.

B.6.3.7.4. Latitudinal Distribution. Various authors have studied the latitudinal distribution of polar faculae in various years. Saito and Tanaka

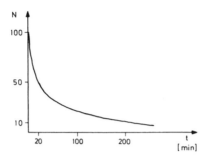

Fig. B.6.6. *Theoretical decay curve of polar faculae in 1954, N - number.*

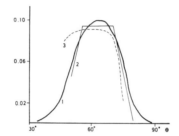

Fig. B.6.7. *Visibility functions of faculae; 1) faculae of the main zone, 2) polar faculae according to Waldmeier (1955), and 3) polar faculae observed at Locarno from 1962 to 1975/76.*

(1957) determined a maximum at around 83° heliographic latitude. Waldmeier (1955) found a flat maximum at around 80°. Observations between 1962 and 1975/76 showed a distinct maximum at around 75°.

B.6.3.7.5. Visibility Function. The visibility function is obtained from the quotient of observed number of facula points divided by the calculated number (Waldmeier 1955, 1962). Figure B.6.7 roughly shows the visibility function of polar faculae. The horizontal axis shows the heliographic angle, and the vertical axis, the proportion of polar faculae, standardized so that a comparison with the visibility function of faculae in the main zone is possible.

The maximum for "normal" faculae is around $\theta = 63°$. The consistency of the polar facula visibility function over a large area of the Waldmeier curve is noticeable, but it should be understood that only a very small number of observations were available for this curve to be generated.

B.6.3.7.6. Temporal Appearance. The temporal appearance can be summarized as follows: sunspots, minimum; polar faculae, maximum. Polar faculae are most likely to appear during decreasing sunspot activity and during a sunspot minimum. They are rarely seen during maximum sunspot activity.

The relative position of the solar equator varies periodically during the year (see B.3.2.1) with the result that sometimes the sun's north pole can be seen, and sometimes its south pole is more visible.

B.6.3.7.7. Amateur Observations of Polar Faculae. In the past amateurs have neglected polar faculae, though there are many observation and evaluation possibilities. For example, one could monitor polar faculae over several hours to determine their average lifetime. Or one could determine positions to evaluate the activity at various latitudes. However, the simplest thing would be to include polar faculae during daily observations of the sun if the projection method is used.

To do so, the projected image has to be shaded from the remaining sunlight as far as possible, and, when searching the polar areas, the rest of the solar image has to be covered with the hand to avoid being dazzled. It is a good idea to carry out projection in a dark room.

To increase the contrast even more, a sheet of white paper should be moved back and forth in front of the screen. The position of a facula is memorized for a moment until it has been marked on the screen. This process may sound complicated but is, in fact, very quickly learned.

Once a search has been completed, all polar facula points are counted separately for north or south. It is important that observation and drawing along the solar limb be carried out quickly, for a momentary representation of polar facula activity is only obtained in under 15 minutes per polar region. Subsequently appearing faculae must not be added to the drawing over the course of several hours as doing so would give the impression of much more intensive activity. It is important to obtain a representative cross section of facula activity. One observation per day and a minimum of five per month are sufficient to record polar facula activity.

B.6.3.8   Recording Observations

There are three sheets which can be used for recording facula activity, facula observations, and facula measurements.

B.6.3.8.1. Facula Activity Sheet.

UT   Observation time in Universal Time
Q, S Quietness and sharpness of the image according to the Kiepenheuer Scale
Re   Sunspot Wolf number
g   Number of sunspot groups
F_t Total number of facula areas
F_{wo} Number of facula areas without spots
F_w Number of facula areas with spots
F_I Individual facula appearances (sum of individual faculae in facula areas
         analogue to f in determining Re)
R_{FA} Facula relative number
D/P Drawing or photograph—enter appropriate letter
Pos. Positioning—mark if applicable
AM   Area measurement—mark if applicable
Obs. Number of observations
0   Monthly mean of F_t, Fwo, Fw, R_{FA}

The relationships are

$$F_t = F_{wo} + F_w$$

and

$$R_{FA} = 10F_t + F_I$$

Facula activity in Month														
Name :														
Address :														
Instrument :								Magnification :						
Date	UT	Q	S	Re	g	F_t	F_{wo}	F_w	F_l	R_{fa}	D/P	Pos	AM	Rem.:
1														
2														
3														
4														
5														
6														
7														
8														
9														
10														
11														
12														
13														
14														
15														
16														
17														
18														
19														
20														
21														
22														
23														
24														
25														
26														
27														
28														
29														
30														
31														
Obs.:				ϕ:F_t=			F_{wo}=			F_w=			R_{fa}=	

Fig. B.6.8. Facula activity sheet.

B.6.3.8.2. Facula Observation Sheet. Each facula area is recorded separately. As the amount of space required for daily observations cannot be predicted, the date should be entered by the observer. Please leave a blank line between two days. See figure B.6.9.

Dat.	Date
Number	Number. Each facula area receives an identification number. The first area observed in a month becomes 1; the second 2, and so forth. If an observation is carried out on one of the following days, the sequence is continued for new faculae. If an area is observed which has been observed previously, the same number as before is used; i.e., during the entire period of being visible it keeps the same number. Should faculae be observed at the beginning of a month which have already been observed during the previous month, the old number is again used and this time circled.
T_{FA}	Facula types. The type need only be marked with a cross; in the case of mixed types several boxes should be marked. "Tot." is the total of individual facula appearances in the facula group. If a group cannot be classified, mark the Tot. box with a question mark.
T_{SP}	Type of accompanying sunspots (Waldmeier classification) to be marked. "Tot." is the total number of sunspots.
QU	Mark quadrant in which the facula is located.
B	Brightness of the facula. Subjective impression to be noted: 0 = "normal" + = bright − = dim

| Date | No. | T_FA | | | | | | T_FI | | | | | | | | | | | QU | | | B | Rem. |
		a	b	c	d	e	Tot.	0	A	B	C	D	E	F	G	H	J	Tot.	N w | o	S w | o		

Facula observations in Month

Name :
Address :

Instrument :   Magnification :

Fig. B.6.9. *Facula observation sheet.*

B.6.3.8.3. Facula Measurement Sheet.

Dat.   See above.
Number   See above. Numbers must be identical to those on the facula observation
                    sheet.
θ Heliocentric angle
                    Positions and areas for facula *and* accompanying sunspots if possible.
                    If observations are carried out in projection, the projection diameter should
                    be entered under "Magnification."

FACULA MEASUREMENTS IN MONTH

Name :
Address :

Instrument :   Magnification :

Date	No.	Θ	Positions facula / spot	Areas facula / spot

Fig. B.6.10. *Facula measurement sheet.*

Chapter B.7

Granulation[†]

B.7.1 Introduction

The problem of granulation is still surrounded by a great deal of controversy among physicists, and there are only gradual improvements taking place with regard to observation material. Furthermore, granulation theory is so complex that the amateur astronomer will generally only concentrate on the phenomenon itself. With this in mind, please refer to the bibliography relating to this section. Observations of interest to the amateur will be set out here without going into great detail about the physics involved.

B.7.2 Description

In still air the sun appears to have a white surface which is not uniformly bright, but gives the impression of a certain degree of graininess. This "granulation" (from the Latin *granulum*, meaning "grain") consists of irregularly shaped cells separated by spaces or "intergranular lanes." In some areas the granules seem to be missing so that larger dark spots appear. These should not be confused with pores (B.2.1) as usually after only a few minutes the "hole" is again filled by granulation cells. Occasionally, however, pores can be formed due to an increase in the dimensions of the intergranular lanes, along with a further decrease in brightness. Using a telescope, one can observe granules of $10''$ or more which, when highly resolved, turn out to be concentrations of several granulation cells with little space between them.

The average diameter of a granule is around $1.5''$ (between $0.5''$ and $2.5''$), but granules only become visible individually when the intergranular

---

[†]Written by Heinz Hilbrecht

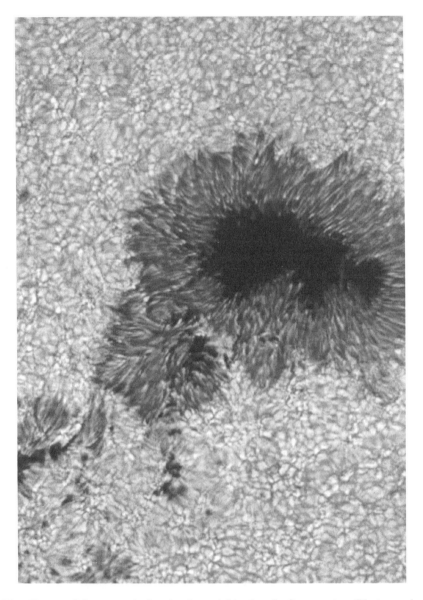

Fig. B.7.1. *Solar granulation in the neighborhood of sunspots. Photography taken on May 22, 1992 by Wolfgang Lille (Stade, Germany) using a 12″ refractor with Herschel prism and interference filter (central wavelength 590 mm, full-width half maximum (FWHM) 0.5 mm). Effective focal distance 45 m. Darkroom work (unsharp masking): Eckhard Slawick (Eggstätt).*

lane is resolved as $1''$. This is near the upper limit of resolution set by atmospheric turbulence (B.1.2), and even professional institutes can only improve on this under particularly favorable conditions. However amateurs have proved that if they have the necessary experience in photography, and a suitable instrument and a good seeing location, they can take pictures which are quite adequate for studying granulation.

B.7.3   Development and Lifespan

Recording granulation, which decays within a few minutes, presents the earth-bound observer with almost insurmountable problems; nevertheless, one should develop proper techniques for high resolution photographs and maintain that quality on a moment-to-moment basis. It is of little use to obtain several good pictures during the course of a single day, for both estimates and measurements show that the individual granules can, on average, be identified as "individual" for only 6 minutes (between 1 minute and 15–30 minutes). There are very few locations on earth where the atmospheric conditions can be so stable as to make experiments worthwhile. Only since the introduction of balloon-telescopes operating from the stratosphere in 1959 have longer intervals with improved resolution been obtained. Wittmann (1978) sets out the evolutionary aspects of solar granulation as follows:

1. All granules are formed from the decay products of former granules.

2. Some granules develop from small bright points in void areas about 3 granules in size.

3. In 2, the increase in brightness appears to be more rapid than the decrease in brightness.

4. The majority retain their shape for 1 to 6 minutes.

5. Granules exhibit elongation. The long axis is 1 to 5 times the length of the short axis (mean = 1.88).

6. In 5% of cases the diameter is approximately $2.5''$. The cells then decay along weak dark lines or from expanding rings of around $4''$ diameter and divide into 2 to 6 parts.

7. The total number of granules formed in a 2.33 square arc second-cell area is approximately 25 per hour.

8. The contrast between the intergranular lanes and the granulation cells diminishes by one third of the maximum contrast shortly after the maximum rate of development per minute.

9. Granules decay by splitting into 2–3 parts in 40 to 50% of cases, by disintegration in 21 to 60% of cases and by fusing with neighboring cells in 4 to 28% of cases.

10. There are too few granules with lifespans of under 5 minutes.

B.7.4 Some Other Features

Counting the granules in limited areas makes it possible to calculate their density, which in turn depends on their size. A number of authors (e.g., Macris [1979], Schröter [1962] and Tchistjakov [1964]) have shown that granules located in the vicinity of sunspots (particularly within the bright ring) become smaller the greater the sunspot's magnetic field, and the longer they last. A possible relationship between the size, shape and lifespan of granulation and the eleven-year solar activity cycle is being debated. Size appears to be constant (Birkle 1967).

B.7.5 Short Theory of Granulation

The evaluation of high resolution spectrograms shows that in the centers of granulation cells there is a flow towards the observer at 1–3 km/sec. The granules are thought to be convective cells in which hot gases from lower levels of the sun rise due to their low density and then cool down, whereupon they sink back along the intergranular lanes. As described in B.7.3, the granules do not form fixed flow cells, but decay through continual changes in shape within a few minutes. This process is known as "non-stationary convection," which may be caused by the fact that the granules are "heated" by a layer which is many times thicker than their diameter.

Today this greatly simplified theory is the subject of intensive research. Granulation evidently transports energy from layers of the sun below the photosphere to the outer layers and thus supplies energy for the processes taking place there. The effects of this phenomenon become clear if it is realized that the heating of the corona (Section C) to over 1 million degrees Celsius is probably caused by the thin corona gas receiving energy from sound and pressure waves produced by turbulent currents of matter.

B.7.6 Options for the Amateur

Amateur data cannot achieve sufficient time resolution to study granule changes but, with the aid of granular counts in predetermined areas, one can study the size and number of granulation cells with regard to overall solar activity or in the vicinity of sunspots. Those interested in determining lifespans can seek photographs from professional institutes. Very often such photographs are used for purposes other than the study of granulation and remain in the archives until someone becomes interested in them. The ultimate solution, however, ambitious but not unrealistic, would be amateur solar observation from space.

Chapter B.8

Amateur Magnetic Field Observation[†]

B.8.1 Introduction

For measuring magnetic fields professional astronomers make use of the Zeeman effect which involves the splitting of spectral lines in a magnetic field. Klüber (1948) and Wiehr (1970) refer to the practical application of the Zeeman effect in solar physics. The small splitting values (around 0.2Å at 4000 Gauss) require the amateur to use apparatus which is beyond his means, making it very difficult to observe this effect. However, once it is realized that certain magnetic field parameters (field strength, polarity distribution) are reflected in the properties of a sunspot (ionized gas is influenced by the magnetic field), indirect methods of observing the field can be worked out. These may not offer the high degree of accuracy of exact measurement, but do provide a certain amount of information about the magnetic field in sunspots.

B.8.2 Magnetic Field Strength

The maximum field strength of a sunspot is related to its area (A in Eq. B.8.1, see Section B.2.4.7). Figure B.8.1 (Jäger 1966, detailing an introduction to the problems and results of magnetic fields in sunspots) shows the relationship which can be given as follows:

$$H_m = 3700 * A/(A + 66) \text{ Gauss.} \tag{B.8.1}$$

The relationship also allows the approximate maximum field strength to be calculated because the strength decreases from the center of the spot

---

[†]Written by Heinz Hilbrecht

towards the edge (Beckers and Schröter 1969), a fact which means that the maximum field strength cannot be determined at a particular point without measurement. In this form, the equation is applicable only to round (H and J) spots. In these cases, it may be necessary to fall back on the information which is regularly published by solar observation institutes. The Boulder Observatory (*NOAA Solar Geophysical Data*) publishes magnetic field charts of the entire sun, but due to their small scale they only permit global readings. The field strengths of individual groups are published in the Russian *Solnyechnye Dannye* (solar data).

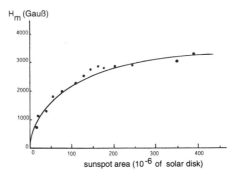

Fig. B.8.1. *Relationship between maximum field strength (H_m) and area (A) for H and J spots.*

B.8.3   Polarity Distribution

In many branches of amateur solar astronomy, delayed information on the sunspot's magnetic field is not enough. For example, it has to be decided when looking through the telescope what the approximate position of the magnetic field is to identify groups that may generate flares. With a little practice a relationship established by Künzel (1969) between the shape of the penumbra and the polarity distribution of magnetic field can be used. The examples shown in Figure B.8.2 and described below occur in 93% of all sunspot groups.

a) Unipolar sunspot with a symmetrical relationship between the umbra and penumbra

b) Two spots of different sizes having the same polarity at a sufficiently great distance so that they do not affect each other

c) Two spots of the same polarity formed one after the other. Parts of the penumbra between the spots are sharply reduced or missing completely.

d) Two umbrae of the same polarity within the same penumbra. Constriction of penumbra indicating separation

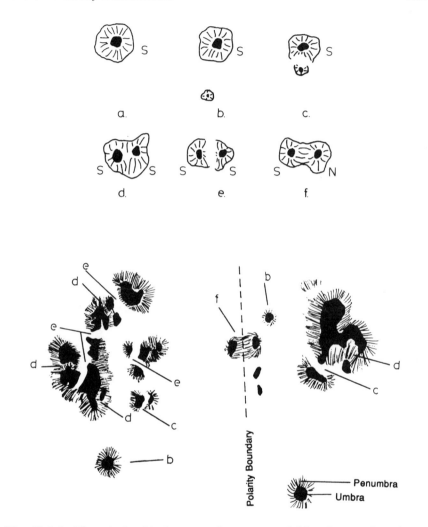

Fig. B.8.2. *The relationship between the magnetic field and penumbra shape. Examples a) to f) described in text.*

e) Sunspots formed at the same time and having the same polarity. This type occurring through separation but also developing without previously being connected.

f) A so-called δ-configuration, i.e., two umbrae of differing polarities in one penumbra. This configuration is unstable (in the case of equally large umbrae there is a tendency towards separation, whereas when the umbrae are of different sizes the smaller one tends to decay).

Because of the relationship between the magnetic field and shape of the penumbra, the amateur is able to include the magnetic classification of sunspots within a routine monitoring program. The beginner should use the Künzel system augmented with data from the Russian *Solnyechnye Dannye*. There are four basic types of magnetic field denoted by Greek letters as follows (see B.2.2):

1. α: Unipolar sunspot groups (e.g., J groups)

2. β: Bipolar sunspot group (usually with distinct p and f spot [see B.2.1])

3. γ: Complex and interlaced magnetic field in which there are two centers

4. δ: Various polarities lying close to one another, partly in joint penumbrae

The system is a suitable supplement to the Waldmeier classification system. Once the position of differing polarities has been determined, the north and south poles of the magnetic field can be worked out using the Hale law of polarities.

The following table shows the relationships.

Sunspot Cycle	Northern Hemisphere		Southern Hemisphere	
	p-spot	f-spot	p-spot	f-spot
1933–1945	N	S	S	N
1945–1954	S	N	N	S
1954–1964	N	S	S	N
1964–1976	S	N	N	S
1976–1988	N	S	S	N

B.8.4   Applications

There is contradictory information about the position of light bridges in the magnetic field. The relationship between the position of light bridges and the distribution of polarities has still not been fully clarified (see B.5). Observers of flares and prominences will be interested in identifying unstable γ and δ configuration groups so that they can be prepared for frequent occurrences of flares and prominences. If the observer makes a study of these phenomena one can quickly work out the likelihood of eruptions taking place and therefore observe such groups more intensely. Veeder and Zirin (1970), and McIntosh (1972) described a process in which lines of identical field strength and polarity distribution were derived directly from the hydrogen alpha image. Veio (1975) (see also A.4.2) describes a method of determining polarity with a spectroscope. Knowledge about the make-up of the sunspot magnetic field is not only of use in specialized studies, but can also be used to make the Waldmeier classification system (B.2.3.1) more reliable.

Chapter B.9

Solar Observation in Hα Light[†]

B.9.1 Introduction

Up to this point this book has described observation opportunities that take place in the photosphere (the "surface") of the sun. Hα observations involve an entirely different area, it is directed instead at a level up to 10,000 km above the photosphere—the lower levels of the "solar atmosphere." This is the transition zone between the photosphere and the solar corona, the chromosphere. In terms of density (approximately 10^{-12} g/cm^3), it is substantially thinner than the photosphere (10^{-8} g/cm^3), but denser than the corona (which continuously decreases with increasing distance from the sun). In terms of temperature, it is between the photosphere (upper level <6000) and the corona (approximately 2,000,000K), but is nevertheless an independently observable feature of the sun. This is of particular interest since many decisive processes become visible in the chromosphere during the build-up and decay of an activity center.

More and more solar observers are constructing prominence telescopes or attachments and other less mechanically inclined observers have discovered that DayStar[T.M.] filters produce consistently high quality views of the sun. Amateurs who own Hα instruments are usually solar observers who have become familiar with the phenomena occurring on the sun. Amateur Hα observers soon learn that while there are many drawings and photographs, there is little in the amateur literature that describes what is going on in these drawings and photographs. In writing this chapter one of my prime objectives is to provide sufficient detail and discuss methods of evaluation so that the reader can begin to appreciate the wealth of information contained in these drawings and photographs.

[†]Written by Peter Völker

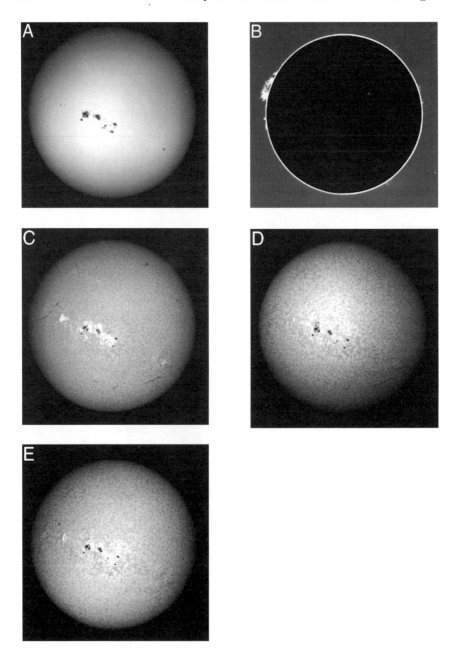

Fig. B.9.1 A–E, (Page Opposite). *The sun as it appeared on 4/27/84. The sun was photographed in white light, through a Hydrogen alpha filter, then through the same filter tuned to a slightly longer wavelength (red sideband), and then a slightly shorter wavelength (blue sideband) to show how the solar atmosphere differs in appearance. Filters such as this can be "tuned" to different wavelengths to see different depths into the solar atmosphere. Observer: Lee C. Combs with a 3" refractor, Hα filter 0.75Å; time UT: a) 18:33; b) 20:12; c) 20:55; d) 20:31; e) 20:48.*

Once the Hα instruments are assembled and the first test observations and photographs become available, one is always struck by the fact that the number of forms of chromospheric phenomena (at the limb and especially on the disk) is so much greater than the photospheric. The same applies to evaluation possibilities. Hα instrument owners can, at one time, investigate three times as much as white light observers, i.e., photospheric phenomena, chromospheric phenomena and the relationship between the two types. In addition, there are *more* details to be seen in the chromosphere than in the photosphere, even if a small instrument is used—and here "small instrument" means just that. With the appropriate filters Hα observation is worthwhile starting with an aperture of 60 mm!

Chromospheric features are very much more difficult to observe because of their lack of brightness than are photospheric features, the light of which is around ten thousand times more intensive. Why they can still be made visible with a filter is described by K.O. Kiepenheuer in *Die Sonne* 1957,

> ...If higher layers are to be made visible, a trick, discovered almost simultaneously by the American Hale and the Frenchman Deslandres around 1890, has to be used. They both realized that the continuous light emitted from the photosphere is, in the layers above the latter, only weakened within the Fraunhofer lines, while in wavelengths between the lines it can escape unhindered. If a solar filter were constructed only to allow sunlight from the Fraunhofer line wavelength through, it would no longer be possible to see as far down as the photosphere...."

B.9.1.1   What is Hα?

Hα is a strong Fraunhofer line in the solar spectrum, the beginning of the Balmer series in the red part of the spectrum. An electron jumps from the third to the second orbit of the hydrogen atom, energy (in the form of light) being released at a wavelength of $\lambda = 6563$Å. A quantum transition from the fourth to the second orbit produces Hβ at $\lambda = 4861$Å. Hγ is produced in a transition from the fifth to the second orbit (4340Å), etc. This phenomenon was described by the Swiss physicist Balmer in 1885 and consequently named for him. The chromospheric features of interest to us are brightest in the Hα line which is why such filters are favored.

It should be mentioned that important chromospheric occurrences can also be observed in other spectral lines, but such filters are still fairly uncommon for amateurs and so will not be dealt with in any more detail.

B.9.1.2 Hα Filters

To select a filter, one should be aware that the narrower the Hα line, the more clearly visible the chromosphere becomes. With filters having a full-width at half maximum transmission (FWHM) of greater than one Ångström, only limb phenomena can be observed, with the surface only becoming visible at FWHM <1Å or, better still FWHM <0.6Å.

To acknowledge the capacity of the Hα filter and to understand the very high price, a closer look at the theory would be worthwhile. From a visible light range of around 4000Å(4000–8000Å), all but approximately 0.5Å have to be filtered out. What does this mean? Imagine the transverse waves of the light. The Lyot filter with a FWHM value of 0.5Å is so narrow that it only transmits around $1/8000$ of the frequency band of visible light (see Fig. B.9.2). Thus, if we consider the visible 4000Å from blue to red as a 40 cm long line, the free area around Hα (= operational effect of the filter) should only be around 0.05 mm. This demonstrates just how strong the filtering must be to even make chromospheric phenomena visible! If compared to the filter curves of "normal" photographic filters, the difference in price brought on by the technical requirements immediately becomes clear.

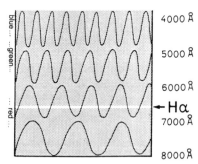

Fig. B.9.2. *Wavelength range of visible light. The position of the Hα line is marked.*

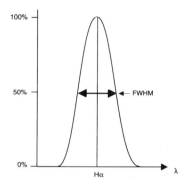

Fig. B.9.3. *FWHM — Full width at half maximum (see text).*

B.9.1.3 What does the frequently encountered expression "full width at half maximum" (FWHM) mean?

A Lyot filter first attenuates the incoming light by polarization. The light then is filtered to Hα. If the intensity of the transmitted light at Hα is set at 100%, the FWHM is the width (in Å) of the wavelength range which is transmitted at 50% (see Fig. B.9.3).

B.9.2 Choice of Instruments

This section is intended as a guide to construct or purchase an instrument such as the Lyot filter. There are various factors to consider to achieve our aim: the type of instrument and filter and the associated variations in quality, resolution, definition, and observation possibilities (observing only the solar limb or the sun's surface as well). Common to all of these, however, is the fact that the filter and not the objective is the heart of all instruments for observations of the chromosphere.

We shall begin by looking more closely at the options available to the amateur: the spectrohelioscope, the prominence telescope or prominence attachment, and the Lyot filter. The operation of these very different instruments will not be dealt with in great detail at this point as it would be beyond the scope of this book.

B.9.2.1 Spectrohelioscope

With a spectrohelioscope, phenomena both at the limb and on the surface can be observed. Someone who enjoys constructing instruments would find pleasure in building a spectrohelioscope, an optically complicated device, which approaches the definition (sharpness and resolution) of a polarizing interference filter. See Fig. A.4.3 for a diagram showing a Spectrohelioscope optical layout.

B.9.2.2   Prominence Telescope/Attachment

These devices are variants of the coronagraph (also invented by Bernard Lyot). They produce an artificial solar eclipse with the aid of a occulting disk built into the tube so that only the limb remains visible. With such an instrument all limb phenomena can be clearly observed, and with a correspondingly narrow filter even the finest details are visible. It is recommended that filters with transmission widths of around 2 to 8Å be used, but given excellent atmospheric conditions, the phenomena can be observed using widths of 60–100Å.

The "traditional" prominence telescope was first made accessible to the amateur by Otto Nögel (1952 and 1955). G. Nemec provides building instructions in a detailed series of articles in *Sterne und Weltraum* 1971/72 which are still valid today. It can, however, also be built as a so-called "prominence attachment."

With a prominence attachment one can achieve the viewing quality of a traditional prominence telescope, with the added option of returning the telescope to its original state at any time (e.g., for integrated-light solar or night-time observations). W. Lille gives assembly instructions in Section A.4.2. The costs of a prominence telescope or attachment are about $750, which can be reduced by $150–200 if the builder is skilled enough and has an adequate supply of lenses (i.e., if auxiliary lens, intermediate objective and iris diaphragm are to be found in his optics collection). Money saved in this way then can be spent on a higher quality interference filter.

B.9.2.3   Lyot Filter

Only the very serious amateur will want to obtain a polarizing interference filter, with which the limb and surface phenomena can be observed simultaneously. With such a device no complicated rebuilding of an available instrument is necessary as it is simply attached to the focusing tube. Of course, there are certain prerequisites: the path of the rays must be as parallel as possible ($\geq f/30$) and an energy rejection filter (ERF) must be used. Good amateur filters (DayStar) cost around $3000. A "University" model is qualitatively superior to an "ATM" model and is also more expensive. Professional filters (Halle for approximately $50,000, Zeiss for over $75,000) have many advantages over the multilayer interference DayStar fi-

Fig. B.9.4. *A Genesis "Solar Kit" refractor with DayStar T-Scanner. The special optics in the Tele Vue Genesis Solar Kit attach to any Tele Vue Genesis or Genesis-sdf telescope and provide full field Hα observing with the DayStar T-scanner. The T-scanner requires no power to operate.*

lters. For example, the greater the stability, the better the homogeneity of the image and rapid shifting from the Hα line (into the red or blue wing). However, these filters are so expensive that they are outside the amateur's means (except for larger amateur observatories) and will therefore not be discussed in more detail here.

Naturally many amateurs will be put off by the hundreds and thousands of dollars being bandied about, but all amateur astronomy associations, public and school observatories, and life-long hobbyists in amateur solar observation will have to seriously consider whether or not to purchase such a specialized instrument, either now or at some point in the future.

Fig. B.9.5. *Top: A Complete DayStar Filter. Bottom: The "insides" of a DayStar Filter consisting of (L to R): 1) an anti-reflection coated optical window, 2) a narrow-band blocking filter, 3) an etalon window, 4) a Fabry-Perot solid spacer crystal, 5) another etalon window, 6) a broad-band trimming filter, and 7) an anti-reflection coated window. This filter eliminates all solar wavelengths except an ultra-narrow passband centered on the Hydrogen Balmer-alpha line at 6562.8Å. The black tilting knob (left of bottom center) is used to center the etalons on this narrow line. The white eyepiece retaining screw (upper photo) is seen on the left. Photos courtesy of Donald Trombino.*

Fig. B.9.6. The sun in the CaII (K) line; note the good visibility of the chromospheric network. Photo taken on September 7, 1981 at 12:48 UT by Günther Appelt who used a 50mm refractor, $f = 1000$, DayStar 1Å CaII (K, 3933Å) line filter.

B.9.3 Chromosphere

We will now turn to the phenomena which can be observed in the chromosphere. Phenomena visible in other lines, apart from Hα, have been omitted. I have tried to cover everything relating to Hα, including those phenomena which are only of very small dimensions (around 1″) and those which are still the subject of scientific debate, whether they be independent (delimited) phenomena or can be related to other phenomena. I believe it is worthwhile to provide as complete a picture as possible since amateur literature is scarce. A short historical overview follows in which there is a list of phenomena as they are most commonly known. As there is not enough space available for detailed descriptions, reference is made to the relevant professional literature. It is well worthwhile doing some further reading to realize how varied are the possibilities of observing the photosphere if we are studying the chromosphere.

B.9.3.1   Historical Background

Before Janssen, Zöllner, Lockyer, Secchi, and Hale, the chromosphere and its limb phenomena could only be observed during a total solar eclipse and few detailed descriptions were available (mostly of large prominences). Around 1850, Airy was still calling the chromosphere "sierra." Although some earlier observers had suspected that such phenomena could have their origins in the sun itself, others believed that they were optical illusions or belonged to the moon. It was even said that prominences were "solar mountains which shone in the reflected light of the sun just like snow-capped mountains on earth" (Secchi 1872). However, while evaluating observations of the solar eclipse of July 18, 1860, both Father Angelo Secchi and, independently of him, Warren de la Rue came to the definitive conclusion that this layer and its phenomena must belong to the sun itself.

Lockyer and Frankland finally coined the term "chromosphere" in 1869. Between 1869 and 1880, the first spicules were observed with a spectroscope as small flame-like objects surrounding the entire solar limb, although initially they were thought to be prominences of lesser height and size than "normal" prominences. Secchi himself describes them picturesquely in 1872:

> The outside of the chromosphere often exhibits a number of small fiery rays or numerous irregular flames and has the appearance of a burning field, looking as if a low area of flax or hemp had caught fire. The height of the flames changes constantly and reaches twice the height of the actual chromosphere below it. The flames are evidently little more than comparatively small prominences (Secchi 1872).

Shortly afterwards it was Secchi himself who realized that the spicules were a phenomenon of the upper chromosphere, subject to their own laws. Finally, by 1892 Hale had established the "chromospheric network" through spectroheliograms using the spectroheliograph he had developed. This is the network of supergranules and the term is still used today, although it is better known from photographs in the CaII (K) line. With the aid of the spectroheliograph and the possibilities it provided, further details of the chromosphere's surface were soon discovered and called "flocculi" on the basis of a suggestion by Hale in 1903 (Hale and Ellerman 1903). In 1904 he wrote:

> The term 'flocculi' is applied indiscriminately to all bright or dark clouds of vapor photographed in projection on the sun's disc, without distinction of level. In other words, a flocculus may be a mass of vapor in the reversing layer, or in the chromosphere, or in a prominence. For this reason we shall speak of calcium flocculi, hydrogen flocculi, etc. (Hale, Ellerman 1904).

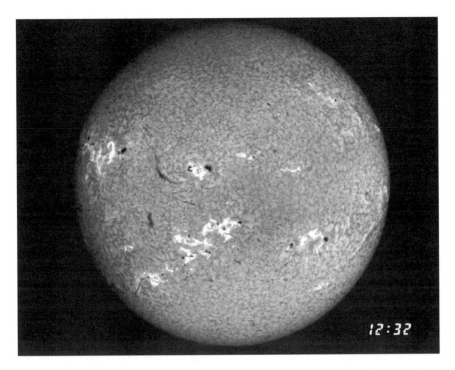

Fig. B.9.7. *The sun in Hα light: structures of the quiet and active chromosphere are visible. Observer: Gordon Garcia, 63 mm Schmidt-Cassegrain, f=2000 mm (stopped down to f/32) with DayStar Hα 0.56Å, July 1, 1990, 17:32 UT.*

As late as 1929 he still only distinguishes between:

"quiescent bright flocculi" (now: plages)
"active bright flocculi"   (now: flares)
"dark hydrogen flocculi"   (now: filaments) (Hale 1929).

Since the invention of the Lyot filter, further individual phenomena have been discovered and differentiation has taken place. It was not until the 1960's that a more precise picture could be obtained through detailed photographs. Today, the following types of chromospheric phenomena are distinguished: (a) fine structures of the quiet chromosphere and (b) fine structures of the active chromosphere.

B.9.3.2 Structures of the Quiet Chromosphere

Spicules: Phenomena at the solar limb (as described above) having an average diameter 1″1 (approx 815 km), but may be larger, are 9000 km in height, and last 5–10 minutes. Average ascending rate 20–30 km/sec.

"Young" (ascending) and "decaying" (descending) spicules are distinguished.

Bright Mottles in the Low Chromosphere: Another phenomenon at the solar limb (at high resolution): bright, round to long knots in the lower chromosphere, i.e., bright areas between the outer edge of the chromosphere (upper limit: the spicules) and the photosphere. On average the size is horizontally $2''$ to $5.5''$ (1450–4000 km) and vertically $1''$ to $3''$ (725–2200 km); lifespan around 12 minutes; height above the photosphere $1''–6''$ (725–4350 km).

Dark Band at Base of Chromosphere: This is a relatively unexplained and not always observable phenomenon between the photosphere (= base of the chromosphere) and the bright mottles (see above). The dark band was first defined by Loughhead (1969) and Nikolsky (1970). The authors indicate a height directly above the photosphere of around $1''\!.5$ (1100 km).

Dark Mottles: These are small, dark, round to longitudinal structures with a size of around $2''$ to $11''$ (1450–8000 km) and a lifespan of 0.5 to 15 minutes. They are full of contrast and spiky in the wings around Hα ± 0.25 – ± 0.75Å.

Chromospheric Network: As already described above, this is a large chromospheric structure discovered by Hale.

In addition, several lesser fine structures are given as phenomena of the quiet chromosphere.

Grains: These occur in the blue end of Hα (Hα – 0.5Å), visible as small, dark points in the interior of the cells of the chromospheric network with a size of $1''–2''$ (Beckers).

Bright Pattern: A still unexplained phenomenon, with discussion centering on whether this is photospheric granulation shining through the chromosphere (Bray, Loughhead 1968; Winter, Janssen and Rogers 1970).

B.9.3.3   Structures of the Active Chromosphere

The best known and most easily observed phenomena for the amateur are prominences/filaments, flares, and chromospheric faculae (plages). Since they are so easily observed in detail and differentiated in Hα, a separate section will be devoted to them (B.9.4). For the present we will limit the discussion to a description of those phenomena in the active chromosphere which are not so easily accessible to amateurs but which form part of the overall picture.

Chromospheric Facular Granules: These are $1''–2''$ in size and are at intervals of around $1''–1''\!.5$ from one another. Previously it was thought (e.g., Kiepenheuer et al. 1953) that these were the same facular granules as the photospheric ones but seen at a different height. More recent studies (Bray and Mussayer 1968) have, however, thrown doubt on this (see also Rothe 1979).

Fibrils, also known as dark fine mottles and bright fine mottles: Here, a distinction is made between the "fibril structure of growing active regions" which are similar to dark mottles in the quiet chromosphere but appear in emerging centers of activity (like the finer structure in the known idealized picture of an emerging center of activity) and the "fibril structure of well-developed active regions." These fibrils have a larger and more complex structure than the others and are concentrated around activity centers (similar to the iron filings pattern in a magnetic field). Individual fibrils are on average around $1''$ to $3''$ (725–2200 km) in width and about $15''$ (11,000 km) long. Their lifespan is considered to be 10 to 20 minutes. There is much evidence that these are spicules, as only fibrils are seen *on* the solar disk.

Dark Coarse Mottles and Bright Coarse Mottles: Both of these phenomena involve a fibril-like basic structure which here means structural links of simple fibrils. They are also known as *rosettes* or *bushes,* particularly as they take on the appearance of the latter (mainly when in the vicinity of the solar limb). They are $5''–10''$ in size and their lifespan around 20 hours (like the cells of the chromospheric network).

Arch Filaments, also known as "Field Transition Arches" (Prata 1971): given as "arch filament system" (AFS) at the NOAA. According to Bruzek (1967), they are described in Tandberg-Hanssen (1974) as "similar to fibrils, but larger and longer (20000 to 30000 km). They are usually to be found in the early stages of most activity centers, and they are particularly typical in the formation of bipolar sunspot groups in the interspot region." Arch filaments are a dark arch-shaped fibril pattern (much smaller than normal filaments) with a short lifetime in the region of hours. Usually they are certain predecessors of rapid developments in the activity centers in which they are located.

Superpenumbrae around Individual Spots: Consisting of fibrils, their appearance is similar to white light penumbrae but larger, and they do not have to be identical to the photospheric penumbra fine structure. The distances between the individual superpenumbra fibrils are around $1''$ towards the umbra and around $2''–3''$ away from the umbra. The average length varies greatly, but is given as approximately $25''$. The lifespan of individual superpenumbra fibrils corresponds to that of "normal" fibrils, although the general fibril structure around a sunspot lasts much longer.

Moustaches (Bright Spots or Ellerman Bombs): Small, *extremely* bright points of light (almost flare brightness!), which are mainly observed at the outer penumbra edge of the principal spot in bipolar groups in the Hα wings. They are not observed in unipolar spots and in decaying faculae, but are present at the ends of small, surge-like dark filaments and in arch filaments. Size is of the order of $1''$ to $5''$ but lifespan is disputed, with average values 4 to 25 minutes discussed. It should also be mentioned that apart from appearance, moustaches are not related to flares as they exhibit neither temporal dependence on the latter nor spectral similarities. One of many assumptions is that the bright points could possibly be the "bright end" of a fibril.

More recent investigations also show the *"Filigree Structure,"* but this is beyond the reach of amateur instruments ($0.25''$) and has still not been definitively explained (first described by R.B. Dunn, 1974). Also, this phenomenon is probably more related to the photosphere than the chromosphere.

B.9.4　Prominences/Filaments

The most easily observable phenomena are prominences and filaments, and for this reason they are the most studied field in amateur Hα observation. Whether only the prominences at the limb or also filaments on the surface of the sun can be observed depends on the instrument and filter, as has already been described. The fundamental principles of the physics of prominences which every serious amateur astronomer should grasp cannot be given here, but they can easily be found in professional books. Once the amateur has set up his Hα instrument he should ask himself how he should record his observations and at a later stage evaluate them. This will be discussed in detail as amateur literature on the subject is practically nonexistent.

B.9.4.1　Observation Records

Records of observations can be either in the form of drawings or photographs.[1] For counting or measurement it is sufficient to record the figures. Figure B.9.8 shows the report sheet for the diagrammatic recording of prominences used for many years at the Wilhelm-Foerster Observatory in Berlin. To facilitate addition of filaments a circle marking only the limb is used. Figure B.9.9 shows a report file in which personally observed values can be entered every month. This enables information to be retrieved very quickly for evaluation purposes and is also suitable for rapid data exchange with other Hα observers.

The seeing conditions are determined in accordance with the Kiepenheuer scale (see B.1.2.3). If one uses a prominence telescope with a occulting disk and relatively broad filter, the transparency becomes very noticeable. As only phenomena at the solar limb are being observed, the brightness of the sky must not be underestimated. In 1968, B. Wedel of the Wilhelm-Foerster Observatory in Berlin proposed that the image contrast should also be determined in such observations. Wedel's scale is as follows:

1 = celestial background very dark, prominences very distinct
2 = celestial background dark, prominences distinct
3 = celestial background slightly bright, but prominences still quite distinct
4 = celestial background bright, prominences only seen with difficultly

In practice this scale has proved extremely useful.

In photographic observations, an accurate observation log has to be kept. Detailed note taking cannot be overstated—errors can easily occur in photography which cannot be rectified once the film has been developed.

---

[1] For photographic Hα observations Kodak Technical Pan 2415 is especially recommended as all other films now available (1995) produce inferior results.

Wilhelm - Foerster - Observatory

Sun 19..

Date: ; Time   ; Instr.:   "; Eyepiece: mm;

Seeing: ; Observer: ;

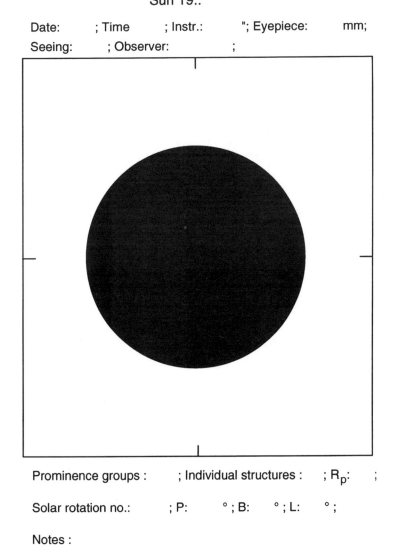

Prominence groups :   ; Individual structures :   ; R_p: ;

Solar rotation no.:   ; P: ° ; B: ° ; L: ° ;

Notes :

Fig. B.9.8. *Report sheet for the diagrammatic recording of prominences.*

Hα Solar Activity in Month													
Name :													
Address :													
Instrument :			Hα – Filter :						Magnification :				
Date	UT	Seeing (vis)	C	H	E	R_p	A_{WM}	A_{mm^2}	HO	Flare R | O		Photo	Rem.:
1													
2													
⋮													
30													
31													
Monthly mean:								Obs. :					

Fig. B.9.9 *Monthly report file for observed values of the solar activity.*

Key to Fig. B.9.9

UT	Universal Time
Seeing(vis)	Visual; in photographic observation only visually possible as no control possible during exposure of the emulsion; Kiepenheuer scale 1–5 to be used.
C	Contrast (only in the case of pure prominence telescopes; Wedel scale)
H	Prominence groups (at limb)
E	Number of prominences (at limb) according to Völker types
R_P	Prominence number according to Völker: 10H+E (visually determined at instrument for prominences at limb)
A_{WM}	(Area) Prominence profile area of prominences at limb according to Waldmeier $1° \times 1''$
A_{mm^2}	(Area) Prominence profile area according to Völker (is determined using 15 cm photographic enlargements and indicates how many mm^2 are filled with prominences).
HO	Heliographic position determination; a cross indicates whether available (for limb and/or surface structures).
Flare	A cross indicates whether present. R means observation of a limb flare (also possible with prominence telescopes) and O means surface observation.
Photo	Number of exposed negatives

Two examples:

1. Underexposure: On the developed film, one or more pictures are blank.
2. Film spooling failure: The film spooling device fails temporarily (e.g., perforation damage) and several pictures are exposed one on top of the other. Where do the usable pictures begin again once the error has been noted and rectified?

After developing the negatives, failed pictures are removed. A negative number is then written on each negative (with drawing ink). The negative number is composed of the date in astronomical notation and the sequence number of the picture in the appropriate observation year, e.g., 19790201–14. In this way each negative is clearly marked and cannot be mistaken for others. This number and all other data on the pictures are entered into a negative list, the final form of the photographic data obtained directly at the instrument in the observation book. These negatives are, of course, placed in negative holders for storage. For detailed statistical evaluation, a positive copy with a 15 cm diameter is produced[2]. For more detailed investigations, the negatives can be evaluated using a measuring microscope. Samples of a negative list and a protocol sheet for photographic enlargements to 15 cm, as used by the Wilhelm-Foerster Observatory in Berlin, are shown in Figs. B.9.10 and B.9.11.

The advantage of drawing is that fine details can be recorded, whereas photography has the advantage that positions and size relationships (proportions) between individual structures are more accurate (particularly important in sequence pictures of prominences).

B.9.4.2 Classifications

After some period of time, the Hα observer will start to think about what he has observed and start to ask questions, usually beginning with "Is there a prominence classification system?" In the case of sunspot groups, we are accustomed to using Waldmeier's classification from A to I. Is there something similar for prominences? A certain amount has been written on the subject of "prominence classification" which I will summarize below, for not only is it of interest and importance to us, but also because a concise summary has not yet appeared. Waldmeier (1941) writes succinctly (page 207) "The range of shapes of prominences is so great that it is impossible to give a general description." On page 209 he continues "Pettit's proposed classification (1932) cannot be used as it is not based on a clear principle and relates to features which are too superficial." We shall return to Pettit's classification later. Other astronomers, both before and

---

[2]This size is recommended by various institutions, see *Catania Annual Reports.*

Wilhelm - Foerster - Observatory,   Sun

Negative list of H–α–photographies from ....to ....

Neg. number	Date	d	S(V)	F	Mat.	t1 (exp)	Type	I	Dev.	t2(m)	Obs.	Proc.	Rem.

Fig. B.9.10. *Sample of a negative list.*

Key

Neg. Number:	Negative number
Date:	Date and time in astronomical terms, UT of photograph
d:	Day of the week of the photograph
S(v):	Seeing determination according to the Kiepenheuer scale; in the case of photographic observations only visually possible, as no verification is possible during the exposure
F:	Filter setting at the time of exposure
Mat:	Material used
t_1 (exp):	Exposure time in seconds
Type:	Type of picture (prom. or fil)
I:	Size of instrument in inches
Dev:	Details of negative developer used
t_2 (m):	Development time in minutes
Obs:	Name of observer
Proc.:	Name of person working on the material
Rem:	Remarks (e.g., C means that a copy of the negative has been made) or "negative scratched" or "failure," etc.

after Waldmeier have thought differently. As early as 1872, P.A. classified nebulous prominences, column prominences, jets, also known as forced discharge prominences, pile prominences, smoky prominences, cloud prominences, also quiescent or hydrogen prominences (Krause 1911), eruptive prominences, metallic prominences (Krause 1911), and bushy prominences. One curious extract from Krause (1911) should be quoted here: "In the faculae which appear so frequently in the vicinity of sunspots, we should generally imagine prominences, but seen from above, not from the side as at the limb."—Popular scientific literature in 1911.

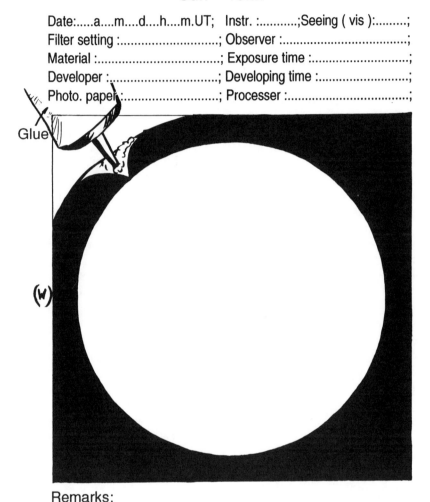

Fig. B.9.11. *Protocol sheet for photographic enlargements with a diameter of 15 cm. They are precut so that they are ready when needed.*

Charles G. Abbot took over Secchi's classification in 1929, but introduces two main types in his book *The Sun* (D. Appleton and Co.), i.e., "quiescent, cloud-formed or hydrogenous and the eruptive or metallic prominences." He provided the following English terms for Secchi's forms which he classified as "subclasses" of the two main classes: spikes, sheafs and volutes, jets, clouds, diffuse, filamentary, stemmed, plumes, horns, vertical filaments, cyclone, and flames. We even find out that Trouvelot suspected the existence of "dark prominences," apparently "clouds of cooler hydrogen that absorb the light of the hydrogen behind them." Tacchini also assumed that there were "white" prominences "which give a continuous spectrum, and are not reached by spectroscopic observation." However, Abbot, who himself did not believe in them, said that the evidence was still lacking! W. Grotrian (Grotrian et al. 1934) also uses the broad categories of quiescent and eruptive prominences.

R.R. McMath (1939) reported that additional prominence types should be included in Pettit's classification (which was then already known—see below) because of the advent of Hα cinematography. These prominence types are: surges, ejections, coronal type streamers, violently eruptive prominences, arch types, and predominance of matter in descent.

U. Becker (1951) noted that prominences can be divided into prominences of the principal or equatorial zone and those of the secondary or polar zone, and that the former at maximum limb visibility have an elongated bridge shape whereas the latter at minimum limb visibility only exhibit a post or pyramid structure. E. Pettit (1961) mentioned "prominences of the coronal cloud type," "tornadoes," and "interactive prominences."

B.M. Rustad (1973) gave further subdivisions to Jager's prominence classification (see below). To IIa: interactive, normal active, corona active; to IIb: quasi eruptive, normal eruptive and eruptive arch; to IIc: normal corona sunspot, loop corona sunspot, active sunspot, flow from corona, coronal rain, funnels; to IId: normal surge and expanding surge (these with illustrations of the corresponding flow conditions).

In 1975 U. Bendel and W. Kunz wrote, with regard to an article in *Kosmos* by K. Schülte entitled "Solar Prominences, Gas Eruptions": "The old division of prominences into three classes (active, eruptive and quiescent) has recently been shown to be inadequate. A few years ago American astronomers therefore established the following division into 6 classes:

1) active prominences,

2) eruptive prominences (ascending prominences),

3) sunspot prominences (surges),

4) tornado prominences,

5) quiescent prominences (stationary), and

6) coronal prominences."

(Bendel et al. 1975). From 1) to 5) this corresponds to the old Pettit classification, with the coronal prominences added.

Engvold (1976) also includes "hedgerow," "suspended cloud," "tree," "tree trunk," and "thick coarse prominences." Shapley et al. (1973) and Mangis (1975) also have "bright surge on limb," "loop prominence system," "spray," and "coronal rain," while Severny (1959) simply uses the old division into quiescent and eruptive prominences. Smith and Smith (1963) use the Menzel-Evans classification (see below).

Tandberg-Hanssen put an end to all these conflicting ideas in his excellent book *Solar Prominences* (1974) in which he lists all the then known important classifications in tabular form in a few pages. These will be reproduced here because of their importance. For readers unable to obtain the book, there first of all follows an explanation of the terms used in the subsequent tables to ensure that the latter are fully understood.

Eruptive Prominences (also called ascending prominences) are ordinary quiescent prominences that for some reason become unstable, erupt (ascend) and disappear. The French term for this phenomenon is disparition brusque, and one often refers to the disparition brusque phase of a quiescent prominence. Generally, the prominence reforms in the same place. According to L. d'Azambuja and M. d'Azambuja (1948) the disparition brusque phase seems to be a normal stage in the development of most quiescent prominences.

Caps are seen above the limb as bright, low-lying prominences near active regions. Their lifetimes range from hours to days. Surges frequently are ejected from the edges of caps (Pettit 1943). They may be the limb manifestation of fibrils and arch filaments (Malville 1968; Harvey 1969).

Knots are seen above the limb as shortlived (15 minutes) very bright features, having heights less than 20,000 km. They lie above sunspots.

Surges are prominences that seem to be shot out of active regions as long straight or curved columns, and return along the same trajectory. They may reach to great heights (several hundreds of thousands of kilometers) and their velocities may exceed several hundred km/sec. Some active regions produce nearly identical surges during part of their lives (*homologous surges*).

Sprays are shot out from flare regions at velocities often exceeding the velocity of escape. The ejection is so violent that the matter is not contained, as in surges, but flies out in fragments.

Coronal Clouds are irregular objects suspended in the corona with matter streaming out of them into nearby active regions along curved trajectories. The coronal clouds last for a day at heights of several tens of thousands of kilometers.

Loops are divided into single loops (see Fig. B.9.13) in which one side streams upwards and the other downwards, usually into the spot, and flare loops (see Fig. B.9.14). The latter result from a flare and both sides stream downwards. A loop system is the manifestation of the highest degree of

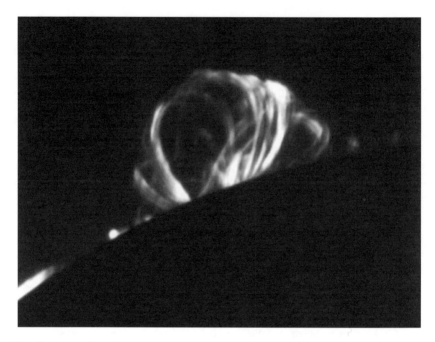

Fig. B.9.12. *Complex loop prominence. Observer: Victor J. Lopez, May 10,*
1981.

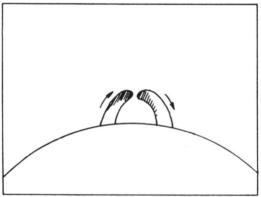

Fig. B.9.13. *Single loop: one side flows up, the other down.*

activity observed optically in the solar atmosphere. At the tops of such
loops the corona is very hot and condensed into a coronal condensation.

Coronal Rain is closely related to loops, but the complete loop structure is
absent giving the phenomenon its descriptive name.

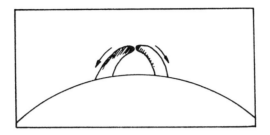

Fig. B.9.14. *Flare loop: both sides stream down.*

Pettit's Classification (1925, 1932, 1936, 1943, 1950)

Class	Name	Description
1	Active	Material seems to be streaming into nearby active center (like sunspots).
2	Eruptive	The whole prominence ascends with uniform velocity (of several hundred km/sec often). The velocity may at times suddenly increase.
3	Sunspot	These are found near sunspots and take the shape of 'water in a fountain' or loops.
4	Tornado	A vertical spiral structure gives these prominences the appearance of a closely wound rope or whirling column.
5	Quiescent	Large prominence masses which show only minor changes over periods of hours or days.

Newton's Classification (1934, 1935)

Class Description

I   Prominences that avoid the neighborhood of sunspots (but not the whole sunspot zone). Long well-defined filaments lasting several days.

II   Prominences that are associated with sunspots or with the plage areas. Generally smaller than objects of class I. Lifetimes of the order of minutes or hours.

  (a) Prominences that show large radial velocities and occur after the appearance of a localized emission (a so-called bright flocculus).

  (b) Prominences originally of class I that become activated by the sudden appearance of an emission object. The emission remains more or less stationary, but it gives the filament a large radial velocity.

Menzel-Evans Classification (1953)

Relation to Sunspots	Place of Origin	
	From above A	From below B
Associated with sunspots, S	Rain, a Funnels, b Loops, l	Surges, s Puffs, p
Not associated with sunspot, N	Coronal rain, a Tree trunks, b Tree, c Hedgerows, d Suspended clouds, f Mounds, m	Spicules, s

What is interesting about this classification system is that structures can be fully described using reference letters, for example, surges are classified as BSs or arch prominences as SA1.

Severny's Classification (Severny 1950 and 1959, Severny and Khokhlova 1953)

Class	Name	Description
I	Eruptive	Quiescent prominences becoming eruptive. Rare, 5 to 10% of all cases. Outward motions with velocities of several hundred km/sec at times exceeding the velocity of escape.
II	Electromagnetic	Electromagnetic prominences. The knots or condensations making up the prominences exhibit motions along definite curved trajectories. Velocities range from several tens to a few hundred km/sec. About 50% of all prominences belong here.
III	Irregular	Prominences with irregular, random motions of individual knots.

De Jager's Classification (1959)

Class	Name
I	Quiescent prominences (a) Normal (low to medium latitudes) (b) Polar (high latitudes)
II	Moving prominences (a) Active (b) Eruptive (c) Spot (d) Surges (e) Spicules

Zirin's Classification (1966)

Class	Description	Object
I	Short lived, associated with flares and active sunspots	1. Sprays, explosions, puffs
		2. Surges
		3. Loops, coronal rain
II	Long lived, quiescent	1. Polar cap filaments
		2. Sunspot zone filaments
III	Intermediate	1. Ascending prominences
		2. Sunspot filaments

This concludes a brief voyage through the history of prominence observation and the attempts at classifying these phenomena.

The Hα observer is faced with all sorts of uncertainties. The current classification systems cannot easily be used without long periods of uninterrupted observation. All systems have as a prerequisite long observation times to classify individual structures according to their development— sometimes using instruments which are simply not available to the amateur.

What can the Hα observer do despite this? E. Leitmeier wrote in 1967 that he had tried to count prominences by category. He determined the number of prominences to establish the development of prominence frequency within the cycle. He writes that he differentiates between prominence types (tornado prominences, filaments, quiescent triangular prominences, tongue-shaped, bushy, active prominences with arches and bridges, mountainous prominences and prominences elevated above the solar limb, which float like balloons, or cloud layers, above the limb; sometimes descending lines are noticeable, like with terrestrial clouds, which rain down on the limb) and prominence groups.

> Entire prominence groups sometimes pose complex problems with regard to counting as it was not always known whether a prominence or prominences should be counted, thus making the count somewhat arbitrary. To have a definite standard for the prominence telescope, I also counted the prominence groups encompassing several prominences over a small arch, in addition to prominences. Here, too, a certain arbitrariness is not excluded, but the positions of prominence groups are much easier to determine.

B.9.4.3 Types of Prominences According to Völker

In 1969, after hundreds of my own observations, I introduced a type categorization which has turned out to be extremely useful for amateur observers (Völker 1970). I noticed that right up to the limit of resolution (instrument size, filter width, perspective effect) the small individual structures within the prominence groups can easily be grouped into three basic

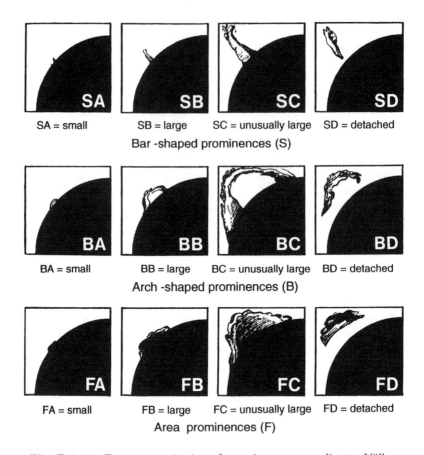

SA = small   SB = large   SC = unusually large   SD = detached

Bar -shaped prominences (S)

BA = small   BB = large   BC = unusually large   BD = detached

Arch -shaped prominences (B)

FA = small   FB = large   FC = unusually large   FD = detached

Area prominences (F)

Fig. B.9.15. *Type categorization of prominences according to Völker.*

forms—bar-shaped, arch-shaped and flat—with possible variations in size. This is what I based my type categorization on. However, it is not a true "classification," just a type categorization on which a numerical record of prominence activity can be based, i.e., the prominence number which will be discussed in more detail at a later stage.

B.9.4.4   Observation Programs

We shall look at which observation programs we can work with in the field of prominence and filament observation.

It should be emphasized that most programs can be carried out using a prominence telescope or attachment. A spectrohelioscope or Lyot filter enables the program to be more complex as limb structures can be observed along with the entire solar surface in Hα light. Our work can be divided into long and short period programs. Long observation period programs are of a statistical nature allowing us to observe the overall activity (over the entire sun) of prominences and filaments in correlation to the cycle(s). Gaps in one's own observation material (time, weather, etc.) can be filled by using an amateur observation network or by adding data from professional observations. Short observation period programs can be used to describe activities brought about by changes in the magnetic field of an activity center, for which minutes, hours, days or, at most, the lifetime of an activity center are sufficient.

Long-Term Observation Programs

1. Prominence/Filament Frequency

   1.1. Prominence profile area according to Waldmeier (unit: $1° \times 1''$) or Völker (unit: 1 mm^2 on a 15 cm-drawing or, better still, photographic enlargement)

      1.1.1. Prominence number according to Völker $R_p = 10H + E$

   1.2. Frequency of filaments according to Catania ($1 =$ total apparent length of all filaments in comparison with the solar diameter)

      1.2.1. Filament number according to Völker $R_F = 10H + E$

   1.3. Frequency of prominences and/or filaments in comparison with the sunspot activity curve

   1.4. as 1.3, with regard to the facula activity curve (photospheric and chromospheric)

   1.5. as 1.3, with regard to the flare activity curve

2. Equatorial Prominence or Filament Frequency (in the sunspot zone)

   2.1. as 1.1 to 1.5, but only for equatorial prominences and/or filaments

   2.2. Do the equatorial prominences and/or filaments follow the sunspots and/or faculae and/or flares exactly in cycle,

      2.2.1. or is their frequency independent,

      2.2.2. as 2.2.1, but according to laws, in different cycles?

3. Polar Prominence and/or Filament Frequency

   3.1. as 1.1 to 1.2.1, but only for polar prominences and/or filaments

   3.2. Polar prominence and/or filament frequency in temporal relationship with equatorial prominence and/or filament frequency; according to the literature prominences and/or filaments are at a maximum two years before the sunspot maximum whereas the equatorial prominences and/or filaments follow the sunspot cycle.

      3.2.1. Is it exactly equal in each cycle or does it vary in different cycles?

   3.3. Polar prominence and/or filament frequency as a quantitative ratio of equatorial prominence and/or filament frequency

      3.3.1 As 3.2.1

   3.4. Correlation of polar prominences and/or filaments to polar faculae?

4. Asymmetry

    4.1. North/south asymmetry of prominences and/or filaments

        4.1.1 Correlation to the north/south asymmetry of sunspots and/or faculae and/or flares

        4.1.2. As 4.1.1, but in the cycle

        4.1.3 As 4.1.1, but for several cycles

    4.2. North/south asymmetry of equatorial prominences and/or filaments

        4.2.1. As 4.1.1

        4.2.2. As 4.1.2

        4.2.3. As 4.1.3

    4.3. North/south asymmetry of the polar prominences and/or filaments

        4.3.1. Correlation to 4.2

        4.3.2. Correlation to polar faculae

        4.3.3. Also 4.2.1, 4.2.2, and 4.2.3 can be investigated again with regard to 4.3.

    4.4. East/west asymmetry (as north/south asymmetry)

5. Positions

    5.1. As 1.3

    5.2. As 1.4

    5.3. As 1.5

    5.4. As 2.2

        5.4.1. As 2.2.1

        5.4.2. As 2.2.2

    5.5. As 3.2

        5.5.1. As 3.2.1

    5.6. As 3.4 (With additional position determination the above, Observation Programs can be evaluated more accurately, and therefore they are included again here.)

    5.7. Position determination of filaments within the activity center in which they occur to connect them

        5.7.1. with the other structures in Hα (fibrils, flares, plages)

        5.7.2. with integral observations (sunspots, faculae)

6. Area Measurements. The areas of individual prominences can be measured using the methods given in 1.1. For detailed area measurements even more precise processes can be used. The following can be investigated:

    6.1. When do most small/large prominences occur in the cycle?

    6.2. Does this have to be so in several cycles? When taking area measurements of filaments, perspective has to be taken into consideration. Precise information about the area of filaments is difficult to obtain, as the angle at which they appear to us has to be known.

7. Photometry (Estimates, Photometers, Equidensity Lines [Isophotes]). "Bright" or "dull" prominence photometry, intensity evaluations or measurements of the "degree of darkness" of filaments. We can investigate the following:

   7.1. When do more bright prominences and/or filaments, and when do more dull ones occur depending on the cycle?

   7.1.1. As 7.1, but is this so for different cycles?

   7.2. Is there a relationship $m_{prom/fil}(t)$ in the cycle at all?

   7.2.1. Is there a heliographic latitude relationship?

   7.2.2. Is there one for the size of a sunspot group belonging to the corresponding center of activity?

   7.3. Are equatorial or polar prominences and/or filaments brighter/duller during the course of a cycle, and if there is a law, is it always the same?

Short-Term Observation Programs. Points 5.7, 5.7.1, 5.7.2, and 7.2.2. given under long-term observation programs can also be incorporated into short-term programs.

   7.4. Photometry of individual bright nodes in active or eruptive prominences in correlation to neighboring structures and as a function of t and h (height) = > light curves. All photometry is only relative. A better evaluation (Δm) is possible with calibration. Unavoidable difficulties (seeing, scattered light) occur if an absolute correspondence is required. Therefore these measurements are hardly realizable by the amateur.

8. Course of Movement. The observation of movements (eruptive prominences and/or filaments, and less "spectacular" occurrences such as material movement in quiescent structures) can take place in the form of drawings. However, for more accurate measurement at a later stage with subsequent evaluation, only the following observation methods can be considered: photographic (photographic camera), cinematographic (cine-camera with stills function), and video. With a photographic camera a series of photographs can be produced on Kodak spectroscopic material in slide format.

   When using cinematography, Super 8 or 16 mm color reversal material can only produce results for limb structures (prominences), with the surface not being shown very satisfactorily. For the surface a 35-mm cine-camera is needed which can be loaded with Kodak spectroscopic material: the cineframe = $1/2$ slide format. Another alternative is the use of special animation film techniques. A detailed description is given in Section A.8. Evaluations can thus be made of:

   8.1. Relative velocity measurements of individual structures in eruptive prominences and/or filaments depending on t and h

   8.2. "Disparition-brusque" phase of filaments

   8.3. "Moreton Waves" (effect of flares on filaments)

   8.4. Streaming conditions in quiescent prominences and/or filaments

   8.5. If these investigations are carried out regularly, the question can arise of when most very active prominences and/or filaments occur in the cycle. Towards the start, at the maximum or towards the end?

8.5.1. Relationship of the heliographic latitude?

9. Lifespan of Filaments. These investigations are only worthwhile for filaments (surface).

9.1. The lifespan of young filaments in whose activity centers faculae and sunspots are still visible

9.2. The lifespan of older (quiescent) filaments after sunspots and faculae have already disappeared from the activity center

9.2.1. As in 9.2, is there a relationship between the lifespan of these filaments and the classification of the former corresponding sunspot group?

9.2.2. As in 9.2, in various phases of the cycle

9.2.3. As in 9.2, in various cycles

9.2.4. As in 9.2.1, in various phases of the cycle

9.2.5. As in 9.2.1, in various cycles

10. Surroundings. Careful attention should be paid to the surrounding area after a filament has disappeared. Is there a structural change in the immediately adjacent areas of the chromosphere?

11. Overall Representation of an Activity Center. The advantage of a national amateur observer network can be seen in the fact that it is possible to follow the life of an activity center from beginning to end, both in integrated and in Hα light. The following can be shown:

11.1. The temporal sequence of the individual phenomena: faculae, sunspots, filaments, flares (when does what change?)

11.2. The positions of the individual phenomena with regard to one another

11.3. The relationship of the individual phenomena with each other

11.4. The overall duration of an activity center

11.5. Are there activity centers in which filaments occur *without* the other known phenomena?

11.6. Are there activity centers in which faculae, sunspots and flares occur without filaments?

B.9.4.5   Prominence Statistics

B.9.4.5.1. Prominence Profile Area. Waldmeier describes how professionals list their prominence statistics. A prominence area is worked out daily, the units of which are given as $1°$ (heliocentric) times $1''$ (geocentric) (see figure B.9.15) (Waldmeier 1941).

From ongoing cinematographic monitoring one 15 cm enlargement is produced every day from a good negative, which is then counted. The daily prominence area thus indicates how many $1° \times 1''$ units are "full" of prominences. The Catania Astrophysical Solar Observatory (description in the preface to the annual *Catania Solar Observations 19..*) uses the same method as Zurich. Wattenberg's essay (1936) is recommended to those

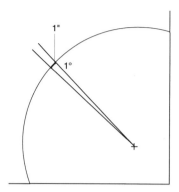

Fig. B.9.16. *"Unit of prominence area ($1° \times 1''$)" defined by Waldmeier.*

who wish to become more involved with Waldmeier's calculation of the prominence profile area.

B.9.4.5.2. Prominence Number. To me, this method seemed too costly in terms of time and material for amateurs, so I endeavored to find a simpler method and gradually the idea of the "prominence number" has evolved. I noticed that prominences at the limb occurred in groups in the same way as sunspots do on the disk. These groups include many smaller prominences which due to their very close proximity, are seen as a joint complex—in the same way as we are used to talking about sunspot groups. Using my classification scheme the individual phenomena within a prominence group can be recorded separately and therefore counted. Again, the various characteristics of sunspot groups lend themselves to comparison, the large with the medium and small, those with penumbrae and those without, and the bright with the dark. They are all of equal value, however, when determining the sunspot number.

After that it was relatively simple. I defined the following: to numerically record prominence activity the number of prominence groups present are counted, the result multiplied by 10 and the recognizable individual structures simply added to the total. This produces the "prominence number" R_P. Expressed as an equation this is: $R_P = 10H + E$. For more experienced solar observers, the conceptual parallel to the sunspot number can now be clearly seen (see Section B.2.4). (H and E in the formula come from the German "Herde" (groups) and "Einzelerscheinungen" (individual structures)).

B.9.4.5.3. A Practical Example of Determining the Prominence Number. In Figure B.9.17 my observation notes from April 14, 1971 are reproduced. Nine prominence groups can be detected around the solar limb. This figure is entered under "Groups." In all there are 28 individual promin-

Wilhelm - Foerster - Observatory

Sun 1971

Date: 71a 04 m 14 d 09h 10m CET ;Instr.: 6 " ; Eyepiece : 40 mm ;

Seeing : 2.5 ;Observer : Peter Völker ;

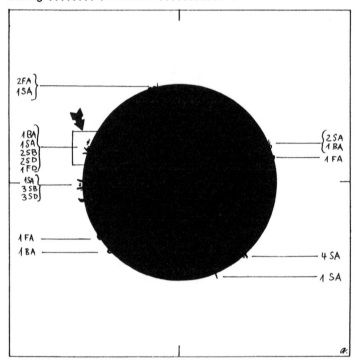

Prominence groups : 9 ; Individual structures : 28 ; R_p:118 ;

Solar rotation no. : ; P : ° ; B : ° ; L : ° ;

Notes :

Fig. B.9.17. *Observation report from April 14, 1971.*

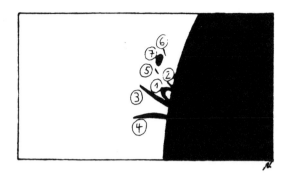

Fig. B.9.18. *Section from the report of April 14, 1971.*

ences. This is entered under "Individual Structures." According to the equation $R_P = 10H + E$ the following is the result $R_P = (10 \times 9) + 28 = 118$. This is then entered at the bottom under R_P.

To understand exactly how the number of individual structures within a prominence group is determined, a detailed drawing of the section of the observation report is shown (see Fig. B.9.18). To fully understand this please compare with the classification scheme (Fig. B.9.15). 1 is BA, 2 is SA, 3+4 are SB, 5+6 are SD, and 7 is FD. The same procedure is used for all other prominence groups.

B.9.4.5.4. Discussion. One argument against determining the number only once a day is that prominences can change dramatically in a short period of time, so that morning and afternoon observations can yield quite different results. On the other hand, it could be said that this is only likely to happen in the case of eruptive structures. Most prominence groups are relatively stable, although it does happen from time to time that a group breaks up and disappears quite quickly. Most prominence groups have a tendency, even if they are active (small changes in the number of individual prominence structures in the group), to remain much the same in terms of extent; i.e., in "large" groups there will always be more individual structures than in "small" ones. In addition, for later statistical evaluation, only means are taken, but short and even noticeable occurrences are canceled out. Very roughly it can be said that for statistical evaluation the following applies: much activity (= many prominences) = high prominence number; little activity (= few prominences) = low prominence number. If this can be recorded using the prominence number, we are able to use our own values to record the maximum, minimum and certain accompanying activities. The same difficulty is encountered as in determining the sunspot number, which is also only determined once a day, yet seems to "work"—small sunspots in groups change within the space of hours, large sunspots become divided and A groups are born and die during the course of a single day.

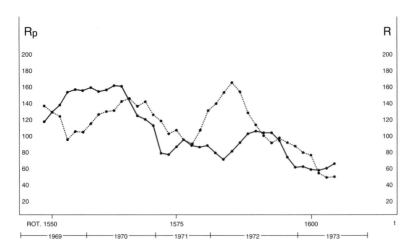

Fig. B.9.19. *Determining the prominence number according to Völker: R_P (full curve) prominence number; R (dashed curve) sunspot number.*

Another argument against the prominence number is that only limb activity is recorded while activity on the disk itself is completely neglected. However, the immediate retort to this is that according to Waldmeier's method the prominence profile area is exactly the same and that only one hemisphere can be used to obtain the sunspot number, despite which, the figures clearly indicate the progress of the cycle. Finally, it could be said against the prominence number that determining it depends very much on the resolution, which is affected by the size of the instrument, the filter width, and above all, the atmospheric conditions (scintillation and brightness of the sky).

All these difficulties are well-known from sunspot observation. Recognizing the individual sunspots also depends on the size of the instrument and scintillation, although, in the case of prominences, the other factors also play a part. The following can be done: if the celestial background is too bright the prominence number is simply not determined, though different filter widths in different instruments do not pose the problem. With a broad width filter, fewer individual structures are observed; with a narrower one, more are seen. All that is important is that the same instrument be used for observation which ensures homogeneity of the observation material. Furthermore, even the weaker filters still enable most prominence groups to be seen, though fewer individual structures. To compensate for this the number of groups is multiplied by 10. So, everything is just the same as in determining the sunspot number.

Finally, there is another strong argument in favor of the amateur using the prominence number. It can be determined easily and quickly, during observation and without the need for photographs, indeed, it has to be determined at the telescope itself as photographs never show the same richness of detail as visual observations (as in planetary observation and in determining the sunspot number).

B.9.4.5.5. The Result of One Evaluation. The data shown in Figure B.9.19 were smoothed by averaging over 5 rotations. All observations: P. Völker. (NB: for evaluation purposes only those days were taken into account on which it was possible to determine both R and R_P).

Interpretation. Both curves follow the falling off in the general course of activity. This proves the correctness and usability of R_P. It is noticeable that the correlation is not as great as is usual if one's own sunspot number is set against the Zurich sunspot sequence. However, this has to be so, as *all* limb structures are included in curve R_P and it is known that only equatorial prominences follow the sunspot cycle whereas polar prominences are at a maximum around two years before the sunspot maximum. The same structures are not involved here. Even Waldmeier writes that prominence activity is expressed differently from sunspot activity. Thus, if the tendency of curve R_P corresponds to the sunspot activity curve, its usability is proved. It would be useful if a prominence observer established two prominence activity curves, one for equatorial prominences and one for polar prominences.

For prominence observers who use photographic methods and do not wish to determine the prominence number R_p visually, the author has conceived another method for statistically evaluating limb activity. Once enlargements have been made, it is, under certain circumstances, possible to determine the prominence profile area $1° \times 1''$ according to Waldmeier. However, it is easier to place a sheet of transparent millimeter paper on the positives (provided they all show the same diameter!) and to count the number of mm^2 which are "full" of prominences: A_{mm^2} (A = area). The values obtained in this way enable a very informative prominence activity curve to be established.

B.9.4.6 Filament Statistics

If the $H\alpha$ observer owns a filter which enables him to observe chromospheric structures on the solar disk, he will see prominences as dark, usually elongated phenomena called filaments. Their frequency can also be statistically recorded.

B.9.4.6.1. Total Apparent Length in Solar Diameter. In the *Catania Annual Reports 19..,* the following method is recommended: for evaluation purposes only quiescent prominences on the disc observed over a period of time are taken into account. From Hα observation negatives, a 15 cm diameter enlargement is made every day. Two values are then determined to be used in later statistical evaluation:

n = daily number
l = total apparent length in solar diameter.

The area is not determined as it is with sunspots and faculae, as filaments are relatively "thin" when viewed "from above." The structures are only characterized by their length, which is worked out using the position of the magnetic poles within an activity center, which in turn changes during its lifetime due to differential rotation. What we see as the filament "area" is related to perspective and short-term material activity (caused by magnetic field activity).

B.9.4.6.2. The Filament Number. In 1974 I developed a simpler method for numerically recording filament activity, similar to that for the sunspot, facula, and prominence numbers.

Filaments also occur in "groups." This has to be so, as filaments, like other phenomena, are part of the activity center, which is known as a group in the case of sunspots, faculae and prominences. During visual observation I noticed that a filament consists of a number of fine structures, such as threads and knots. The larger and longer a filament is, the greater the number of fine structures it contains. Introducing a filament number was therefore a simple matter. The equation used is: $R_F = 10H + E$. Determining the filament number R_F is done in the same way as for the prominence number R_P, but there is no classification of the individual filaments.

B.9.4.6.3. Discussion. The fact that the filament number is worked out only once a day is not a disadvantage in terms of the information it provides for statistical purposes. Even professionals (Catania, see above) work this way. Furthermore, the same is true for determining the sunspot, the facula and prominence numbers. Catania works out the number of filaments and their apparent length separately. The filament number includes the number of filament groups and the number of individual filaments contained in them. We rightly assume that there are many individual phenomena in a long filament whereas there are fewer in a short filament. Thus, the total apparent length of the filaments is included in the filament number. The advantage of the filament number for the amateur is that it can be worked out quickly and visually during observation.

B.9.4.7 Determining the Position of Chromospheric Phenomena

If the positions of chromospheric phenomena are recorded in sufficient detail they can be analyzed. A long term data gathering program should include the following: The latitudes of prominences and/or filaments can be recorded visually in butterfly diagram form and numerically. Of particular interest is the link with sunspot and facula movements. Here borderline situations should be noted: Mattig (1963) writes,

> Accurate analysis of zone movements has recently shown that a second sunspot zone exists. The sunspot zone forming at the beginning of a cycle in particularly high latitudes divides with one area moving to the pole rather than the equator. This secondary sunspot zone can only be detected, however, during the increasing phase of the cycle until the maximum is reached.

The problem the amateur can investigate is how it relates to the prominences and filaments.

In position evaluations, polar and equatorial prominences and/or filaments are treated separately as both have their own cycle. The investigations we can make have already been described under points 5.5, 5.5.1, and 5.6. (see Section B.9.4.4 Observation Programs). To compare one's own prominence position results with those from professional institutions the following can be done. The amateur can consult the annual book of tables published by Catania in which the longitude (east or west limb) and latitude of all prominences are listed for (almost) every day. Also available are the NOAA figures published monthly, although positions have to be worked out by oneself from a small drawing (one drawing per day), which takes up a lot of time. The advantage is that the NOAA figures are available after an interval of 3 to 4 months, whereas the Catania figures are not published for 18 months. Further, NOAA publishes an Hα surface photograph for each day so that the amateur with the right equipment can compare these positions, too.

All these observation programs can be carried out by observers who own a prominence telescope or attachment and therefore can observe only limb structures. With a filter of the DayStar- or Lyot-type, with which the surface of the chromosphere is visible, the phenomena can be monitored more extensively and therefore there are fewer gaps. However, the accuracy of the information about the cycle or even several cycles is not substantially increased.

There are of course observation programs for Hα position determination which can be carried out with a DayStar- or Lyot-type filter alone. These belong under points 5.7, 5.7.1, and 5.7.2 (see Section B.9.4.4 Observation Programs). Here we leave statistics and go on to look at a single activity center, observing the positions of separate chromospheric phenomena with regard to one another and how they change during the lifetime of an activity center. Observation time is not

Fig. B.9.20. *A bi-filar micrometer used with the DayStar TS-11 0.6Å Hα filter permits the observer to determine the length and height of solar prominences, and to calculate the size of sunspots, flares, filaments, and other features in the sun's photosphere and chromosphere. Note the small tuning knob at the top of the Hα filter. It is used to "fine tune" the Hα filter pack (etalon). Turning it slightly will shift the filter off of the H-α center line for Doppler shift observations. When tilted sufficiently the filter will reveal white light or "continuum" features such as sunspots. Photo courtesy of D. F. Trombino, Florida, U.S.A.*

years or decades (which makes statistics worthwhile) but at least minutes or hours (the effect of flares on the positions of prominences and/or filaments), or at most several months (total lifetime of an activity center). All investigations are of more interest if they also become part of integral observations. In conjunction with this I would also like to mention a method conceived by Bendel (1975) which is used to determine the longitudinal extent of a filament. His article is concerned with determining the extent of sunspot groups using a micrometer plate, but can also be used for filaments.

  Methods: The observation methods used to determine the position of prominences and filaments are more restricted than those for sunspots. The projection method is not included at all. Although it is possible to read off the positions from prominence or filament drawings (visual observations through the eyepiece) using a covering grid, it is not recommended due to the high degree of inaccuracy. Only detailed sequential drawings of short-

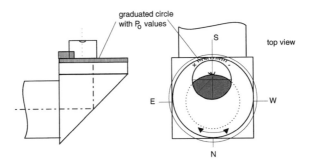

Fig. B.9.21. *Simple device for measuring positions of prominences.*

term changes can be considered here, but even these will be imprecise, however carefully they are made; errors will remain unacceptably great. Only the photographic method is of use here. For heliographic position determination there has to be double exposure to establish the east-west direction. Producing and evaluating double exposures for determining directions is described in Section B.3.2.4.1 and 2. Although all these methods relate to sunspot positions, they are the same for prominences and filaments. Once the positions of a number of main points (e.g., p and f spots in a sunspot group) have been established from the double exposure, detailed photographs taken at the same time can be combined with it.

For the amateur a simple method of interest for measuring the position of prominences during observation (without photographs and drawings) is described by Schröder. Using his techniques measurement is carried out directly at the instrument. The attainable accuracy is between 1 and 3 degrees in heliographic latitude depending on the care taken. The principle is to read the position of the eccentric of a limbus. With correct adjustment the position of the prominence can be read off in the middle of the eyepiece (use a graticule).

For many years I have been using the following (see Fig. B.9.21). Apart from convenient viewing, adjustment is simple. The bottom edge of the zenith prism is adjusted parallel to the mounting which is generally accomplished through simply taking bearings. South is then directly forward in the direction of the objective lens. Next, the graticule is arranged so that one thread is radial, for which it must come vertically out of the cone. The scale is then calibrated, the eccentric moved so that the graticule is parallel to the tube in a radial direction. One eye can thereby look into the eyepiece and the other can see the tube, and by moving the eccentric the thread can be aligned with the edge of the tube. The zero marker of the indicator on the eccentric is now set above the south marker of the limbus.

The limbus can be added on a strip of stiff paper measuring $3.14 \times$ the diameter around which it is coiled. The P_o-angle of the sun can be taken into account and added on the indicator, always being read off under the appropriate P_o value rather than the zero marker.

The accuracy of this method also depends on how exactly the center of movement of the eccentric lies in the optic axis, i.e., the center of the cone. The eccentric can be adjustable incorporated in a larger casing.

B.9.4.8   Measuring the Velocities of Prominences

We are now going to look at how our own observations can be used to express prominence velocities and their changes in numerical terms. Initially, prominences (at the solar limb) will be considered. Sequential series have often been seen as drawings or photographs published in amateur circles (e.g., Klepešta [1967], Völker [1969], Maiwald, Paech, Völker [1978]), but they are never evaluated with regard to velocities. The first attempts at doing this were made by G. Klaus (1974) and W. Paech (1978) in conjunction with Paech (1979). Movements in all types of active prominences can be investigated—sunspot prominences and eruptive phenomena, including surges and the disparition-brusque phase, which are mostly very large prominences.

What must a prominence sequence series be like to make evaluation worthwhile? First of all, a comment by Waldmeier (1958) should be mentioned, according to which even visual observations can be used. (He himself worked like this and published his evaluations (1938, 1939) before the introduction of cinematography into Hα observation.) However, errors made by drawing are so great that photography or cinematography are highly preferable. Of course, the amateur must be equipped for prominence observation with a camera (or a cine-camera in some cases). Two important prerequisites for successfully evaluating the rise of a prominence can easily be overlooked in selecting a set of photographs for study. First, "heliographic adjustment points" are needed for the sequence of pictures. In the event of very lively prominence movement or even its release from the surface, the individual images can only be superimposed if somewhere on the solar limb there are two or more quiescent structures which can be used. Second, "knots" which can be measured must always be present in the active prominence. These should not have *too* short a lifetime and should be present over at least 6 individual pictures. This is only a reference point, with longer lasting knots being preferable as the curves become more definite.

How is a selected sequential series evaluated? In the same publication (1958) Waldmeier writes that measuring the knots is better carried out using the projection method (photographic enlarger or slide projector) rather than with a measuring microscope, since the limited field of this device makes it difficult to find and connect points. However, with the projection method a good projection lens must be used. Maintaining the optical axis must be strictly observed as inaccuracies will result in measuring errors. With 20× enlargement Waldmeier was able to incorporate the knots to an accuracy of around 1 mm, which corresponds to approximately 2″. This method was also used by Dara and Macris (1978). For us amateurs the recommended use of enlargers makes our work a great deal simpler, as measuring microscopes are only rarely available.

For evaluation purposes, a drawing of each negative is made by tracing the knots in the projected image with extreme precision. Once this drawing is completed, each knot is measured with regard to the center of the sun (which has to be marked, of course) rather than to the solar surface, as this would result in inaccuracies.

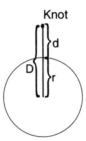

Fig. B.9.22. *Measuring the knot in a prominence.*

The following relationships apply here (see Fig. B.9.22): r is the solar radius of the image in centimeters, D is the distance of the node to be measured in the prominence from the center of the sun in centimeters, thus $d = D - r$ is the height of the knot above the solar limb. If R is taken to be the radius of the sun in kilometers, then h has to be the height of the knot over the solar limb in kilometers:

$$h = \frac{R}{r}(D - r); h = \frac{R}{r}d. \tag{B.9.3}$$

The vertical velocity of a knot is obtained by comparing each measurement of the knot height with the one before it in terms of time. Radial velocity is expressed as $v_r = h/t$ where h and t show the height *and* time difference with regard to the previous picture. Mostly, values of $v_r =$ several km/sec will be obtained. Velocities are given a positive prefix if the height of the knot increases with time (movement away from the surface of the sun) and a negative prefix if the height is reduced (movement towards the sun).

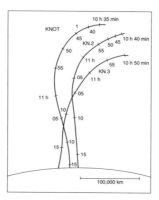

Fig. B.9.23. *Diagram of the movement of measured knots.*

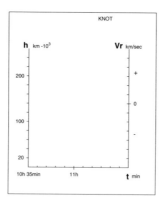

Fig. B.9.24. *Movement diagram with h, t, and v_r.*

There are many ways of showing the measuring results in diagrammatical form. Two will be described here, but if any further information is required there is extensive literature (e.g., Waldmeier [1941, 1961, and [1976], Izsák [1958], Klepešta [1967], Bruzek [1969], Westin [1970], Klaus [1974]).

The first method (see Fig. B.9.23) relates to the solar limb, with points being drawn onto it through which the measured knots have traveled. At the curve points, time markings are added (those of the picture) and a scale is shown. The second method shows three values on one diagram: x-axis −t since the start of the observed movement (usually in minutes); y-axis on the left −h in km × 10^3, and on the right −v_r in km/sec. Figure B.9.24 shows this. During evaluation the values obtained for each knot are added to such a diagram and then joined by a curve.

Finally, the question arises of what time intervals should be selected for prominence rises. Unfortunately, there is no strict answer as it depends on the velocity of the prominence. Rapid movements require a higher temporal resolution (short intervals = many photographs), slower ones require fewer photographs. But as this can only be decided afterwards, as a *guideline* a figure of 1 picture every 10 to 60 seconds can be given here.

B.9.4.9 Measuring the Velocity of Filaments

In the preceding section a method is described which enables amateurs to determine the velocity of chromospheric structures in the sky plane (e.g., prominences). Of course, the Hα observer will also wish to measure velocity components in the direction of vision to obtain a spatial picture of the movement. Apart from amateurs, professional astronomers believed up until the 1960's that by using a Lyot filter and the line shifter, the sun could be represented three-dimensionally (making use of the Doppler Effect). Theoretical studies, including those carried out at the Kiepenheuer Institute, however, showed that this is not the case. Owners of Lyot filters who wish to work on an observation program based on these considerations to measure the velocities of chromospheric structures are therefore warned that in some cases can lead to incorrect results! Here is an extract from the professional literature (edited by H. Hilbrecht and K. Reinsch).

A method known from other areas of astrophysics for measuring the line-of-sight velocity of an object is the use of the Doppler Effect. If a source of rays is moving towards the observer its spectrum appears shifted towards the blue, i.e., the spectral lines are observed at shorter wavelengths than in a quiescent source. On the other hand the spectrum moves towards larger wavelengths (red shift) if the source of rays is moving away from the observer. From shift $\Delta\lambda$ between wavelength λ' and wavelength λ of a spectral line in a quiescent source, the relative velocity on the line of sight between the observer and the source can be calculated using the formula:

$$v_r = \left(\frac{\Delta\lambda}{\lambda}\right) c \qquad (B.9.4)$$

where $c = 299793$ km/sec is the speed of light. It seems quite clear that this method can be used for objects in the solar chromosphere and amateurs have published work on this (Seebald, Ruder, Schwarz: SuW 19, 87 [1980]). Unfortunately the Doppler shift process fails in this case! To understand this rather surprising fact, a detailed study has to be made of the theory of stellar atmospheres and line formation. Of course, it is not possible to go into detail on the theoretical guidelines in this chapter. Therefore reference should be made to the relevant literature (Unsöld 1955, Scheffler, Elsässer 1974). Instead, an attempt will be made here to clarify the mechanisms which cause changes and shifts in spectral lines using a few basic theoretical concepts. In quantum theory an absorption process is described by the transition of an atom from one state of (discrete) energy E_m into a state of higher energy E_n. A photon (light quant) is hereby absorbed whose energy $E = h \times \nu$ (ν: frequency of radiation, $h = 6.626 \times 10^{-34}$ Jsec: Planck's Constant) corresponds exactly to the energy difference $E_n - E_m$. In the spectrum a gap occurs at frequency ν. As such absorption also takes place in other atoms which are in a state of energy E_m, a (dark) absorption line is finally observed in the spectrum at frequency ν. The reverse process from a state of higher energy E_n to lower energy E_m with the simultaneous release of a photon is known as emission and produces (bright) emission lines in the spectrum. Emission can be caused spontaneously or by a radiation field.

Due to radiation damping during the absorption process the spectral lines have a finite width, the so-called natural line width $\Delta\lambda_N = 1.18 \times 10^{-4}$Å. (Wavelength λ and frequency ν are linked by the speed of light $c : \lambda \times \nu = c$.) In addition to radiation damping, Doppler broadening and pressure broadening affect the profile of a spectral line. Doppler broadening is a result of the thermal movement of individual atoms, which leads to different Doppler shifts of their absorption frequencies (see above). The same effect is caused by turbulent movements of the gas (microturbulence) and the stellar rotation. Doppler broadening results in a Gauss profile of the line with a Doppler width of $\Delta\lambda_D$. Pressure broadening is caused by the interaction between the absorbing atoms and other particles which increases with rising pressure. As the natural line width is usually very small with respect to Doppler and pressure broadening, a typical line profile looks very like Figure B.9.25, with extended pressure broadened damping wings being superimposed on the rapidly reducing Gaussian-shaped Doppler core.

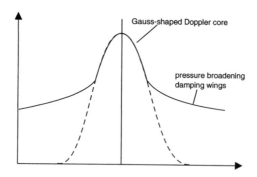

Fig. B.9.25. *The extended pressure broadening damping arms superimposed on the Gaussian-shaped Doppler core of a spectral line.*

The above influences all yield symmetrical changes in the line profile. So far it has been assumed that the absorption and emission processes take place in a state of thermodynamic equilibrium (in physics this means a gas in an enclosed system in which no energy is produced; i.e., the temperature is constant in terms of space and time). At each point of the system precisely as much radiation energy is emitted as absorbed. The fact that we can actually see a star, in other words

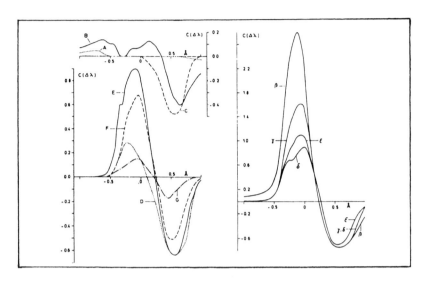

Fig. B.9.26. *Contrast profiles for various velocity distributions and heights of the moving layer (according to Athay).*

we can perceive the radiation from it, proves that the thermodynamic equilibrium is only present in small areas in the interior of the star. Of greater astrophysical significance for the external layers of the star is the assumption that there is local thermodynamic equilibrium (LTE). This state is characterized by the fact that spatial temperature changes are small with regard to the free path distance of the photons. The relationship between the emission and absorption coefficient is known as the source function S_ν.

With a reduction in the density of the stellar atmosphere the interaction between the atoms becomes less frequent while at the same time the mean free path distance of the photons increases; i.e., the state of local thermodynamic equilibrium can no longer occur, resulting in non-LTE. This principally concerns the chromosphere and the corona in particular. Non-LTE systems can only be dealt with using comprehensive numerical model calculations. Another important consequence of non-local thermodynamic equilibrium is that the profile of the spectral lines becomes much more complex than described above. Grossmann-Doerth and von Uexküll (1971) have worked out Hα line profiles for two different chromospheric models. The first, which goes back to Athay (1970), describes an atmosphere in which certain layers move at given velocities. Figure B.9.26 shows the resulting contrast profiles $C(\Delta\lambda)$ for

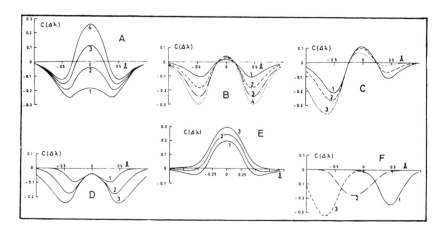

Fig. B.9.27. *Contrast profiles for various source functions S, optical depth t_o, Doppler shift $\Delta\lambda$ and Doppler broadening $\Delta\lambda_D$ (Becker's model).*

various velocity distributions and moving layer heights. (As a contrast profile here, deviation $(I - I_o)$ of the observed line intensity I is shown with regard to line intensity I_o in a quiet atmosphere: $C(\Delta\lambda) = (I - I_o)/I_o$. Where $C(\Delta\lambda)$ is positive, a bright structure can be observed against the surroundings. On the other hand a structure appears dark if $C(\Delta\lambda)$ is negative.) The second model, which was first studied by Beckers (1964) assumes that each structural element in the chromosphere consists of a "cloud" above an otherwise undisturbed atmosphere. The resulting line profiles (see Fig. B.9.27) are distinguished by the assumptions made for the source function S, the optical depth t_o, the Doppler shift $\Delta\lambda$ (by mass motion along the line of sight) and the Doppler broadening $\Delta\lambda_D$.

It is only possible to come to a conclusion as to which model best describes the structure of the chromosphere by comparing the calculated line profiles with measured high resolution spectra. Grossmann-Doerth and Uexküll found that the chromospheric fine structure (mottles) observed in Hα are better described by the Becker density model than by the Athay velocity model, i.e., the spectral lines are more strongly affected by local changes in density and temperature than by ascending and descending masses. For the amateur this means that the Doppler shift measured by shifting the central wavelength of a Hα filter can be used to measure the bulk motion of filaments above the chromosphere but can lead to completely incorrect results for the line-of-sight velocity of chromospheric structures. Figure B.9.28 is intended to show the erroneous interpretations which are possible using the Doppler shift method in NLTE systems.

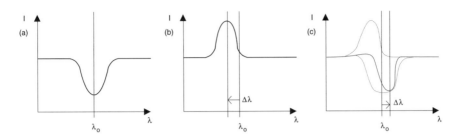

Fig. B.9.28. *a) Line profile of the undisturbed chromosphere; b) emission profile of a superimposed structural element with* $\Delta\lambda$ *Doppler shift; c) superimposition of line profiles a) and b) measured by the observer.*

Figure B.9.28 a) shows the line profile in the undisturbed chromosphere. Superimposed on this is a structural element which has an intrinsic emission profile with a $\Delta\lambda$ Doppler shift (Fig. B.9.28 b)). The observer however measures a superimposition of the two line profiles (Fig. B.9.28 c)). The result is that instead of a blue shifted emission line, an absorption line shifted in the opposite direction is seen! This means that an interpretation of the shift as a Doppler Effect would appear as a descending motion rather than an ascending one!

B.9.5   Flares

B.9.5.1   History

On September 1, 1859, Carrington and Hodgson observed an eruption in a group of sunspots, which was brighter than the photosphere. A flash of light which seemed to move, was visible only for about five minutes and then disappeared again. According to Abetti (1962), this is how the record of the first observation of a solar flare reads; it was also accompanied by speculation as to possible effects on the earth's magnetic field since it was closely followed by the appearance of strong northern lights, which were even visible at low latitudes. Since then, many such eruptions have been observed; however, the first appreciable increase in observational material did not come until after the introduction of new astronomical instruments shortly before the turn of the century. In 1892, Hale made the first spectroheliogram of an eruption. In 1931, he collected together all known records of phenomena of this kind, and since 1936, a regular list of flares has been compiled (*Quarterly Bulletin of Solar Activity of the I.A.U.*). Presently, the most meticulous observation programs run by the largest monitoring institutes incorporate regular flare monitoring. Periodicals on the subject include *Solar Geophysical Data* (NOAA, Boulder, Colorado, USA), *Solnechnye Dannye* (Academy of Sciences, St. Petersburg, Russia), *Quar-*

terly Bulletin on Solar Activity, I.A.U. (Eidgenössische Sternwarte, Zurich, Switzerland), *Solar Observations* (Osservatorio Astrofisico, Catania, Italy). The study of flares is making great advances. Zdeněk Švestka wrote in 1976:

> The physics of solar flares develops very rapidly. If one compares the last book on solar flares, twelve years old (by Henry J. and Elske v. P. Smith), one finds that there are very few sections which might be taken over without substantial changes.

Today, research considers solar flares as follows, in the context of solar activity as a whole (G. Elwert 1978):

> ... Of late, the idea that the Hα flare is a secondary product of a coronal instability above the chromosphere, possibly in the area where it gives way to the corona or in the corona itself, has been developed. X-ray images taken using the telescope belonging to the Aerospace Corporation showed the following: in the case of statistical material relating to over 100 flares, all Hα flares were accompanied by brightening in the X-ray area, but this did not apply the other way round. Evaluation of the X-ray images showed that a large percentage of the X-radiation originated from a well-defined core, embedded in a less sharply defined emission area. Normally, when a flare occurs, the only thing to change is the brightness of the core, while its structure remains essentially the same ...

This brief summary of recent decades should suffice. In the following text, it will be assumed that the reader has a knowledge of theoretical considerations and long-standing results from the study of flares, taken from general or widely available literature, (Abetti, Kuiper, Kiepenheuer, Menzel, Waldmeier, et al.). We do not intend to quote professional technical publications, but rather to make suggestions regarding the amateur's own Hα solar observations. The extensive literature index to this volume is intended to provide more in-depth information.

B.9.5.2   The Flare Phenomenon

Flares are sudden bursts of light in the sun's chromosphere. In other words, they are not eruptions of matter, which is why the term "chromospheric eruptions," used by eminent German and French authors, (Waldmeier, Kiepenheuer et al. up to the late 1950s), is somewhat misleading. Flares manifest themselves as flashes of light, phenomena which are substantially brighter than their environment. Although they are mainly observed in Hα and in other narrow regions of the spectrum, they may even (although seldom) be observed in integrated light (white light flares). The flare energy (visible light, UV, X-radiation ...) is so high that it gives rise to, or influences, solar-terrestrial phenomena (earth's magnetic field, radio communications, aurorae, etc.) in a decisive manner.

Kiepenheuer (1957) describes flares in an extremely simplified, yet, illuminating and unambiguous manner:

> ...Wherever there are magnetic fields, there must also be flows of electric current. Consequently, it is hardly surprising if storm-like phenomena occur there. The sun actually has its own form of lightning!... As may be expected, [storms] only occur near sunspots. They are called chromospheric eruptions, although this does not mean that they are eruptions of matter. It merely refers to an eruption of light.... There is certainly little doubt that an eruption must be a sort of gas discharge, like a flash of lightning or a spark, in other words, the balancing of a great electrical voltage differential. During this discharge, electrical energy is converted into light and heat.

Flares can be recorded in wavelengths of between 3 km (100 kHz) and < 0.06Å (>200 keV). Nowadays flares are roughly divided into "low temperature flares" and "high temperature flares." Low temperature flares differ from high temperature flares, both in terms of their physical properties and the methods of observation used to record them. With the exception of flares whose temperatures differ from low temperature flares by two or three orders of magnitude, high temperature flares are those which are primarily observed in the X-ray, EUV (extreme ultraviolet) and radio area, and will therefore be inaccessible to most of us. However, except for the difference in the radiant flux, both are at home in the chromosphere.

B.9.5.3 Light Curve

Flares are very short-lived phenomena. The life of small flares (so-called subflares) stretches from probably a matter of seconds to a few minutes while the very large ones may last up to a maximum of a few hours. Their surfaces cover areas stretching, in the case of the smallest phenomena, down to the theoretical resolution capacity of the observation instruments and up to 1200 millionths of the visible solar hemisphere in the case of the largest phenomena. In terms of development, they all follow virtually the same pattern: the brightness increases suddenly and, by contrast, decreases relatively slowly (Fig. B.9.29).

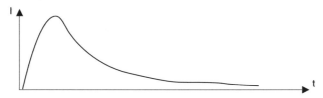

Fig. B.9.29. *Light curve of a flare.*

B.9.5.4 Types of Flares

Let us now look at the different types of flares and the variations we should observe in the phenomena.

Plage flare, or confined flare: This is a flare phenomenon which occurs in a (chromospheric) facula region or coincides with an existing area of faculae.

White Light Flare: In the flash phase of a flare, it is sometimes found that the brightest parts are visible in integrated light. Under these rarer circumstances, the brightness must be greater than the quiet photosphere. Such phenomena occur most frequently in large complex groups of sunspots, for example, the famous group of August 1972, and in the main sunspots which show a contrasting internal magnetic polarity. Points, pairs of points or small surfaces are visible in, or in close proximity to, the penumbrae and then always next to the magnetic inversion line. Duration is roughly 10 minutes, maximum brightness 50% above that of the photosphere.

Limb Flare: Flares which are visible at the limb differ from "normal" flares in that they must achieve an exceptional height. In addition to certain physical features, the following optical criteria distinguish them from prominences occurring at the solar limb—active prominences demonstrate movement over a large area at the limb; flares do not. Furthermore the timing of their development differs. Doubts as to the precise identity of the flares can arise only if they are mistaken for very small loop prominences at an early stage of development (see B.9.4.2 and figures B.9.13 and B.9.14). In the case of sprays, there are even interactions between prominence and flare regions.

Flare Kernels or Hot Cores: These are particularly bright points in a flare region and have a very wide spectral line profile. Some of the flare kernels can develop into white light flares.

Two-Ribbon Flare or Two-Strand Flare: These are usually linked to existing filaments in active regions, in which case the filament fills the line of magnetic flux, but the flare appears on both sides of this line. The flare phenomenon often detaches an existing filament, thereby enabling flare loop connections to form from one side of the flare to the other. However, in active regions with sunspots, the presence of an existing filament is not absolutely essential for a two-ribbon flare, and the latter may occur without one.

Hyder Flare or Impact Flare: Here it is assumed that filament matter descending towards the sun (inside and outside active areas) gives rise to flare phenomena on both sides of the filament.

Homologous Flares: In active regions, flare phenomena may occur repeatedly at the same point. In these cases, the structure and development are almost identical to those of the previous ones.

Flare-Associated Phenomena: These include the surge, spray and loop prominences. All associated flare phenomena are described so well in Bruzek (1966), p. 231, that no more than a reference to them shall be made at this point. Instead, we intend to examine the phenomenon of the Moreton Wave (Flare Blast or Flare Wave).

Moreton Wave (Flare Blast or Flare Wave): As a consequence of the flash phase of a flare, wave motions may be generated. This involves an up-and-down movement of the neighboring chromosphere. (Illustration: wave propagation in water, away from the center of the disturbance. However, please consider this analogy only as an aid to understanding. Small "wave rings" do not occur in the chromosphere, but instead, a single wave, which is in fact also curved.) The up-and-down movement of the neighboring chromosphere can be demonstrated using a line shifter. The phenomenon is bright in the Hα line and dark in both wings. Speeds of around 1000 km/sec are reached, and these waves can be monitored up to a distance of several 100,000 km from their center.

This phenomenon may be accompanied by movements in remote filaments which are otherwise stationary. Observations include the way in which the filaments are stimulated (reeds swaying in the wind, for example) and even their total disappearance, in which case they reappear once the wave has passed and recover their former stability—a particularly rewarding observational assignment for the Hα astronomer!

In addition to the types of flares described here, there are also impulsive flares, electron flares, proton flares, X-ray flares, hard X-ray flares, particle flares, or energetic flares, etc. There is no need for us to describe them all here since the observation and effects of these phenomena lie outside the Hα line.

B.9.5.5 Observation Records

The amateur Hα astronomer should carefully maintain observations of flares using a record sheet. The one shown in Figure B.9.30 has proved reliable. The sheet is not lined. The date should be entered by hand. This is necessary, since we cannot predict how many flares we are likely to register on any observation day, and we need *a line for every phenomenon* in the observation record. Below is a key to the abbreviations used in the observation record:

Flare Activity in Month																
Name : Address :																
Instrument :					H α – Filter :						Magnification :					
Date	ph	v	I	TB	TE	TM	Lat.	L	Imp.	O		T	AP	AC	F	Rem.:
				F | O	F | O	(UT)				P | C		(UT)				

Fig. B.9.30. Flare Activity Record.

Date		date (day of the month);
ph		photographic observation or observational sequence;
v		visual observation or observational sequence (simply mark "ph" or "v" with a check mark);
I		condition of the heliogram investigated (1 very poor ... 5 very good);
TB	F	(UT) beginning of the flare;
	O	(UT) beginning of the observation;
TE	F	(UT) end of the flare;
	O	(UT) end of the observation;
TM		(UT) of the flare maximum;
LAT		heliographic latitude;
L		heliographic longitude; according to Catania (Catania Solar Observations, annually), two separate flare phenomena are involved, if the distance between two flare "knots" is $> 3°$, or the time of appearance differs by more than 5 mins. Otherwise, all "knots" are assumed to constitute a common phenomenon, and the center of the phenomena is taken as its heliographic longitude and latitude.
IMP		importance and intensity grading according to tables under "classification";
O	P	partial observation;
	C	complete observation (full record of the phenomenon); simply check "p" or "c" in each case;
T		(UT) of the measurements;
AP		projected area in millionths of the solar disc at maximum;
AC		corrected extent in degrees^2 (if the heliocentric angle is smaller than 65°);
F		maximum intensity referred to local undisturbed chromosphere.
R		Remarks according to international rules as follows:

A   Eruptive prominence whose base is $> 90°$ from central meridian;
B   Probably the end of a more important flare;
C   Invisible 10 mins earlier;
D   Brilliant point;
E   Two or more brilliant points;
F   Several eruptive centers;
G   No sunspot visible in the neighborhood;
H   Flare with high velocity dark surge;
I   Very extensive active region;
J   Distinct variations of plage intensity before or after flare;
K   Several intensity maxima;
L   Existing filaments demonstrate sudden signs of activity;
M   White light flare;
N   Continuum tends towards polarisation;
O   Observation conducted in calcium II line H or K;
P   Flare shows helium D in emission;
Q   Flare shows the Balmer continuum in emission;
R   Considerable asymmetry in the Hα line;
S   Brightening follows disappearance of filament at the same pos.
T   Region active throughout the day;
U   Two bright branches, parallel or converging (II or Y shape);
V   Occurrence of explosive phase;
W   Great increase in area following maximum intensity;
X   Unusually wide Hα emission;
Y   Onset of a system of loop-type prominences;
Z   Major sunspot umbra covered by flare.

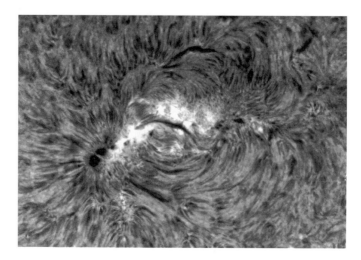

Fig. B.9.31. *Spots, umbra-penumbra-superpenumbra and filaments with flares. Observer: Wolfgang Lille, Stade, Germany; 12″ refractor $f_{equi} = 12$ m, DayStar Hα filter 0.5Å October 7, 1993.*

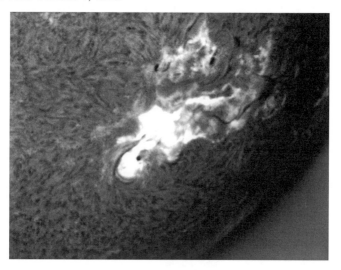

Fig. B.9.32. *Large 3b flare. Observer: Robert O. Morris, Colorado, U.S.A.; Meade 4″ refractor with DayStar Hα filter 0.6Å, October 22, 1989, 18:49 UT.*

B.9.5.6   Classification

There is a system of classifying flares according to their importance, based on the area of the flare. Previously, this had been -1, 1, 2, 3, 3+, but was changed on January 1, 1966, to S, 1, 2, 3, 4, ("S" stands for "subflare"). In addition, there are the intensity grades, f, n, or b (faint, normal, bright or brilliant). Thus a flare observation may be described as, 1n, 2f, or 3b, etc. It should also be added that the "importance" classification should take place at the moment of greatest intensity and *not* at the moment when the flare reaches its maximum area. This maximum area often does not occur until a later stage of development. The area covered by the flare is given in millionths of the solar hemisphere (allowing for distortion in perspective). The following tables may provide further assistance:

Intensity Grades

Code	Intensity
f	≤ 1.5
n	$1.5 - 2.0$
b	>2.0

Importance

Code	Heliographic Degree^2	Arc Seconds^2	Surface 10^{-6} vis. hemisphere	Hα Line width	Lifetime
S	< 2.06	<600	< 100	1.5	< 4 min
1	2.06–5.15	600–1500	100–250	3.0	4–43 min
2	5.15–12.4	1500–3500	250–600	4.5	10–90 min
3	12.5–24.7	3500–7200	600–1200	8	20–155 min
4	>24.7	>7200	>1200	15	0.9–7.2 hr

Some reference should be made to a minor yet annoying problem. It is not easy to determine the importance classification "Imp." Since, according to the definition, classification must take place at the moment of maximum intensity rather than the moment when the area of the flare is largest, we must expect errors to creep in. The intensity of the flare increases so rapidly that (particularly with larger phenomena) the actual maximum intensity may not be situated at the center of the Hα line, but next to it. And if we are observing the center of the line, at some point we assume that the moment of maximum brightness has been reached when, in fact, it has not yet been reached or has long since passed. It is possible to counterbalance this source of error by also conducting observations in the wings. Since the maximum flare intensity may lie some distance from the center of the Hα line, a spectrohelioscope is better suited to this type of practical investigation than a genuine DayStar- or Lyot-type filter, for these usually show only a shift area of roughly ± 1Å birefringent (exceptions are the very expensive Halle and Zeiss filters, which are beyond the reach of all but the most determined amateurs).

B.9.5.7   Observation Programs

Our suggested observation programs can be divided into long-term and short-term programs. The first should stretch over one or, if possible, several cycles, the minimum requirement running into years. To achieve reasonable results from the short-term programs, hours, days or, at the most, a few rotations are sufficient. However, both require the most thorough observations possible; the individual, therefore, will find making long-term programs extremely difficult because of the time involved and the weather conditions. Under these circumstances, a national astronomer's network is the only answer. Furthermore, scientific publications may be used to supplement one's own material, at least with regard to long-term statistical investigations.

Long-Term Observation Programs

1. Frequency with which the importance classification occurs in the cycle. It is well known that subflares occur most frequently, and 4+ flares are the least common. However more precise details are still desirable and significant. Above all, these investigations may be conducted from scratch in each cycle to see whether the result coincides with previous ones, or whether variations occur.

2. Occurrence of the S-4 importance classification in the course of the cycle. A continuation of program 1, except that, in this case, a connection is made with the course of other solar activities.

   2.1. Frequency with which flares with an S-4 importance classification occur (individually and collectively) in relation to the sunspot activity curve

   2.2. As 2.1 in relation to the facula activity curve (photospheric and chromospheric)

   2.3. As 2.1 in relation to the prominence and filament activity curve

   2.4. Correlation between the frequency with which the individual classifications occur in the cycle

   2.5. Frequency with which the individual classifications occur in the cycle as a function of t

   2.6. Checking against Waldmeier's Law, according to which the frequency with which flares occur is $E \simeq 0.05R$ (R = sunspot number). Is this true for various cycles, and is it true at all stages (minimum-rise-maximum-decline) in the cycle?

3. Asymmetries

   3.1. North-south asymmetry. The frequency with which flares occur follows the north-south asymmetry often observed with sunspots. In this case, it is possible to investigate whether flares of this asymmetry always follow in the same proportion (in different cycles)

3.2. East-west asymmetry (as 3.1) (Waldmeier 1959)

4. Ratio of the frequency with which surface flares occur to the frequency with which limb flares occur. The visibility function, according to Behr (1952), of all classes of flare towards the limb should be $\sim \cos\theta$ since flares are assumed, on average, to be "flat." According to Švestka (1976), more than 30% of flares cannot be seen; only some 25% have heights in the region of 10,000 km and rarely reach 30–50,000 km. This observation program could investigate the following phenomena:

    4.1. the number of limb flares which appear in one cycle

    4.2. the correlation existing between the visibility of surface flares and frequency with which they occur

    4.3. the correlation between limb flares and prominences

    4.4. the correlation between limb flares and the sunspot number R

    4.5. the correlation between limb flares and the frequency with which photospheric faculae occur (which can also only be observed towards the limb)

5. The frequency of flares in class A-I sunspot groups for the importance of classes S-4

6. Lifetime

    6.1. Average lifetime of the individual importance classifications in the cycle

    6.2. Average lifetime of the individual importance classifications in the sunspot group classes A-I

        6.2.1. Degree of dependency on the group's class, size (extent), and age

        6.2.2. Variations in 6.2–6.2.1 during the various cycle phases

        6.2.3. Variations in 6.2–6.2.1 during various cycles

7. Positions

    7.1. Frequency with which the flares occur in relation to the latitude migration

    7.2. Determining the position of flares to ascertain whether it follows the sunspot migration precisely, according to the same laws in each cycle phase and in different cycles

    7.3. Determining the position of flares within the center of activity where they occur in order that they can then be linked as outlined below:

        7.3.1. to other Hα phenomena (fibrils, filaments, plages, sunspot umbrae)

        7.3.2. to integrated light observations for: determining the location of the flare within and/or outside a group of sunspots

    7.4. Influence of a flare phenomenon on an existing light bridge or one that is forming (as a result?) and other parameters in the sunspot (number of spots, appearance, etc.)

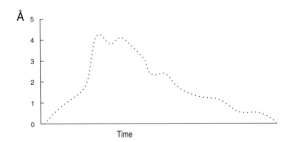

Fig. B.9.33. *Plotting the line width of a flare against time.*

Short-Term Observation Programs

From among the points mentioned under "long-term programs," 2.1–2.3, 3.1–3.2, 4.2–4.5, 5, 6.2–6.2.2, and 7.3–7.4 may be applied in exactly the same way for short-term programs, to achieve more rapid (preliminary) results. However, the following are regarded as "genuine" short-term programs:

    8. Light curves. To describe the course of *one* flare phenomenon, we use the light curve. There are two possibilities open to us:

        8.1. We can observe the flare's line width and plot this against time (Fig. B.9.33); (also see notes under "Classification" regarding flare intensities in and around the Hα line).

        8.2. We can observe the Hα center and plot the brightness values obtained there against time. We take the intensity of the quiet chromosphere (I_o) as a connected value. (Take care here! This value should not be determined in the direct proximity of the flare since flares frequently occur in chromospheric facula areas, and even faculae are brighter than the quiet chromosphere [Figure B.9.34]).

        8.3. If several bright points occur in a flare phenomenon, it is desirable to produce a light curve for each one since they do not necessarily all have the same course.

The light curves of flares are both interesting and important. Since they vary with each phenomenon, it is, however, possible to identify certain common features and even hazard an attempt at collating them into a few "light curve types," and yet, due to the wealth of observational material, every good light curve is still of value. It is not only the point of maximum intensity ("flash phase") which is significant in obtaining a comprehensive overview of the development of a flare, but also, above all, the stage which precedes it ("preheating" or "preflare"). There are flares which are relatively slow in reaching their flash point, after which they slowly subside, while there are others which reach their flash point with barely any preflare, and even some which lose brightness during their preflare phase, only to suddenly switch to the flash phase.

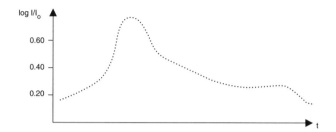

Fig. B.9.34. *Plotting the Hα intensity of a flare against time.*

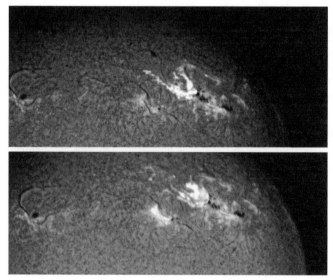

Fig. B.9.35 a) and b). *Short-term programs: rapid changes in a flare, in this example changes can be seen in the second photograph taken 40 minutes after the first. Observer: Robert O. Morris; Meade 4″ refractor with DayStar Hα filter 0.6Å, January 18, 1989; a) 18:13 UT; b) 18:51 UT.*

9. Cinematography. In this case, what is said in the section entitled "Prominences/Filaments" under "Observation programs, point 8" applies to an equal extent. Consequently, the following should be investigated:

   9.1. Determining the precise extent of the area covered by flare phenomena

   9.2. Fine structure, determination thereof

       9.2.1. Velocities

       9.2.2. Flare detail flow ratios

9.2.3. Flare detail flow ratios are achieved by underexposing the negative so that the details of the flare which are overexposed during "normal" exposure of the chromosphere appear. (Loughhead 1968; Bray and Loughhead 1974)

10. Environment. We should still pay some attention to the environment in which the flares appear.

   10.1. Appearance before the flare occurs

   10.2. Appearance afterwards? Are there any structural changes? Point 7.3.1 should once again be included here.

11. Radio observations. Although we do not intend to deal with the monitoring of flares in radio frequencies in the context of these Hα observation programs, we would recommend anyone who is interested to observe the short wave reception using a "normal" receiver with large optically recorded flares to learn of any radio effects from the phenomenon. It would also be possible to determine the time delay without a great deal of expense (see Chapter A.4.5).

12. White light flares. Course and connection to subsequent photospheric changes (sunspots, faculae)

B.9.6   Chromospheric Faculae (Plages)

Chapter B.6 contains an in-depth account on the observation of photospheric faculae. At this point I intend to make a few suggestions regarding the observation of chromospheric faculae (plages). We shall begin with a brief, general description.

The word "plage" comes from the French term "plage faculaire." Tandberg-Hanssen (1974) maintains that a continuous transition from photospheric to chromospheric faculae exists. Both have the same form, the same appearance, and the same relationship to sunspots. The NOAA (Mangis, 1975) stresses that plages must continue to be observed since, through their growth or disappearance, they provide a good overview of whether an active region is in development or decline: "Their presence most often indicates emerging flux and is often good evidence that rapid development will soon take place in the active region wherein they lie." Moreover, the author makes it clear that the general arrangement of plages corresponds to the magnetogram structures in the same areas quite well.

Chromospheric faculae are visible over the whole solar disk in contrast to photospheric faculae, which we can only see towards the solar limb (except when using special methods; see Chapter A.5.5). The boundaries of the facula groups, which are often difficult to locate in white light, are easily discovered since the perspective is omitted. In the case of groups migrating

, 2.2, 3.4, 4.1.1, 4.3.2, 5.7.1, 5.7.2, 9.2, 11.1, and
11.6. Monitoring chromospheric faculae with the aid of cinematography is
also rewarding; in this way, the faculae and all their associated changes can
be observed in motion over the whole solar disk. A detailed description of
the equipment and techniques is given in Chapter A.8. It is important to
emphasize that flares should not be mistaken for chromospheric faculae and
vice versa, although relationships may exist in individual cases. See "Plage
flare" (B.9.5.4).

Mention must be made of an obvious distinction in relation to all other
phenomena in the active chromosphere: all phenomena are of a short-lived
nature—spicules, flares, prominences/filaments, etc. In other words, they
demonstrate an "active" growth and disappearance within a short period
of time; chromospheric faculae do not. Waldmeier writes (1941), p. 187:
"Never has the sudden disappearance of a group of faculae been observed;
instead, the groups appear to be larger and more dispersed at each rotation,
until, finally, they can no longer be distinguished from the basic structure
of the chromosphere."

Finally, a comment on another rewarding aspect of monitoring chromospheric faculae. As we already know, an imminent center of activity first becomes evident due to the appearance of faculae, after which sunspots (may)
also form. Tandberg-Hanssen (1974) writes: "Sunspots nearly always occur in pre-existing faculae." In other words, by observing chromospheric
faculae, we are in a position to predict where sunspots may form. And if
faculae were observed, but no sunspots have formed, we can conclude that,
although there was a center of activity, it must have been extremely weak.
Consequently, by observing and monitoring chromospheric faculae, we are
in a position to determine the formation, strength and total lifetime of a

center of activity more precisely and thoroughly than by merely recording the sunspot activity in integrated light.

Chapter B.10

The Aurora[†]

B.10.1   Introduction

The word "aurora" is Latin for "dawn," and it is the resemblance of
the aurora at times to the pre-dawn glow that has given it that name. The
aurora is caused by an electrical discharge in the upper atmosphere which
produces light in the same way as it is formed in a neon or sodium lamp.
Electrified particles arriving from outer space collide with the atoms and
molecules in the rarified pressures found in the high atmosphere, and some
of the particle energy is converted into visible light.

B.10.2   Appearance of the Aurora

The aurora appears as diffuse glows or as discrete forms such as arcs,
bands, veils, and rays, or as combinations of these forms (Fig. B.10.1). Between altitudes of 400 and 150 kilometers above the earth's surface, red
colors are found. From 150 down to 80 kilometers white, green, blue and
yellow may be seen, green being the most usual color. From 95 down to 80
kilometers the bottom border of a display may show a red fringe. Brightness may vary between the barely visible to the most intense level sufficient
to cast a shadow. The classic auroral storm in mid-latitudes usually begins
with a glow on the horizon in the direction of the magnetic pole. This
is followed by the development of an arc which rises above the horizon.
The arc may duplicate or change into curved bands. Rays then form and
stretch upwards. If the aurora travels equatorwards towards the observer,
the rays seen from immediately below will, by reason of perspective, appear
to converge at one point in the sky. This structure is known as a corona.

[†]Written by R.J. Livesey

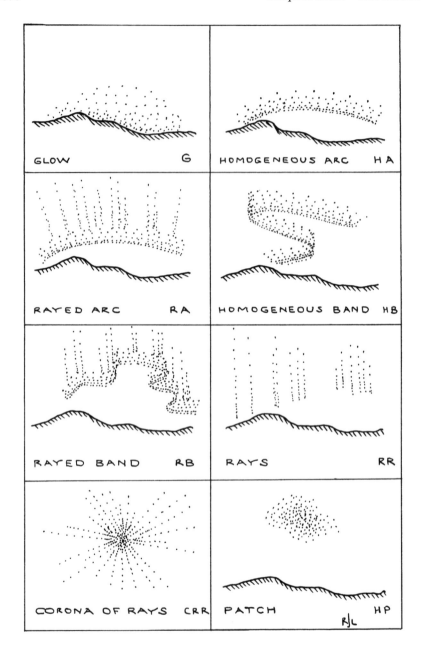

Fig. B.10.1. *Examples of auroral forms.*

It does not form at the true zenith but at the magnetic zenith because the lines of force along which the rays are forming lie at an angle to the vertical. The value of this angle depends upon the observer's latitude. In severe storms the auroral activity may appear equatorwards of the observer and extend down into tropical latitudes. At the peak of the storm the quiet forms and the brightness change, sometimes suddenly, so that there is movement of the forms and a flaming and flickering of the light. Rays may be seen to drift westwards or eastwards. Less violent pulsing of the light may also be seen. After this phase, the aurora calms down and, with the disappearance of rays, patches of light may be left in the sky. These fade in due course. The whole sequence of events may repeat itself an hour or so later. Of course only part of the storm may develop and never proceed to completion. On the other hand, the observer may see only the top of a storm which is taking place below the horizon.

The polar aurora consists of two eccentric oval haloes of activity, one encircling each magnetic pole. On the day-side, the oval is normally about 15° of arc from the magnetic pole; on the night side the distance is about 20°. The earth rotates under the ovals. On the night-side observers on the surface of the earth are carried under the oval.

The auroral zone is defined as the corresponding oval on the surface of the earth joining places at which the polar aurora is most frequently seen. In 1873, H. Fritz published his map of isochasms or lines joining points on the earth's northern hemisphere having similar frequencies of auroral visibility. During periods of quiet conditions, the polar aurora remains generally within the ovals. The balance may be disturbed, however, when the oval, as a consequence of increased activity, is made to expand towards the pole and towards the equator. This constitutes an auroral storm, and it is during these events that the storm aurora becomes visible in mid-latitudes.

B.10.3 Source of the Aurora

The source of the polar aurora lies in the sun, from which a steady stream of electrified particles and associated magnetic fields are being ejected into interplanetary space. On encountering the earth's magnetic field, some of the particles are guided and accelerated in towards the earth's polar regions. As these particles can only travel parallel to or helically along magnetic lines of force, they reach down into the atmosphere of the polar regions where the magnetic field lines are relatively perpendicular to the earth's surface, but are unable to do so in the equatorial regions where the field lines are approximately parallel with the surface (Fig. B.10.2).

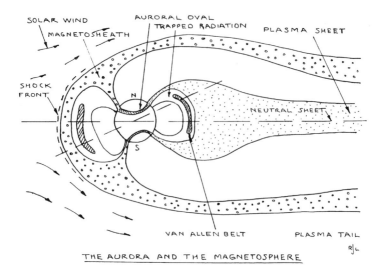

Fig. B.10.2. *The aurora and the magnetosphere.*

There are two principal types of solar disturbance that cause the auroral storms to form:

1. The first is the solar flare, the disappearing filament, coronal mass ejection, and similar types of explosive transient activity on the sun which correlate with the sunspot cycle. These events discharge clouds of energetic electrified particles, which, if they encounter the earth, trigger a magnetospheric storm accompanied by aurora. Transient aurorae are often quite strong and can produce brilliant displays. Their frequency of occurrence relates to the sunspot cycle, though there may be variations in frequency and in the timing of the auroral maximum relative to sunspot maximum as it differs from cycle to cycle and with the place of observation.

2. The second is the coronal holes in the sun's atmosphere. These are areas of open solar magnetic fields from which energetic electrified particles may escape in the form of a jet stream. As the sun rotates, the jet of particles rotates with it and, if the alignment is opportune, this jet will strike the earth each time the sun rotates, so long as the coronal hole exists. These jet streams activate the aurora, but more quietly than do the transient events, and the aurora then caused does not penetrate so far down into the mid-latitudes.

Recurrent aurorae may appear for up to several nights in succession. The sequence will repeat itself at 27 day intervals with every rotation of the

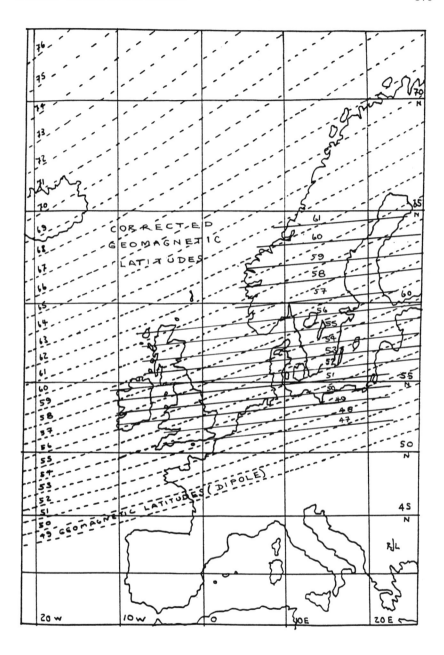

Fig. B.10.3. Dipole geomagnetic latitudes and corrected geomagnetic latitudes.

sun so long as the coronal hole remains active and consists mainly of quiet glows, arcs and, possibly, ray structures. Coronal holes reach a maximum effect in the last few years of the sunspot cycle before the beginning of the new cycle. During this period the aurora is predominantly of the recurrent form. Consequently, observers in the lower latitudes experience a single maximum of annual auroral frequency while higher latitude observers may observe a double maximum during the course of a sunspot cycle. The geomagnetic latitudes shown on the chart (Fig. B.10.3) refer to an idealized magnetic field due to a dipole magnet assumed to be placed at the center of the earth with its axis passing through the magnetic poles. In fact, the real space field above the earth's surface is distorted by the solar wind with the result that in Europe the corrected geomagnetic latitudes are lower in value and align more truly east to west than the dipole latitudes. Consequently, for a given dipole latitude the aurora tends to penetrate further towards the equator in North America than in Western Europe. Further, there is a similarity of aurorae between north Scotland and southern Finland than the dipole geomagnetic latitudes might suggest.

B.10.4   Spectroscopy

As the aurora is caused by the light formed in gaseous discharges, the principal emissions are at discrete wavelengths, as given in the table below.

Principal emission lines of the aurorae.			
Wavelength Å	Relative Light Strength	Origin	Altitude Range km
3914	47.4	N_2^+	
4278	24.4	N_2^+	
5577	100	OI	90–150
6300	10–600	OI	150–400
6364	3–200	OI	150–400
6563	–	Hα	(Polar Proton Aurora)
6611	–	N_2–1P	65–90
6624	–	N_2–1P	65–90
6696	–	N_2–1P	65–90
6705	–	N_2–1P	65–90
6789	–	N_2–1P	65–90
6875	–	N_2–1P	65–90

Between the heights of 400 and 150 kilometers above the earth's surface, red aurorae at 6300Å and 6364Å may be found due to the collision of electrons with atoms of oxygen. Between 150 and 90 km the aurora is principally green at 5577Å because of denser layers of oxygen. Between 90 and 65 km the lower border may be tinged with red molecular emissions of nitrogen. In average strength aurorae, the greens and reds of oxygen may be mixed with the violet of singly ionized molecular nitrogen at 3914Å to produce grayish yellow hues. Generally speaking, the aurorae are colored green, white, red, blue, and yellow in order of rarity.

Type A aurorae consist of high level red emissions due to low energy electrons moving down the direct connections between the inter-planetary and geomagnetic field lines. Type B aurorae are caused by high energy electrons moving along enclosed field lines from the tail of the magnetosphere and penetrating deeply into the atmosphere to where molecular particles exist, thus causing the lower red border of the auroral forms in a strong auroral storm. The most commonly observed line is oxygen 5577Å. The red oxygen lines may be more intense but lie at wavelengths at which the eye is less sensitive to light, thus causing the red light to appear fainter. White is generally associated with scotopic vision due to very low levels of luminance when the aurora is very faint and the cones that provide color vision in the eye are not being stimulated.

In areas free from town lighting pollution, spectral lines may be observed visually in a spectroscope, but some are not readily visible due to their faintness or to their position relative to the variable sensitivity of the eye with wavelength. In cloudy or hazy weather, or if sodium light or moonlight is present, the green light may be effectively detected using an interference filter tuned to this wavelength. In the filter the green glow may be detected between the clouds, which, backlit by the aurora, stand out black.

Spectrophotography requires large aperture instruments together with long exposures when the aurora is faint. Professional spectrographs have focal ratios in the region of $f2.5$ to $f0.5$. Slit, slitless and grating instruments have been used. The successful detection of identifiable auroral emissions has been achieved by an amateur observer with a standard 35-mm camera fitted with a series of interchangeable interference filters. By using this method, red emissions not visible to the naked eye have been recorded. Normal color photography also provides information on the various emissions present.

B.10.5 Photographing the Aurora

Any camera having a focal ratio of $f2.8$ or less may be used. The camera is set up on a rigid mount and pointed towards the aurora. A cable controlled time exposure is used. Cameras laid flat on the ground may be fitted with fish-eye lenses to take all-sky pictures. Catadioptric systems are used on professional all-sky cameras to reduce focal ratios down to $f1.4$ or thereby to enable short exposures to be used. The length of exposure should be as short as possible to prevent sky glow from fogging the film, especially near towns, and to minimize the elongation of star images. However, the exposure must be long enough to capture the aurora. If the aurora is changing form, long exposures are undesirable because of fuzzing of the sharpness of form. Exposures may be attempted at between 5 seconds and 60 seconds at intervals of 10 seconds on ISO 400 film at $f2$. For faint aurorae a 30 second exposure is a good first trial. Because the aurora varies in brightness, no standard may be given. For brighter aurorae exposures between 3 and 10 seconds are usually satisfactory.

When using a standard 35-mm camera set at $f2.0$, Kodak T-Max 400 at ISO 400 can produce good black and white photographs of bright aurorae down to 10 seconds exposure, bearing in mind that color film has greater sensitivity than black & white film. To make color slides Kodak Ektachrome 400 is satisfactory, while to make prints Fujicolor 400 has often been used. Ektachrome 200 offers capacity for greater contrast. Agfa CT21 at ISO 100 has been used, but Agfa CT18 is too slow.

Various films give different ranges of sensitivity across the spectrum. Some are better at detecting the true aurora spectroscopically; others image it more truly to match the sensitivity of the human eye. For example, AGFA CT21 is red-green sensitive. Some experimentation in film, exposure and lens is worth while. ISO 1000 has been used for fast exposures especially in the polar auroral zone, but amateur observers generally recommend film speed to be limited to ISO 400.

B.10.6   Stereoscopic photography

Two observers situated up to 60 km apart, preferably in a line parallel with corrected geomagnetic latitude, may arrange to take simultaneous photographs in agreed-upon directions. The stereographic pairs may then be used for locating the forms. The cameras are set up on permanently constructed rigid clamps pointing to the magnetic north at an altitude of about 30°. The directions of the cameras are calibrated by taking timed photographs of the stellar background. When an aurora takes place, the two observers agree by telephone to take simultaneous photographs at given times to the nearest second. Synchronized digital watches now make this task an easy one. On completion, pairs of photographs may be examined and the location of the auroral forms deduced by reference to the parallactic shift between the aurora and the stellar background. The original graphical method devised by Professor Carl Størmer may be used, but computer programs such as that operated by Dr. M. Gadsden of Aberdeen University, Scotland, are available for this purpose.

B.10.7 Visual Observation

Observation sites with clear horizons and freedom from artificial lighting are best. High latitudes are better in winter, but the polar summer twilight blots out higher observers. BAA data indicates that aurorae are more likely at the equinoxes. Observers in North America are better placed to see summer aurorae than European observers because the American aurorae stretch down into lower geographic latitudes where the nights are darker.

In favorable conditions, the simplest observation to make is merely to record that aurora is present. The date, time, time standard, and location of the observer are noted. The observation is enhanced by adding a description of the event accompanied by a sketch, if possible. Useful data may be recorded by making simple measurements of angular height and width of auroral forms. Horizontal angles are measured from 0° to 360° eastwards from true north, using the Pole Star as a zero base. Vertical angles are measured from the true horizon. To obtain these accurately, a cloud alidade or some other device with a plumb bob or levelling bubble to determine the position of the horizontal plane is effective.

A home-made rule marked to show units of five degrees when held at arm's length is helpful. The outreached hand may be used on the assumption that thumb to pinkie approximates to 20°, and a knuckle corresponds to 2°. A shaded flashlight and notebook and pencil are required, and a table to rest equipment upon is a decided advantage.

Detailed observations of an auroral storm are usually recorded at about five minute intervals with additional observations at each change in activity and form. There is an internationally accepted code for recording auroral activity which was used in the International Geophysical Year in 1957 and updated for the International Year of the Quiet Sun in 1964. Details of the code are shown in Table 10.1. (Noting the difference between capital and small letters.)

$$a_3 \text{ c f } R_2 \text{ B 3 c 25 30 330 020}$$

This example represents a rapid horizontally moving, coronally converging, fragmentary, medium length, rayed band. It is as bright as a moonlit cumulus cloud and is green in color. The base of the band is at an elevation of 25°, and the top at 30°. The azimuths of the two extremities are 330° and 020° (true), respectively.

Observations in code together with sketches may be set out in standard format on a report sheet, together with date and time (Fig. B.10.4). As aurorae occur at night, it is usual to quote the dates of the beginning and end of the night, for example, 27/28. Times are quoted in Universal Time regardless of location on the earth. The observer may quote geomagnetic

Table 10.1
International Aurora Report Code
(See B.10.7 for explanation and example.)
Elevation

Base	Angular height from horizon to bottom edge of form.
Top	Angular height to top edge of form.

Direction

Azimuth	Compass bearing (true) to point being measured.

Condition

q	Quiet. No movement of form, brightness or activity.
a	Active. Movement in structure or brightness. Undefined.
a_1	Active. Bands which are folding or unfolding.
a_2	Active. Rapid change of shape of lower form.
a_3	Active. Rapid horizontal movement of rays.
a_4	Active. Forms fade quickly to be replaced by others.
p	Pulsating. Undefined.
p_1	Pulsating. Rythmic change of form as a whole.
p_2	Pulsating. Flaming with light variations moving upwards.
p_3	Pulsating. Flickering with rapid irregular variations.
p_4	Pulsating. Streaming of irregular horizontal variations in homogeneous forms.

Qualifying Symbol

m	Multiple. Several groups of the same type or form.
f	Fragmentary. A part only of an auroral form.
c	Coronal. Rays converging overhead at the magnetic zenith.

Structure

H	Homogeneous. Uniform in shape and intensity.
S	Striated. Lines of brighter and darker light.
R_1	Rayed. Short length rays.
R_2	Rayed. Medium length rays.
R_3	Rayed. Long length rays.

Auroral Form

G	Glow.
N	Unspecified form. Unidentifiable form. Auroral Light.
A	Arc. Uniformly curved arch of light.
RA	Rayed arc. Arc from which rays reach upwards.
R	Ray. A shaft of light reaching upwards.
B	Band. A partial arch or twisted band of light.
RB	Rayed band. Band from which rays reach upwards.
V	Veil. Curtain like structure, which may be folded.
P	Patch. An isolated cloud or surface of auroral light.

Brightness

1	Weak. Barely visible.
2	Bright as moonlit cirrus cloud.
3	Bright as moonlit cumulus cloud.
4	Bright enough to cast a shadow.

NOTE: Observers tend to over-estimate brightness.

Color

a	Red in upper portion of form only.
b	Red in lower border only.
c	White, green or yellow.
d	Red in main region of form.
e	Red and green mixed.
f	Blue and purple.

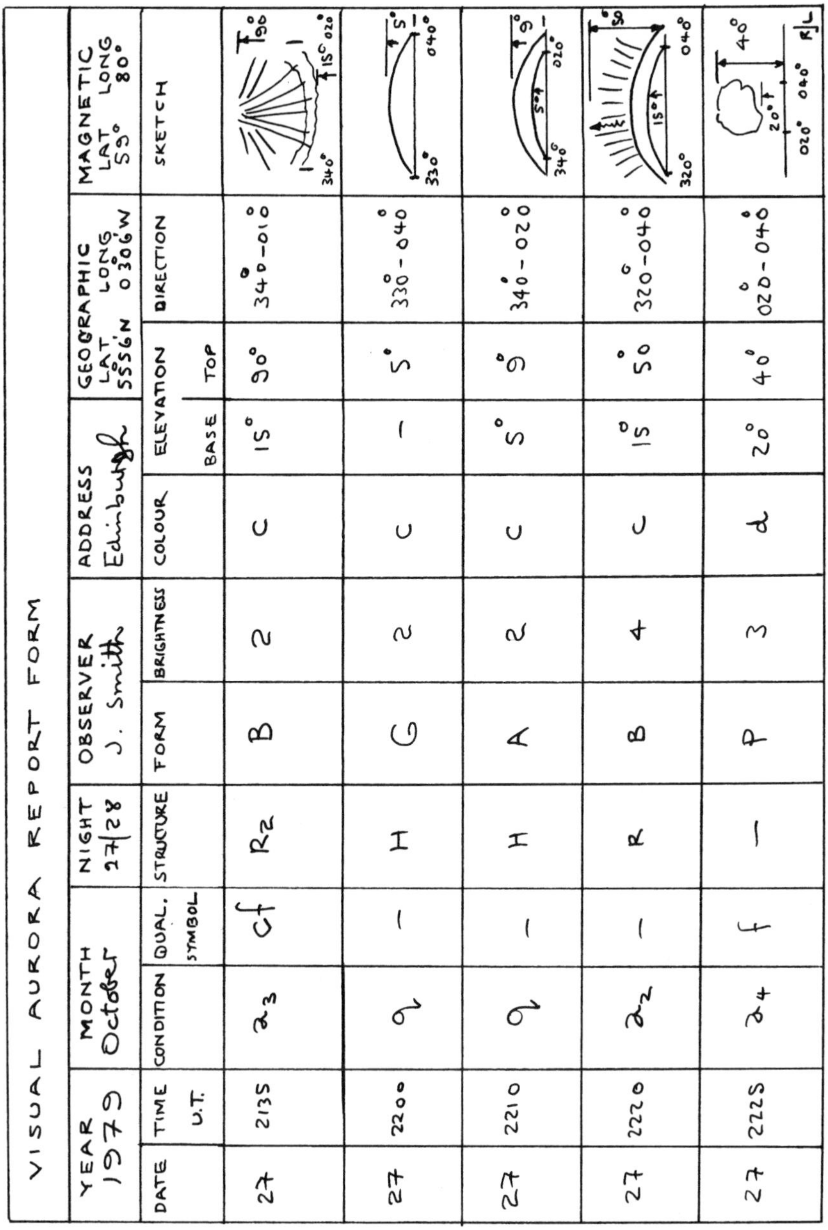

VISUAL AURORA REPORT FORM

YEAR 1979	MONTH October	NIGHT 27/28	OBSERVER J. Smith				ADDRESS Edinburgh			GEOGRAPHIC LAT 55°56'N LONG 03°06'W		MAGNETIC LAT 55° LONG 80°
DATE	TIME U.T.	CONDITION	QUAL. SYMBOL	STRUCTURE	FORM	BRIGHTNESS	COLOUR	ELEVATION BASE	ELEVATION TOP	DIRECTION	SKETCH
27	2135	?3	cf	R2	B	2	C	15°	90°	340-010°	
27	2200	?	(	I	G	2	C	(	5°	330-040°	
27	2210	?	(	H	A	2	C	5°	G°	340°	
27	2220	?	(	R	B	4	C	15°	5°	320-040°	
27	2225	?	cf	—	P	3	d	20°	40°	020-040°	

Fig. B.10.4. *Example of aurora report.*

latitude as the zone and longitude as the sector position. Alternatively, quote geographic latitude and longitude from which the zone and sector may be obtained from magnetic maps. Completed observations should be submitted to the local national association that organizes the collection and the analysis of astronomical records.

Very recently amateur visual aurora observers in mid-latitudes have become aware of the occasional apparition of what is now known as the flash aurora. This type of auroral event suddenly appears for 5 to 10 seconds and then vanishes, no other general auroral or magnetic activity being present that night. The phenomenon is a mystery and any observations of such an event are important.

Occasionally in summertime, auroral forms and noctilucent clouds have either appeared simultaneously or alternately on the same night. Any observations or particularly photographs of such events are of great value to professional researchers.

B.10.8   The Radio Aurora

Auroral activity causes ionization clouds to form in the upper atmosphere at the base of auroral forms. These may act as scatterers or absorbers of radio waves, and the presence of these clouds together with their effects on radio signals is known as the radio aurora. Such ionization may or may not be associated with a visible aurora near to the radio observer. Conversely, a visible aurora may be present without detected radio effects.

Ion clouds in the E layer at a height of about 112 km can absorb HF and scatter VHF radio signals, thus increasing transmission distances in VHF from 80 up to 1600 km between stations, especially where they lie approximately on the same line of geomagnetic latitude. When scattered, a normal high pitched Morse signal takes up a low pitched rasping sound. Distortion increases with frequency. Higher latitude radio beacons may not normally be heard, but during the presence of auroral ionization, their signals may be scattered equatorwards so that their detection by mid-latitude receivers acts as an indicator of auroral activity. Similarly the radio operators' horizon expands with increased strength of the aurora and the clouds, causing the VHF signals to scatter, expand equatorwards, and recede back to the auroral zone as with the visible aurora itself. The amplitude peak of radio aurora coincides with peak of the break-up phase of visible aurora and the peaks of magnetic disturbance.

Many European radio aurorae take place in two distinct periods in the afternoon and in the evening. In the United Kingdom, for example, radio

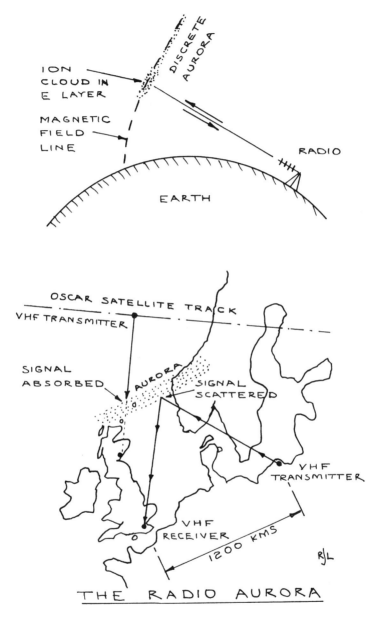

Fig. B.10.5. *The radio aurora showing examples of aurorally propagated VHF transmissions and signal absorptions from satellites.*

aurorae may be detected in the afternoon phase between 1500 and 1900 U.T. and in the midnight phase between 2200 and 0300 U.T. During very strong activity radio aurorae can take place outside these periods. Afternoon aurorae are stronger than the midnight events because the primary input of electrons into the atmosphere from the earth's magnetotail takes place on the evening side of the planet. British and German amateur radio records suggest that taken over a sunspot cycle as a whole, radio aurorae tend to be more probable in the spring and autumn and less frequent in summer and winter. In general, radio aurorae follow the sunspot cycle in frequency with distinctions between the transient and coronal hole forms of solar activity. The seasonal variations may be due to the McIntosh effect, especially in the declining years of the sunspot cycle, whereby the sun's southern hemisphere magnetic field is best oriented towards the earth in springtime and the northern hemisphere field in autumn. Activity in solar mid-latitudes tends to show a seasonal effect upon the earth but solar equatorial activity had no such tendency.

There is a tendency for radio aurorae to peak at 1900 hours local time with a secondary peak at 1500 hours L.T. There is an annual peak of radio aurorae in northwest Europe at the autumnal equinox with a secondary peak at the spring equinox. There is a zero point in midsummer and a secondary minimum in midwinter. The radio aurorae follow the pattern of the solar cycle through the years.

Coronal hole activity on the sun is more often detected in lower latitudes as radio rather than as visible aurora. The radio signal is unsteady and tends to peak activity at 1400–1700 and 2100–2400 hours L.T. These events fall towards the end of the sunspot cycle. Aurorae following solar flares produce steady radio effects, often with visual events which appear in the lulls between radio events and after the radio effects have ceased. A similar effect takes place on the breakup of a solar filament. Another type of event consists of one or more bursts of activity each lasting ten minutes or so, consisting of solar radio frequency flux detected between 1700 and 1900 hours L.T., unaccompanied by a magnetic storm and seldom by visible aurora. Strong visible aurorae penetrate deep into the atmosphere where molecules are to be found. Ion clouds form at lower levels which can absorb radio signals and disrupt radio traffic. On the other hand, other ion clouds which may assist in scattering radio signals in V.H.F. may themselves absorb signals from transmitters placed behind them such as the signals in the VHF bands from an Oscar series satellite. (Fig. B.10.5b).

Suitable radio observations of the aurora may be made with amateur band V.H.F. equipment using a movable directional antenna. Two stations make contact with each other using auroral scattering transmission (Fig. B.10.5a radio aurora). They determine the directions of their respective aerials to give best results from which the probable location of the ion cloud may be determined. A single station may determine what stations of known geographical location can or cannot be heard due to auroral scattering and enhancement of transmission range. An assessment of the radio horizons can give some clue as to the probable location of the scattering cloud. By tracking Oscar satellites transmitting on amateur bands, it is possible to track the zones of absorption along the satellite's transmission path. Details should be reported to the radio operator's local national radio association, for example, The Radio Society of Great Britain, Potters Bar, England or the American Radio Relay League, West Hartford, Conneticut in the United States.

B.10.9   The Magnetic Storm

At any magnetic observatory the earth's field can be measured in terms of three components. The vertical component Z and the horizontal component H are measures of field strength, while horizontal component D measures the angular direction of the field. Auroral structures extend along magnetic field lines which are not necessarily vertical to the earth's surface.

Geomagnetic latitude (°)	62	61	60	59	58	57	56	55	54
Tilt from vertical (°)	17	18	18.5	19	20	20.5	21.5	22	23

The general sequence of a transient magnetic storm is as follows. A cloud of interplanetary plasma impacting the earth's magnetic field provides the first opportunity for observation. The suddenness of the field change is called a *Storm Sudden Commencement* (S.S.C.). Thereafter the value dips below the quiet field value as the incoming particles enhance the ring current around the earth whose orientation tends to demagnetize the planetary magnetic field. This current slowly disperses and returns to normal, allowing the field strength to increase. During this period, however, instabilities in the tail of the magnetic field on the side away from the sun cause interplanetary particles to be guided and accelerated into the auroral regions of the atmosphere to cause the aurora to form.

This depends very much upon the alignment of the interplanetary magnetic field with respect to the earth's magnetic axis. This is favorable to the development of an aurora when the I.M.F. can interconnect with the earth's magnetic field. If the observer is close to the aurora, he can detect violent magnetic disturbances which can be correlated with the changing auroral forms. It is possible to have magnetic storms which contain an initial S.S.C. enhancement of flux but no subsequent diminution of a demagnetizing current. Some storms have no enhancement but only the diminution.

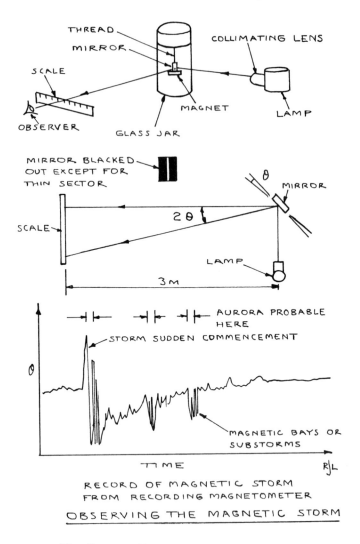

Fig. B.10.6. *Observing the magnetic storm.*

The interplanetary plasma contains its own magnetic field, which may be resolved into three components, one of which is parallel to the earth's axis. If the axial component points northwards, parallel to the earth's field, aurorae will form in the auroral zone. If the component is strong, then the aurorae contract polewards. In this situation, neither the aurorae nor their associated local magnetic field disturbances will be detected in midlatitudes. If, however, this component points south, its reaction with the earth's magnetic field causes the aurorae to migrate equatorwards so that they become visible in mid-latitudes. The degree of equatorward extension depends upon the strength of the impacting plasma and its associated magnetic field.

Professional observations of local terrestrial magnetic fields are made at Göttingen and other specially equipped magnetic observatories situated world wide. Global averages of the degree of field disturbance are prepared at three hourly intervals using data from a selection of magnetic observatories. These are issued on a logarithmic scale called the Kp index, daily averages are issued on a linear scale called the Ap index. The comparison of the two scales is as follows:

Kp	0	1	2	3	4	5	6	7	8	9
Ap	0	3	7	15	27	48	80	140	240	400

An Ap index of 0–10 is considered to represent a quiet field, 10–20, represents a minor storm, 20–50, a storm, and over 50, a major storm. Over 80 the field is very disturbed. While very disturbed conditions are usually associated with visible aurora, lesser values of Ap may not be.

Amateur observers can follow the course of a magnetic storm by constructing a simple suspended-magnet magnetometer (Fig. B.10.6). Those with experience in electronics can construct a self recording suspended-magnet magnetometer utilizing a light sensitive diode to detect the location of the light beam reflected from the apparatus. Alternatively magnetoresistive units may be employed to detect the position of the magnet. Such equipment records variations in the direction of the horizontal component of the earth's field. A self-recording fluxgate magnetometer can be fabricated to measure the variations in the intensity of the field. The British Astronomical Association is currently operating a network of magnetic observatories incorporating examples of the above equipment. Suspended magnet magnetometers are used in the northern part of the country to act as an early warning system for the onset of auroral conditions.

B.10.10 Plotting of Observations

It is useful to adopt the technique developed by Bartels to investigate magnetic storms so that the 27 day periodicity becomes evident, where it exists. The diagram consists of a horizontal row of 27 consecutive dates followed immediately below by the next 27 dates thereafter, each row starting from the left hand side, and so on. The presence of aurorae, radio aurorae and magnetic data are plotted in the square for each date. Recurrent activities will tend to appear one below the other as the sun rotates. Such a diagram may be used to predict the possibility of further active periods in the subsequent rotations. If the observer also measures sunspot activity,

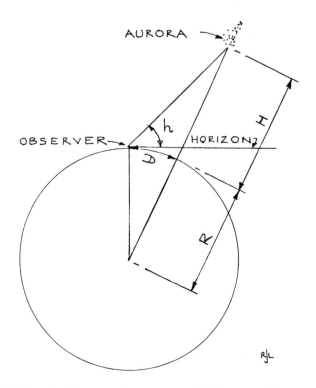

Fig. B.10.7. *Plotting the approximate geographic location of an aurora in relation to an observer.*

the numbers of aurorae seen may be related to the mean daily frequencies of active solar areas and plotted together against a scale of time.

It is possible to monitor the southern migration of the aurora and plot its approximate geographic location in relation to an observer. Assuming the atmospheric height of the base of an auroral arc, by measuring the angular altitude from the horizon to that base, the distance along the surface of the earth from the observer to the aurora may be inferred. As shown in Fig. B.10.7 let

$h =$ the angular altitude of the aurora

$H =$ the assumed height in kilometers

$R =$ the radius of the earth at 6367 km

$D =$ the distance along the circumference of the earth from the observer to the aurora in km

$\Psi =$ the angle subtended at the center of the earth between the radii through the aurora and the observer.

Then,

$$\tan h = \cot \Psi - \frac{R}{(R+H)\sin \Psi},$$ (B.10.10.1)

and

$$D = \frac{\pi R \Psi}{180}.$$ (B.10.10.2)

A graph may be prepared to solve these equations on a regular basis.

B.10.11 Conclusion

The future of amateur work in the observation of auroral activity lies in the integration of visual, radio, and magnetic observers into a combined network spread over a wide geographic area. Records of auroral events stretch back to Biblical times and are apparent in Chinese, Japanese, and Korean records. Thus the modern amateur contributes to the continuance of man's observation of this phenomenon. Artificial satellites, radar, and other high technology systems are now making scientific studies of the aurora, but these do not detract from the beauty, wonder, and awe that the aurora holds for the ground based observer.

Part C

Solar Eclipses

Chapter C.1

An Introduction to Solar Eclipses

C.1.1 Preparing an Expedition to Observe a Solar Eclipse[†]

To observe a total solar eclipse, one is usually obliged to travel great distances. An expedition to observe such an eclipse involves substantial costs, and as the phenomenon is very uncommon, very careful preparation should go into an expedition.

C.1.1.1 Long-term Preparations

Lists of eclipses can be found in a number of popular books, the most complete being in Meeus (1966, Figs. C.1.1 and C.1.2) and Oppholzer (1887, 1962). Eclipses until the end of the century are described by Pasachoff and Covington (1993). Maps in these books aid the choice of the continent and country in which observation is to be carried out. Many personal computer programs are available which cover every aspect of eclipses in former and future times. During the first phase of preparation, it should also be decided whether to travel alone or in a small or large group.

C.1.1.2 Medium-term Preparations (about one year before the eclipse)

During this phase, NASA Goddard Space Flight Center publishes a circular with detailed forecasts for the eclipse, weather, etc. Forecasts can also be found in astronomical periodicals (see Appendix A for ordering information). In addition, weather information can be obtained from the appropriate national meteorological services. Their addresses or

---

[†]Written by A. Hänel, R. Beck, and D. Staps.

397

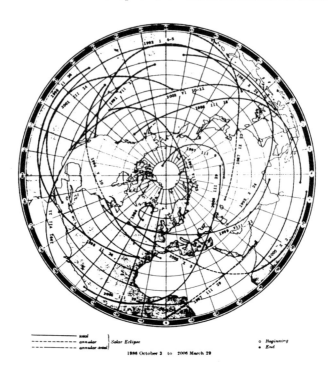

Fig. C.1.1. *Chart of eclipses in the Northern Hemisphere from Meeus, Canon of Solar Eclipses, 1966.*

general information can be obtained from university meteorological institutes, airport weather services, regional weather centers (addresses in the telephone book), or national meteorological offices. This information will provide a basis for selecting an observation point. In the case of groups, teams of up to four or five should disperse to different points to reduce the weather risk (see also C.1.5). To determine the exact path of the central line, a map with a scale of 1:500,000 or better will be adequate, but a topographical map is always preferable. These maps can be obtained from book shops. In general, however, it is better to contact a national (often military) geographical institute directly. These are usually located in the capital. At this point in time the journey should have been booked and international car rental companies contacted as a vehicle is often a necessity. Local authorities, astronomical associations

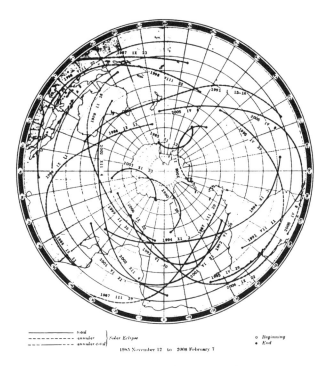

Fig. C.1.2. *Chart of eclipses in the Southern Hemisphere from Meeus, Canon of Solar Eclipses, 1966.*

or universities should also be contacted at this stage (StarGuides, 1994). An expedition requires a high degree of cooperation between members of a team (for example, the occupants of a Landrover), and for this reason nothing should be left to chance when putting together observation groups. For instance, conflicts can easily arise between smokers and non-smokers, stay-at-homes and globe-trotters, scientists and stargazers.

By now ideas about what kind of instruments to take should take on a more concrete form. All the instruments should be set up at home, and the eclipse observing program should be tested using a stop watch. The program should allow for at least 20 extra seconds during totality, because the excitement of being present at an eclipse usually results in mistakes being made during a complex program. There should also be a little time left over for enjoying the eclipse with the naked eye. As international air travel regulations usually limit luggage to 20 kg, it may be necessary to come to an arrangement with the airline about excess baggage. Alterations to the instruments could also be made. The apparatus being taken should be robust, lightweight and easily assembled and operated. Too many cameras can never be taken if for no other reason than to avoid changing film during the eclipse! Exposed films must be kept air-tight and protected against dampness (resealable plastic bags).

C.1.2   Visual Observations of Total Solar Eclipses[†]

The direct experience of witnessing a total solar eclipse with your own two eyes cannot be replaced by a photograph, however good it is. Therefore, the duration of the eclipse should not be completely spent behind a camera. The naked eye, and with binoculars, is a sensitive measuring instrument which can record fine details in the corona. Simple drawings can record the event. Astronomers in previous centuries had to rely on this method of observation and developed it to perfection (see also Lockyer (1900), U.S. Naval Observatory Report (1880), and Fig. C.1.3). During the eclipse the naked eye can also be used to observe other phenomena such as the brightness and color of the horizon light, the visibility of planets and fixed stars, the approach of the lunar shadow and shadow bands (see Sections C.1.3.4.2 and C.1.4). In addition to astronomical observations, meteorological (see C.1.5) and biological observations can be set up, which to a certain extent can also be carried out in cloudy conditions. It is therefore possible to take measurements during adverse weather conditions as the flora and fauna react to the reduction in brightness during the eclipse. Some authors even state that the best time to study these phenomena is when an eclipse is heavily clouded out (Stratton 1927).

Probably the best description of a solar eclipse (1842) is to be found in the works of Adalbert Stifter:

> ... and finally the effect became visible on Earth, and ever more so as the glowing crescent in the sky became narrower; no longer did the river shimmer but became a grey colored band. Dull shadows lay all around, the swallows became restless and it was as if a breath had tarnished the soft glow of the sky. A cool breeze arose and blew towards us. An indescribably strange, but leaden light lay over the meadows, and over the forest all movement disappeared with the light. There was calm—not the calm of slumber but rather the calm of unconciousness—and the countryside became ever paler and stiller. Our shadows lay empty on the walls, faces became ashen. This gradual dying in the middle of the morning freshness which had existed

---

[†]Written by Dietmar Staps and Rainer Beck

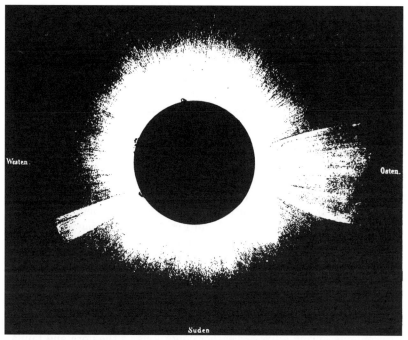

Fig. C.1.3. *Solar eclipse of September 7, 1858 in Brazil (Paranagua) observed by Liais (Mädler 1861).*

but moments before was unnerving. We had imagined that this twilight would be like dusk without the red glow of the setting sun, but we had not realized how ghostly twilight without a sunset could be. This twilight was quite different; it was an oppressive alienation of our nature. In the south-east there was a strange yellowish-red darkness which covered the hills and even the Belvedere—at our feet the city sank lower and lower like an insubstantial interplay of shadows, it was as if people driving, walking or riding across the bridge were being observed in a black mirror. Tension rose to a peak. One more look through the telescope and it was my last. It was as if the glowing crescent had been cut into the darkness with a knife and would disappear at any moment. As I looked up, I saw everyone else discard their glasses and stare upwards, no longer having any need of them. Like the last glimmer of an expiring candle, the last ray melted away, probably through the canyon between two lunar mountains. It was a very sad moment as one celestial disk covered the other, but it was precisely this moment which was truly heart-rending. An "ah" was uttered in unison by all—and then deathly silence. This was the moment God spoke and all men listened.

The complete description appeared in Waldmeier (1959). In works from the last century there are also precise details about the behavior of animals and plants during eclipses. An example is this extract by J. Mädler (1867), who accurately described the effects of a solar eclipse on animals and plants:

> This year's eclipse had a relatively insignificant effect on the animal and plant kingdoms, the effect having been much greater at Brest-Litovsk in 1851, even though the phenomenon could not then be observed as the sky was completely covered, whereas it was perfectly clear in Vitoria. However, the effect in 1851 was much greater than in 1860 which can be explained by the much wider lunar shadow. From this we can conclude that it is the darkness which is inappropriate for the time of day which confuses and disturbs the animals, and that the phenomenon itself, which is enjoyed by the human looking up at the sky and not by the animal looking at the ground, has little to do with it directly. Animals can sense a coming change in the weather, both sudden and gradual, but not a solar eclipse. Nothing happens in the atmosphere to cause a change, and so during the eclipse the only influences on the animals are those of confusion and fear. While some, such as birds, hide and flee to their nocturnal resting places, other, such as bats and nocturnal moths, leave the places where they remain hidden during the day. Then, when the light reappears, everything takes on its previous liveliness and all traces of restlessness are gone.

C.1.3   Photographic Observations[†]

In contrast to naked eye observations, photographs provide a record of the size, brightness etc., of the corona, and years later can still provide information about the corona. To take photographs of the corona, substantially longer exposure times are required than for photographing the photosphere. Moreover, colored phenomena occur in the corona (prominences, condensation) so that color film should be used. The corona can extend over $10°$ in the sky with the result that practically all focal lengths of a camera with interchangeable lenses can be used to record the corona.

In the following section the amateur is given some hints on photographing the corona and then evaluating the photographs.

C.1.3.1   White Light Photographs of the Corona

The sun travels across the sky at approximately 15 arc seconds per second. To make use of the theoretical resolution of a 5 cm diameter lens, the exposure time of a stationary camera should not be longer than $1/4$

[†]Written by Rainer Beck, Dietmar Staps, and Adolf Merz

second. Due to the film grain of medium to highly sensitive emulsions, the theoretical resolution cannot be obtained, with the result that exposure times of approximately 5 seconds (normal lens) to approximately 0.5 seconds (500 mm tele) are possible without a guiding system. This makes equatorial mounting unnecessary, thus saving a great deal of weight. There are no problems of movement blurring with Super-8 cameras as the exposure time is usually only $1/30$ second. Depending on the exposure time, f-stop, and film sensitivity prominences, the inner or outer corona can be photographed.

Gibson (1973) gives the following definitions:

- Inner corona: Distance from the sun 1.02 to 1.30 radii (1.02 due to the chromosphere)

- Middle corona: Distance from the sun 1.30 to 2.30 radii

- Outer corona: Distance from the sun over 2.30 radii.

Exposure tables are given at the end of the section. Normally the extreme corona (more than approximately 5 solar radii) can not be photographed without filters as it attains the same brightness as the sky in the background (see Fig. C.1.4). If the sky is exceptionally clear or if observation is carried out above 2000 m, the corona can be observed for up to 10 solar radii (Palem, India, 1980 Fig. C.1.5) or 30 radii (total diameter approximately 15° [1954 eclipse, Waldmeier 1961]).

1.3.2.1. Low Resolution Photographs. With extremely wide angle lenses (possibly even fish-eye lenses) the changes in the surrounding landscape during an eclipse and the whole sky can be recorded. The use of highly sensitive color films (at least 400 ASA) is recommended.

The prevailing light conditions are similar to those during a full moon. In areas which are not in the core shadow of the moon, there are wonderful displays of color on the horizon. Focal distances of 28 mm to 80 mm can be used to photograph the outer corona.

1.3.2.2. Medium Resolution Photographs (around 10 arc seconds). The best photographs of the entire corona (assuming the total diameter of the corona is around 3° in the sky), showing a number of the features to be described in later sections, can be obtained with telephoto lenses having a focal length of between 200 mm and 600 mm and an appropriate film. The advantages of a lightweight compact camera, which is not likely to be faulty, cannot be too highly stressed.

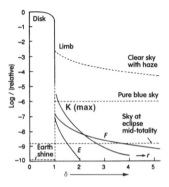

Fig. C.1.4. *Relative intensity of the components of coronal light. K corona = continuous spectrum due to electron scattering. F corona = inner zodiacal light; E corona = combined light of emission lines. The best blue skies observable at mountain altitudes have $\log I = -6$. I is normalized so $\log I_{disk} = 0$. (After van de Hulst 1953)*

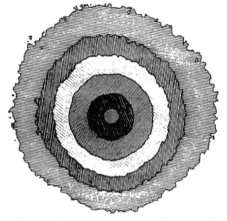

Fig. C.1.5. *Corona (Palem, India Feb. 16, 1980), extending approximately 10 solar radii. Orientation: East is right, North is up. (Pröll, Staps, Wenzel)*

1.3.2.3. High Resolution Photographs (under 3 arc seconds). With

a focal length of over 600 mm, the fine structure of the inner and middle corona can be recorded, and if the exposure time is kept correspondingly short, there is no need for equatorial mounting. However, the sun moves away from the center of the field of view relatively quickly with the result that tracking is desirable. Without an equatorial mounting, tracking is difficult, but with an equatorial mounting with a clock motor drive one can produce photographs which are only limited by the optical system and the local seeing conditions. Professional photographs (e.g., Koutchmy

1988) normally have a resolution of approximately one arc second, and with the right optical system the amateur can produce comparable results. Subarcsecond coronal structures are visible on images taken during the 1991 eclipse with telescopes at Mauna Kea (Vial *et al.* 1992).

1.3.3.1. Photographs with Polarization Filters. Taking photographs of the solar corona with polarization filters is one of the amateur's most gratifying tasks as the inner corona is strongly polarized (see Fig. C.1.6). Just three photographs (see Figs. C.2.8–C.2.10 and Chapter C.2.3) using filter orientations of 0°, 60°, and 120° provide all the information on the degree of and angle of polarization in the corona. The filter should therefore be marked in degrees and absorb as much as possible perpendicular to the direction of polarization. Evaluation is facilitated by accurate guiding and calibration on the same film. The optical system should have a focal length of at least 400 mm.

1.3.3.2. Photographs with Interference Filters. The strongest emission lines of the solar corona in the visible spectrum are 530.3 nm and 637.4 nm. Interference filters with a FWHM of 0.6 nm make for interesting observation programs (relative line strength, structure of the corona, polarization, etc.). Films which can be used are the Kodak spectroscopic emulsions (103a-) or Kodak 2415 Technical Pan. Exposure times are in seconds. Extensive testing of the filters using bright sources of light must be carried out (ghost images, reflections!). (See also Section C.2.4.)

1.3.3.3. Infrared Photographs. In the infrared spectrum the solar corona can be detected up to greater distances than in white light. False color film (Ektachrome Infrared) has only a slight infrared sensitivity and has properties similar to a color slide film (using an orange or red filter). A comparison of the two now available (1995) infrared films (Kodak High Speed Infrared and Konica Infrared 750 nm) was published in *Foto und Labor* (1993). Konica film is less sensitive than Kodak but has finer grain and is much easier to handle. On the other hand, the Kodak High Speed Infrared black and white film requires special handling—it can only be loaded in the dark, and the camera must then be kept in an aluminium case and protected from sunlight until just before the photographs are taken because most camera shutters do not block infrared radiation (see also Section C.2.4). With exposure times of over one second (using a normal or small telephoto lens with guiding), the inner corona should be covered by a screen at the film plane or positioned about 3 m from the objective. Precise distance should be determined by trial and error several days in advance of the eclipse. (See also Section C.2.4.)

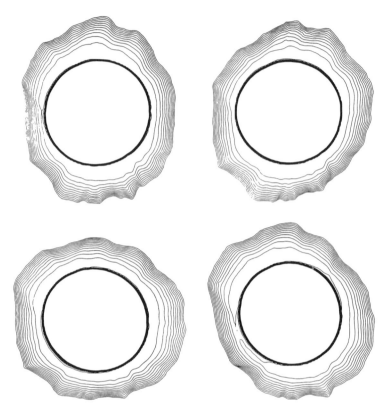

Fig. C.1.6. *Isophotes of polarization photographs of the corona taken with filter settings of 0° (upper left), 45° (upper right); 90° (lower left), and 135° (lower right), Eclipse Feb. 16, 1980 Palem, India (Pröll, Straps, and Wenzel).*

1.3.3.4. Radial Gradient Filters. If exposure times are short, the inner corona is clearly defined, but not so the outer corona. With longer exposure times the outer corona can be clearly seen, but the inner corona is over-exposed. To photograph the entire corona clearly, several pictures have to be taken because the brightness of the corona decreases radially the further the distance from the solar limb (see Fig. C.1.4). If a filter which compensates for this decrease (i.e., absorbs more strongly in the inner corona than in the outer corona) is placed in front of the film, all parts of the corona can be photographed equally well in one shot (for details see Newkirk 1970). Priced at around $300, the cost of radial gradient filters is prohibitive for most amateurs. Less expensive devices that achieve nearly the same effect have been used by amateurs (Todd 1901, Wedel 1980). Certain photographic techniques ("unsharp masking") or digital image processing (see Chapter A.7) are also very promising.

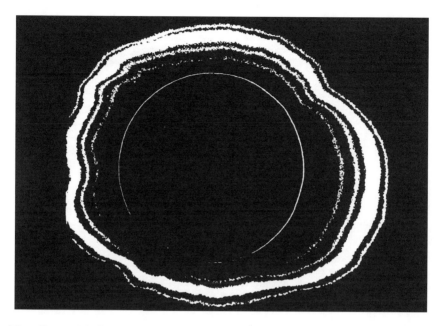

Fig. C.1.7. *"Agfacontour"-Isophotes of the corona (R. Beck, Eclipse of June 30, 1973).*

1.3.3.5. Photographing the Corona with Color Films. The most impressive pictures of the entire solar corona are obtained using color slide film and a focal length of around 400 mm to 1200 mm. On the other hand, with color negative film the individual colors can later be separated with appropriate filters. Thus one shot can yield up to three different color pictures (Koutchmy 1978).

1.3.3.6. Organizational and Photographic Tips for One's First Solar Eclipse.

The following will be needed:

1. Reflex camera 35-mm

2. Telephoto lens 400 mm, approximately 1:5.6

3. Color slide or negative film (approximately 100 ASA)

4. A good tripod

5. Polarization filters

6. Tape recorder (optional)

Example of a Program for a Solar Eclipse			
Picture no.	Text		Time (secs)
1.	1–6	Partial phase with solar filters	
2.	7–12	2nd contact at $1/1000$ sec	10
3.		About 10 secs after 2nd contact photographs of the corona at:	
	13	$1/1000$ sec	
	14	$1/250$ sec	
	15	$1/60$ sec	
	16	$1/15$ sec	
	17	$1/4$ sec	
	18	$1/2$ sec	
	19	1 sec	30
4.		Attach polarization filter	20
	20–22	Photographs with polarization filter set to 0°, 60° and 120° and exposure time 1 sec	20
	23–25	As above at 1/60 sec	20
		Remove polarization filter	10
5.	26–31	Photographs of third contact	10
6.	32–36	Photographs of partial phase with filter	

Additional notes:

1. The differences with factor 2 exposure times (e.g., $1/1000$ and $1/500$ sec.) are small; therefore, it is better to use a factor of 4 or 8.

2. Exposures are longer at mid-eclipse as diffused light in the earth's atmosphere is at a minimum. Also, light from the chromosphere and photosphere is brighter than the inner corona close to the second and third contacts.

3. The program assumes a three-minute solar eclipse with about 60 seconds set aside for other visual observations—adjust for your eclipse's particular timing at the site where you plan to observe. The example shown above or, alternatively, one's own program, should be run through several times before departure. A good subject for conducting your dry run is the full moon, as lighting conditions are similar to those during a total solar eclipse. By examining the pictures obtained of the moon, the effects of, for example, shake and reflexes can be determined.

4. After some practice the time you take to carry out the program should stabilize and fall into a familiar routine. This time should be 20 to 30 seconds shorter than the calculated duration of the eclipse.

C.1.3.2   Filming the Corona

1.3.4.1. Filming the Moon's Shadow and the Landscape. Film and video cameras with fast lenses can record the approach of the moon's shadow and the surrounding landscape and people during a total solar eclipse. Precise exposure times cannot be given. Lighting conditions are approximately 0.1 to 1.0 times those of the full moon (dependent to a small degree on the phase of the sunspot cycle, Nye 1992).

Fig. C.1.8. *Shadow bands observed during the total eclipse of Dec. 22, 1870 (Mullar 1870).*

1.3.4.2. Filming Shadow Bands. A few minutes before second contact and a few minutes after third contact, when only a narrow crescent is visible, the scintillation phenomenon known as shadow bands occurs. According to various reports, the width of the shadow is between a few centimeters and 20 cm, the interval between them several decimeters to one meter, and their velocity several meters per second. Shadow bands are particularly clear on white surfaces (see Fig. C.1.8). The contrast is less than 1%, being at its greatest in ultra-violet and blue light. As the solar crescent grows narrower, the shadows become longer and greater in contrast and faster. The best way of recording shadow bands is by using a camera with a very fast lens to film a white cloth in slow motion (exposure time less than $1/100$ sec., [Young 1972, Marschall 1994, Zirker 1984]).

1.3.4.3. Filming the Flash Spectrum. At second and third contact the emission spectrum of the chromosphere is visible for a few seconds. This phenomenon can be filmed using a prism or diffraction grating and camera set to maximum slow motion (see also C.2.1).

1.3.4.4. Filming without Guiding. As the exposure time of movie cameras is generally $1/30$ of a second, there is no danger of blurring from movement. During totality the solar corona cannot leave the film frame, for the longest focal lengths obtainable with movie cameras, approximately 60 cm, correspond to only around 400 mm in 35-mm format. The longest available focal length should be used to film the eclipse. Prominences are filmed at aperture 8 (25 ASA film), the inner corona at aperture 2.8, and the middle corona at 1.4. The outer corona can only be filmed with fast video or CCD cameras (Pasachoff and Covington 1993).

At second and third contact the greatest time-lapse should be used (36 or more pictures), but during totality, time lapse or normal speed should be used (e.g., 5 frames per second), the continuous opening of the aperture providing an impressive transition from the inner to the outer corona.

1.3.4.5. Filming with Polarizing Filters. A film camera with a long focal length is used with a polarizing filter which is continuously rotated. Following each cycle of the filter the aperture is changed so that the polarization of the inner to the middle corona can be demonstrated. A high level of precision is required here if the continuity is to be maintained in the final film strip (slight slow motion, 24 to 36 frames/sec).

1.3.4.6. Filming with Guiding. Expensive movie cameras have removable lenses. With a 135 mm or 200 mm lens, prominences and the inner corona can be filmed that fill the 8mm format, provided the telescope is guided. A camera, without its lens, can be placed behind the telescope's eyepiece and Baily's beads (slow motion), the chromosphere and prominences at one section of the solar limb can be filmed. Time-lapse views of the moon covering a sunspot during the partial phase are always of interest.

C.1.3.3   Evaluating the Photographs

More detailed information on evaluating photographs of a solar eclipse can be found elsewhere (see Section C.2 and its corresponding bibliography), and for this reason only a few brief notes will be given here. High resolution black and white photographs of the inner and middle corona (1–2 solar radii) are ideal originals for "Agfacontour" isophotes (Beck and Hünecke 1974 and Fig. C.1.7; see also Chapter A.6). If isophotes are to be found through the outer corona, two negatives with exposure times differing by a factor of 10 (focal length around 500 mm) are required. The film should be of medium sensitivity and should not be developed to show too much contrast. By using the isophote technique the elliptical form of the solar corona (see C.2.2) and its variations with regard to distance from the sun can be easily determined.

Using digital techniques, one can determine surface luminosity in the solar corona (see Chapter A.7). Negatives are scanned and digitized using a microphotometer, all data being stored on magnetic tape for further processing. If the film is to be calibrated with the aid of the darkened sun or another standard light source, a surface luminosity chart for the corona can be established (Beck and Pröll 1974; Pröll and Staps 1979). Digital processes for suppressing noise and increasing contrast can be em-

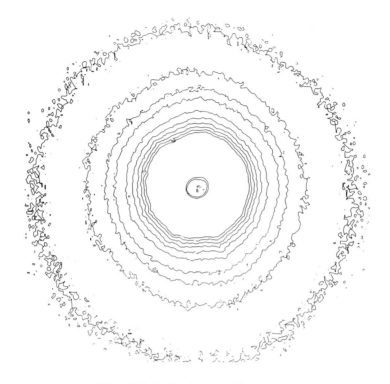

Fig. C.1.9. *Isophotes of the corona.*

ployed to show the outer corona. For example, attempts could be made to show lunar formations on the new moon which should be visible in the earthshine. The three (calibrated) polarized intensity charts can be combined in a computer to form a chart of the degree and angle of polarization (Beck and Pröll 1974).

C.1.4   Photocells[†]

As in all sectors of astronomy, there are numerous applications for photocells in observing solar eclipses. Modern photocells are inexpensive and available for practically all regions of the spectrum.

C.1.4.1   Optoelectronic Recording of the Solar Corona

In photometry of the solar corona, a field of view of about 1.5° is required. For measuring the reduction in luminosity during second and third

---

[†]Written by Manfred Belter

contact and the diamond ring effect, it should be only a few arc minutes. As photocells have a large field of view, it has to be optically reduced. Modern photodetectors for measuring purposes (e.g., PIN-Photodiode BPW 34) have a clear aperture approximately 4 mm in diameter. To maintain a field of view of around 1.5°, focus a 135 mm focal length lens on the photocell's light-sensitive area.

The simplest and least expensive method is to record the photometric data on magnetic tape using a small battery-operated cassette recorder. For this purpose the analogue values obtained by light falling onto a photocell (10 Hz to 10 kHz) first have to be electronically digitized. The appropriate components (Analog-to-Digital converters) are inexpensive and can also be built into the recording device. Slightly more difficult is the later evaluation of the recorded data. Frequency variations have to be interpreted as changes in luminosity and, if necessary, compared with intensity measurements of the sky. For this there are frequency voltage transformers which convert sound frequency changes into corresponding variations in voltage.

C.1.4.2   Optoelectronic Recording of "Shadow Bands"

The most important aspect of recording the shadow bands which occur shortly before and after a totality is to determine a difference in luminosity or change in frequency. With very sensitive calibrated photocells variations in luminosity can also be given in absolute values. As the shadow bands are only a few centimeters in width and travel at several meters per second, it is worthwhile to use a view-finding telescope with a focal length of 30 cm to 50 cm and a sensitive photocell positioned at the focal point. Scattered and incident light radiation can be reduced by mounting a tubular light shade in front of the lens. The photocell and the optoelectronic transducer form a unit and are located in a housing that is firmly mounted to the telescope. The entire apparatus is set up so that the objective is directed upwards towards the zenith. If the likely direction of the shadow bands is known, it is possible to measure the speed by simultaneously using two detectors to sense any fine structure that may be present. A detailed investigation of shadow bands would require an entire system of light-sensitive detectors and the use of a recording device with several channels.

C.1.5   Meteorological Observations[†]

In addition to astronomical observations, meteorological observations can also be carried out during a total solar eclipse. During the eclipse solar

---

[†]Written by Rainer Beck and Dietmar Staps

radiation onto the eclipse path is reduced for around three hours, resulting in a drop in temperature of 5° to 6° centigrade and a rise in humidity. Atmospheric pressure does not fall noticeably (several torrs).

A phenomenon which is often observed is the "eclipse wind." Shortly before the beginning of totality, a strong wind begins to blow, the direction of which can change during the eclipse. This is not always a regular feature, and the "eclipse wind" does not blow during every eclipse.

Frequently observers have noted that the sky was completely covered, and it was even raining. Suddenly the cloud cover around the sun broke up, and for several degrees around it there were no clouds at all—the sun being clearly visible. As the eclipse progresses, observations of the corona are carried out according to plan, and at the end of the eclipse the sky is completely covered again. The cause of the cloud cover breaking up might be caused by the drop in temperature and the eclipse wind. The ground and air temperatures, atmospheric pressure, humidity, cloud cover, brightness, and the coloring of various parts of the sky can be recorded.

The meteorological effects should also be taken into consideration when planning an expedition. The devices should be set up rigidly because of the eclipse wind, and a windbreak may be necessary. Depending on the location an umbrella (and sunshade) and warm clothing should be readily available for the protection of both people and equipment.

C.1.6 General Photographic Data

Neutral Density Filter Factors

Neutral Density	Filter Factor	Exposure Extensions (Stops)
0.1	1.26	0.33
0.2	1.58	0.66
0.3	2.00	1.00
0.4	2.51	1.33
0.5	3.16	1.66
0.6	3.98	1.99
0.7	5.01	2.33
0.8	6.31	2.66
0.9	7.94	2.99
1.0	10.0	3.32
2.0	100.0	6.64
3.0	1000.0	9.97
4.0	10000.0	13.29
5.0	100000.0	16.61
6.0	1000000.0	19.93

SOLAR ECLIPSE – EXPOSURE CHART

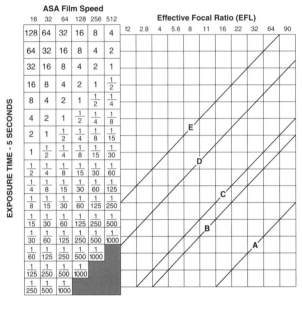

A – Partial Phases – Number 4, Neutral filter   D – Totality – Inner corona – no filter
B – Partial Phases – Number 5, Neutral filter   E – Totality – Outer corona – no filter
C – Totality – Prominences – no filter

Fig. C.1.10. *Adapted from: P.C. Sherrod and T.L. Koed:* A Complete Manual of Amateur Astronomy, *Englewood Cliffs, 1981, p. 252.*

EXPOSURE GUIDE for the Solar Eclipse					
Film Speed		**f/ratio of optical system**			
25	1.4	2	2.8	4	5.6	8
50	2	2.8	4	5.6	8	11
100	2.8	4	5.6	8	11	16
200	4	5.6	8	11	16	22
400	5.6	8	11	16	22	32
Feature of Interest					
Prominences	–	1/1000	1/600	1/250	1/125	1/60
Inner Corona	1/1000	1/600	1/250	1/125	1/60	1/30
Middle Corona	1/60	1/30	1/15	1/8	1/4	1/2
Outer Corona	1/8	1/4	1/2	1	2	4
Extreme Corona	1	2	4	8	16	32
			exposure in seconds		

Fig. C.1.11. *Source: R. Berry: "Film the Eclipse,"* Astronomy *Nov. 1978, p. 44.*

Chapter C.2

Observable Phenomena

C.2.1 Flash Spectrum[†]

The chromospheric spectrum is visible for a few seconds before the second and after the third contact in a total solar eclipse. For this reason the chromospheric spectrum is known as the "Flash" spectrum. To observe it the edge of the moon is used as a natural slit in conjunction with a spectroscope. There are various methods of photographing the flash spectrum, two of which are described here.

With W.W. Campbell's "moving plate spectrum," a narrow slit is set parallel to the spectrum, and a film, which is moving in one direction, is exposed (see Fig. C.2.1). The photograph shows the chromospheric emission lines which are distinguishable from the Fraunhofer lines occurring in the background by their different lengths. The height of emission above the photosphere can be derived from the length of the chromospheric lines (Mitchell 1951). However, it is difficult for the amateur to build a moving plate device, and it is recommended that the second method, devised by Mitchell and improved by Menzel, be used.

A grating or prism is placed in front of an optical system (telescope or telephoto lens), and the solar limb is photographed through this arrangement using a motor driven SLR, video, or CCD camera. The same system in front of a binocular allows the flash spectrum to be observed visually. To save film the series of photographs can begin when the flash spectrum first appears in the binocular. By using a grating (and thus linear dispersion), it is possible to select a particular spectral range by inclining the grating in front of the objective against the optical axis. Redman (1942) recommends a range of between 300 nm and 400 nm. Most emission lines from the flash spectrum occur in the blue range of the spectrum, and this is the range

---

[†]Written by Dietmar Staps and Teoman Topcubasi

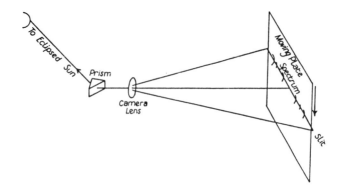

Fig. C.2.1. *Moving plate spectrograph.*

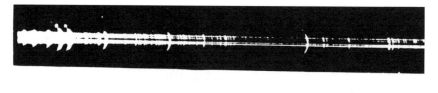

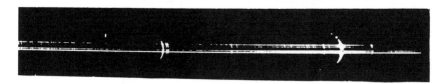

Fig. C.2.2. *Flash spectrum 375 nm–675 nm on Feb. 16, 1980 (from a photograph by R. Beck).*

where the amateur with the means at his disposal should concentrate. Because of the light intensity very good photographs are possible (Figs. C.2.2 and C.2.3).

The exact moment of second and third contact has to be calculated for the observer's position and used accordingly. It is best to begin taking photographs approximately 15 seconds before second contact. The exposure time of each photograph should be as short as possible. The calculated moment of third contact should be noted and, as before, filming should last 15 seconds. Mitchell recommends beginning approximately 5 seconds before third contact. The flash spectrum is similar to the reverse of the Fraunhofer spectrum, except for the majority of ionized metal lines and neutral atoms (He, O) in a highly excited state. If the pictures are calibrated, one

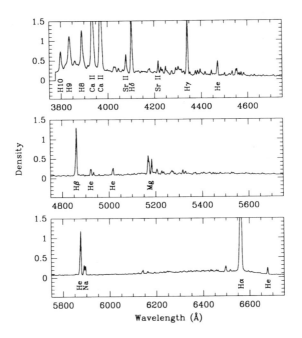

Fig. C.2.3. *Microdensitometer evaluation of a flash spectrum taken on Feb. 16, 1980, region 375 nm–675 nm (Photograph by R. Beck, analysis by K. Reinsch).*

can evaluate the flash spectrum with microdensitometry and photometry. Chromospheric spectra are studied to establish the following:

1. wavelength
2. line intensity
3. the height of emission.

The interpretation of the results given in tabular form by Bray and Loughhead (1974) extends from determining the gas pressure to non-thermally conditioned atom velocities in the chromosphere (Bray and Loughhead 1974). Using the velocities determined from the spectrum, one can also calculate the kinetic temperature of the chromosphere. The flash spectrum can be different from eclipse to eclipse as a consequence of the 11-year solar cycle and activity zones in the limb areas.

Extensive catalogues of flash spectrum lines have been published by Dunn *et al.* (1966), Pierce (1968), Hiei and Fukatsu (1974), and Qi-De (1986). Good illustrations and practical instructions can be found in Mitchell (1951) and Redman (1942).

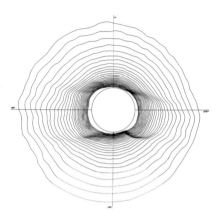

Fig. C.2.4. *Isophotes of minimum corona of July 9, 1945 according to Ramberg (1951).*

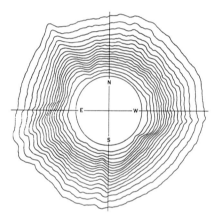

Fig. C.2.5. *Isophotes of maximum corona, March 7, 1970 according to Waldmeier (1970).*

C.2.2   Corona Shapes and Parameters[†]

In the 1880s Ranyard noted that the shape of the corona changed depending on the phase of the sunspot cycle. During minimum sunspot activity the corona has noticeable polar plumes and a large equatorial extension (Fig. C.2.4). At sunspot maximum the corona is almost circular (Fig. C.2.5). This phenomenon has resulted in the shape of the corona being described mathematically. The method which is generally accepted today was introduced by Ludendorff in 1928, and is:

[†]Written by Dietmar Staps

$$\varepsilon = \frac{\overline{D}_A - \overline{D}_P}{\overline{D}_P} \tag{C.2.1}$$

where

$\overline{D}_A$ = mean equatorial corona diameter and
$\overline{D}_P$ = mean polar corona diameter.

The mean diameter is calculated from the equatorial or polar corona diameters and the diameters inclined at $\pm$ 22.5° thereto. Corona isophotes (lines of equal brightness) are required as a starting point for these measurements. These can be obtained by photographic equidensity (Löchel 1965) or by measurements with a microphotometer. Ludendorff originally obtained the isophotes by covering photographs with transparent paper and tracing the isophotes. Comparisons with more accurate methods have not shown any systematic differences (Layden *et al.* 1991). Following evaluation of the isophotes, a curve similar to Fig. C.2.6 (Pröll and Staps 1979) is obtained. In the region up to approximately 1.7 solar radii, the ε values exhibit a linear increase, which can be expressed by the equation

$$\varepsilon = a + b(\overline{R}_A - 1). \tag{C.2.2}$$

Values a and b are an index for the shape of the corona. The $(a + b)$ values are then shown graphically against the sunspot cycle phase.

The phase can be shown in two different ways. First,

$$\Psi_1 = \frac{T - m}{m - M_1} \tag{C.2.3}$$

and

$$\Psi_2 = \frac{T - m}{M_2 - m} \tag{C.2.4}$$

where

T = epoch of solar eclipse,
M_1, M_2 = epoch of preceding or following maximum, and
m = epoch of minimum.

Formula (C.2.3) or (C.2.4) is taken depending on whether the solar eclipse is in the decreasing or increasing part of the cycle. Second,

$$\Psi = \frac{T - m_1}{m_2 - m_1} \tag{C.2.5}$$

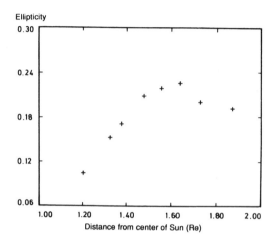

Fig. C.2.6. *Relationship of ellipticity of the corona with distance from the center of the sun.*

where m_1, m_2 = epoch of preceding or following minimum. Figure C.2.7 shows values obtained from previous eclipses.

Calculating the $(a + b)$ value of a total solar eclipse is not difficult and could be one of the objectives obtained during an expedition to observe an eclipse. The maximum and minimum corona isophotes in Figs. C.2.5 and C.2.4 can be used to calculate $(a + b)$ values, the results of calculation having to correspond to the values of Fig. C.2.7. As can be seen from Fig. C.2.7, the data from around twenty historical eclipses which have been photographically recorded are missing. Determining the missing values and those of each new eclipse would be a worthwhile activity for the amateur.

Absolute photometry, which provides initial information about the corona, is more difficult than the relative photometry described above. To do absolute photometry, exact calibration of the film, in astronomical magnitudes, is required to provide data on the corona brightness.

Amateurs who are interested in this field are referred to four publications which deal with the topic. Ramberg (1951) covers calibration, absolute photometry, scattered light correction, and measurement errors (see Fig. C.2.4). Dürst (1973) covers the same areas as Ramberg but is more comprehensive. In addition, he covers polarimetry and calculation of electron density. Koutchmy (1978) deals with photometry using stars. Guhathakurta (1991) evaluated CCD images taken during an eclipse combined with data obtained with a coronagraph.

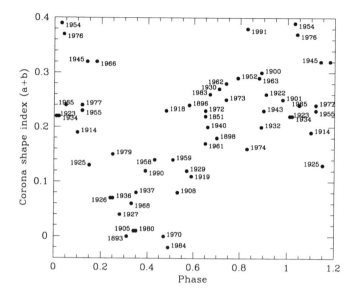

Fig. C.2.7. $(a + b)$ values against sunspot cycle phase.

C.2.3 Polarization of the Corona[†]

Coronal light consists of various components, the most important of which are the F, E, and K coronas (see Fig. C.1.4). The F-corona spectrum looks the same as the Fraunhofer spectrum. The F-corona (= zodiacal light) is produced by the scattering of photospheric light on interplanetary dust. The E-corona is the combined light of the emission lines.

The K-corona occurs only in the immediate vicinity of the sun, and its spectrum exhibits a continuum with barely noticeable absorption lines. The light of the K-corona, which up to a distance of two solar radii is the principal contributing factor of corona intensity (Fig. C.1.4), is scattered on free electrons of the inner corona and is very strongly polarized.

The term "polarization" is used to mean the orientation of the oscillating plane of light which normally oscillates in all directions perpendicular to the plane of observation. The degree of polarization has a maximum of 60% at a distance of about 10 arc minutes (Clette *et al*, 1985). During the 1991 eclipse values to 70% were measured (Clette and Gabryl 1992). The direction of polarization is radially outwards with certain variations (Beck and Pröll 1974 and Figs. C.2.8 to C.2.10). Polarization of the corona can be observed using simple commercially available polarization filters. If it

---

[†]Written by Rainer Beck and Dietmar Staps

can be captured on film, the changing shape of the corona is particularly impressive (see also C.1.3).

To determine the degree and direction of polarization requires at least three pictures taken with the polarization filter set at 0°, 60°, and 120°. The intensity reaching the film is thus

$$I_{a,b,c} = \frac{I_u}{2} + I_p \cos^2(\alpha - \theta) \qquad (C.2.6)$$

where $\alpha = 0°, 60°, 120°$. I_p is the intensity of the polarized radiation components; I_u, that of the unpolarized ones. The contribution of the F-corona can be neglected up to around 2 solar radii. θ is the angle between the plane of polarization and the 0° plane of the filter.

The results of the three equations (Eq. C.2.6) with differentiation and the use of the addition theorems are

$$2I_a - I_b - I_c = \frac{3}{2} I_p \cos 2\theta \qquad (C.2.7)$$

and

$$\theta = \frac{1}{2} \operatorname{arccot} \frac{(2I_a - I_b - I_c)}{\sqrt{3}(I_b - I_c)}. \qquad (C.2.8)$$

The degree of polarization is defined as

$$P = \frac{I_p}{(I_p + I_u)}. \qquad (C.2.9)$$

(C.2.6) gives

$$\frac{3}{2}(I_u + I_p) = I_a + I_b + I_c. \qquad (C.2.10)$$

(C.2.7) gives

$$I_p = \frac{2}{3} \frac{(2I_a - I_b - I_c)}{\cos 2\theta}. \qquad (C.2.11)$$

With

$$I_b - I_c = \sqrt{3}/2 I_p \sin 2\theta, \qquad (C.2.12)$$

we obtain

$$I_p = \frac{4}{3} \left((I_a + I_b + I_c)^2 - 3(I_a I_b + I_a I_c + I_b I_c) \right)^{1/2}. \qquad (C.2.13)$$

For the degree of polarization

$$P = \frac{2}{I_a + I_b + I_c} \left(I_a(I_a - I_b) + I_b(I_b - I_c) + I_c(I_c - I_a) \right)^{1/2}. \qquad (C.2.14)$$

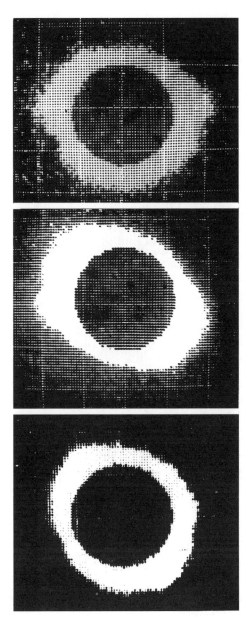

Fig. C.2.8. *Polarization photographs of the corona with filter settings of 0°, 60°, and 120° (Eclipse of June 30, 1973, Beck and Pröll 1974).*

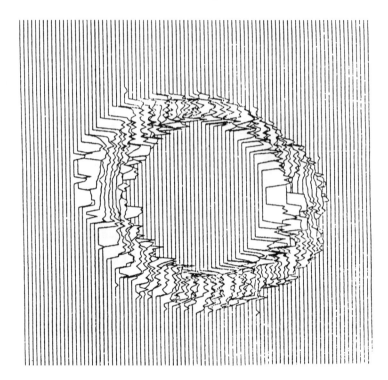

Fig. C.2.9. *Relief picture of the distribution of polarization in the solar corona June 30, 1974 (Beck and Pröll 1974).*

The direction of polarization is calculated using (Eq. C.2.8). Measurement of the degree of polarization can be carried out with only two pictures (0° and 90°). Four pictures (0°, 45°, 90°, 135°), however, produce more accurate results, for one picture can be used to check the other three. The formulae for two to four pictures are described in detail in Billings (1966).

The following polarimetric observation program can be carried out:

1. How does the average degree of polarization change with distance?

2. Are there local variations in the degree of polarization?

3. Where do variations in the angle of polarization from the radial direction occur?

4. Does the degree of polarization depend on the spectral range (possibly also in spectral lines (C.2.4))?

5. Does the degree of polarization change along the zone of totality (C.2.6)?

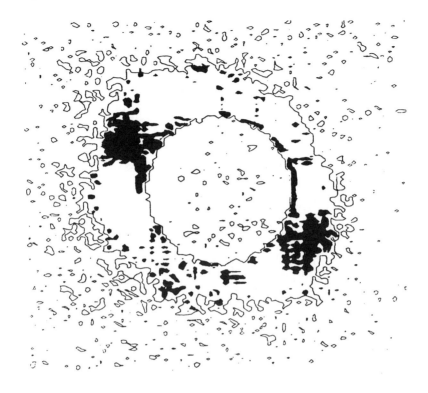

Fig. C.2.10. *Polarization in the solar corona (June 30, 1973).*

C.2.4 Infrared Corona and Coronal Lines[†]

The differences in the form of the corona in the visible range, with a spectral resolution of around 20 nm, are relatively small. Of more interest are pictures in the near infrared. Using a combination of an 87C Wratten filter and Kodak High Speed Infrared film or Aerographic infrared film, an effective wavelength of 880 nm can be achieved. Light is scattered by molecules in the earth's atmosphere. This scattering, which is stronger with shorter wavelengths, is known as Rayleigh scattering. The coefficient of scattering is proportional to $(1/\text{wavelength})^4$. Light at an effective wavelength of 880 nm is scattered 16 times less than light at a wavelength of 440 nm. The positive effect of this fact is that in the infrared the sun's corona can be observed for up to 12 radii and more (Lillequist 1970). In photographs taken in the visible range, the solar corona normally cannot be distinguished from scattered light at 5–6 radii (see Fig. C.1.4).

[†]Written by Dietmar Staps

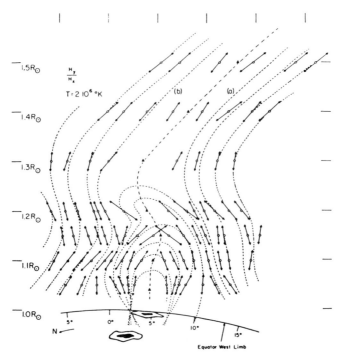

Fig. C.2.11. *Projected orientations of the magnetic field in a coronal condensation (solar eclipse of Feb. 25, 1962, Newkirk 1967).*

In addition to the continuous (K-corona) spectrum, the corona also has an emission line spectrum (E-corona), observations of which go back to 1869. This corona exhibits a changing form in the emission lines. Advantages of observation in the emission lines are as follows:

1. The inner corona can be observed in the emission lines with the aid of a coronagraph on a suitable site even when there is no total solar eclipse taking place, and

2. The contrast between phenomena is greater in the emission lines than in white light.

The amateur will perceive the advantages of item 2 above, but the line widths of the coronal lines are relatively small and the instrumental cost is high.

The coronal lines can be divided into four groups according to ionization energy (Dollfus 1971; Zirin 1966; Gibson 1973; Billings 1966; Beck 1979). Ionization energy is the minimum energy required to remove n electron(s) from the atom. $Fe\ X$, read "Iron ten," has lost 9 of its 26 electrons due to high temperatures in the corona (1–2 million K). "$Fe\ I$," iron one, indicates neutral iron. The main representatives of the groups are as follows:

1. 569.4 nm, Ca XV, 814 ev
2. 530.3 nm, Fe XIV, 355 ev
3. 637.4 nm, Fe X, 235 electron volts (ev)
4. 670.2 nm, Ni XV, 430 ev

C.2.4.1   569.4 nm

In the yellow calcium coronal line areas become visible which are connected with intense solar activity. Waldmeier (1956) showed that in almost every F group (B.2.3) emissions at a wavelength of 569.4 nm can be observed. However, groups in higher latitudes appear to correlate more with emissions at 569.4 nm than in lower latitudes.

C.2.4.2   530.3 nm

Observations in this green iron line are principally carried out outside eclipses, but then only the inner corona up to a distance of several angular minutes from the solar limb can be seen. During a total solar eclipse, the corona can be observed much more extensively in this line. As *Fe XIV* has a large equivalent width, amateur observations are restricted to this and the 637.4 nm line. During periods of intensive activity, the yellow calcium line can also be used in certain circumstances. Green line emissions correspond to facula activity (see Section B.6). However the accompanying sunspot group must have already developed. As the faculae have a longer lifespan than the accompanying sunspot group (B.2.2), emissions in the 530.3 nm line can be observed for a long period and they sometimes even last longer than the corresponding faculae.

C.2.4.3   637.4 nm

Emission in this red iron line is less clearly associated with sunspot activity than in the previously discussed lines. It occurs principally in regions of low to medium activity. The distribution of coronal activity in this line is given by Waldmeier (1971). Using one's own and other people's eclipse observations, it is possible to connect emissions with centers of activity, but, as the precise spatial position of the structures can be determined only by polarization measurements, by comparison with earth-bound coronagraph observations, or by x-ray data over a longer period of time before and after the eclipse, such observations also have to be used. (Data are published in Solar Geophysical Data, etc.).

In addition to photographing structures in individual lines, the amateur can also take photographs of the coronal spectrum. To record the weakest lines, exposure times range from several seconds to minutes. A list of the most important lines discovered is shown in the Table C.1.

Table C.1

Lines in the Coronal Spectrum

Wavelength (nm)	Identif.	X_i(eV)	A_{max}	I_{max}
332.8	Ca XII	592	0.7	1.0
338.8	Fe XIII	330	11.1	16.4
345.4			1.4	2.3
353.4	V X	206	(1.0)	
360.1	Ni XVI	455	1.1	2.1
364.3	Fe IX		(0.7)	2.0
380.1	Fe IX		(0.4)	(1.9)
398.7	Fe XI	261	0.2	0.7
408.7	Ca XIII	655	0.3	1.0
423.1	Ni XII		0.8	2.6
425.6	K XI	504	(0.1)	
435.1	Co XV	412	(0.1)	
441.2	Ar XIV	687	(0.3)	
456.6	Cr IX	185	0.3	1.1
511.6	Ni XIII	350	1.2	4.3
530.3	Fe XIV	355	27.5	100.0
544.5	Ca XV	814	(0.15)	0.3
553.9	Ar X	423	(0.4)	<2
569.4	Ca XV	814	(0.3)	1.5
637.4	Fe X	235	2.8	8.1
670.2	Ni XV	430	(1.2)	4.5
706.0	Fe XV	390	(0.8)	2.5
789.2	Fe XI	262	(6.0)	15
802.4	Ni XV	430	(0.3)	0.8
1074.7	Fe XIII	330	48	66
1079.8	Fe XIII	330	30	41

Abbreviations:

X_i = ionization energy in electron volts (eV)

I = intensity related to line 530.3nm (=100)

A = equivalent width of the line in nm

C.2.5   Phenomena in the Solar Corona[†]

During a total solar eclipse, a number of different structures can be picked out on good photographs. These phenomena have been classified by many authors, the most important of whom are Bugoslavskaya (1949); Vsessviatsky (1944); Newkirk (1967); Dunn (1971); De Mastus (1973); Billings (1966); Koutchmy (1977, 1988); Orrall (1973); Munro and Sime (1985); Burkepile and St. Cyr (1993)). In the available literature most phenomena are given several names, a situation which leads to confusion. Interesting works dealing with the time development of individual phenomena

[†]Written by Dietmar Staps

are provided by Newkirk (1967) and Bohlin (1970). Important data relating to coronal phenomena are set out in Table C.2 (Newkirk 1967), which represents a first step towards systematizing the individual phenomena. An extension of the table with satellite data and high-resolution earth-bound solar observations would be appropriate.

The amateur should take the above literature into account when evaluating photographs of eclipses and investigate the following:

1. the heliographic distribution (determine the East-West orientation by double exposure [Treutner 1978, see Section B.3.2])

2. the variations with the phase of the sunspot cycle

3. the relationship of the structures with phenomena in the photosphere and chromosphere

4. precise photometry

5. movements in the structures (see C.2.6)

A good example of classifying coronal phenomena was published by Teske et al. (1970). One of the best evaluations of coronal structures using ground-based high-resolution photographs with radial gradient filters and observations of the outer corona obtained from aircraft was published by Vsekhsvyatskii *et al.* 1981. For the first time coronal structures ranging from 1–14 solar radii are described along with their dynamical evaluation (see also C.2.6). Figure C.2.12 shows a picture by Strong and Mitchell (1973) and Table C.3 the corresponding evaluation of the coronal structures. One of the above classification schemes should be taken and points 1 through 5, or parts thereof, worked through. As extensive material has been published in journals and books since 1851, the amateur wishing to work on these or similar problems has a wide range of activities at his disposal without even needing to have observed a solar eclipse.

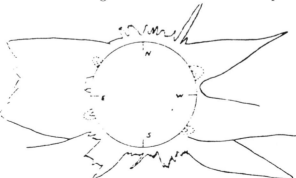

Fig. C.2.12. *Schematic representation of coronal phenomena, June 30, 1973 according to Strong and Mitchell (1973).*

Table C.2

Structure	Diam. (km)	Height (km)	D.inc.	Assoc. surface and emission line phenomena
Active region enhancement	200000	200000	<2	Young active region plage, 5303, 6374 intens. inc, age of region 2 weeks, lifespan 2-3 weeks
Active region streamer	300000	several radii	2–5	Faculae and sunspot regions, type E, often with flares, loop prominences, 5303, 6374 intens. inc. age of reg. 3 weeks, lifespan 2–3 weeks
"Permanent" Condensation	50000–130000	80000	5	Faculae and sunspot regions, type E, often with flares, loop prominences, 5303, 6374 intens. inc. age 3 weeks, lifespan several days
Sporadic Condensation	20000	20000–80000*	50–500	Faculae and sunspot regions, type E, often with flares, loop prominences, 5694 and continuum, age 3 weeks, lifespan mins-hours
Helmet streamer	300000	several radii	7–25	Prominence, extended magnetic fields, age 8 weeks, lifespan several months
Equatorial streamer	300000	several radii	–	Lifespan months-years
Polar plume	30000	several radii	4–8**	Bright polar faculae
Narrow ray	30000	several radii	?	?

Abbreviations:

D.inc. = typical density
enhancement

Diam. = diameter at one
solar radius

* – can appear as an isolated
cloud above the surface

** – is a lower limit

See also Fig. C.2.16

Table C.3
Evaluation of the Corona Structures in Fig. C.2.12

Pos. angle	Corona Structures
322–017	Northern polar plumes
020–127	Complex overlapping helmets and rays (oriented parallel to the solar equator)
050–059	Corona arches, height approx. 3.3 arc minutes (prominence at foot)
070–087	Condensation, centered at position angle 77 with prominence, length approx. 1.3 arc minutes at position angle 82
105–115	Corona arches, height approx. 2.6 arc minutes (prominence at foot)
127–138	Short curved featherlike rays
139–168	Series of faint rays (inclined 27°)
168–196	Faint southern polar plumes
176	Long faint ray, inclination 50° east of radial
190	Short ray, inclination 51° east of radial
196–223	Helmet streamer, inclination 30° north of radial
220–231	Corona arches, height 3,9 arc minutes
223–269	Helmet streamer, (asymmetrically diverging, oriented parallel to the equator)
269–280	Coronal hole
280–322	Helmet streamer (radially oriented)
281–301	Corona arches, height 3.6 arc minutes (prominences at foot)
328	Long ray (radially oriented)

C.2.6 Movements in the Corona[†]

To determine movement in the corona the following conditions have to be met.

1. Resolution should be better than 5 arc seconds

2. The time interval between observations should be as great as possible; the minimum should be around 30 minutes (observation at various points in the zone of totality!)

3. The photographs should be calibrated and taken with telescopes of the same type.

In the *Handbook of Astrophysics,* Mitchell (1929) notes are given on movement in the corona, according to which only small movements can be detected, and the greatest possible resolution is required. A summary of values obtained at various eclipses is contained in the following table by Bugoslavskaya (1950).

[†]Written by Dietmar Staps

Table C.4

Arches above prominences	2 km/s
Helmets	<4 km/s
Arch-shaped structures and sunspots	10 km/s
Small coronal clouds	15 km/s
Knots and clouds above sunspots	47 km/s
Displacements in thin streamers	45 km/s
Displacements in polar plumes	0.6 km/s
Extension of outer limits of streamers	1 km/s
Coronal mass ejections	100–960 km/s

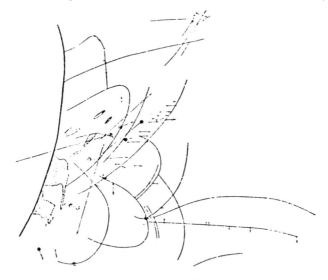

Fig. C.2.13. *Movements in the corona (Bugoslavskaya, Oct. 21, 1941).*

Figure C.2.13 shows a very effective summary of movements in the corona in 1941, obtained from Russian observations. In more recent times, movements in the corona have been measured during all major eclipses. As in the chromosphere, there are movements in the corona which partly exceed the sun's escape velocity of 619 km/s. If one is fortunate enough to observe these movements during a total solar eclipse, the above instrumental requirements can be substantially reduced. Even low resolution photographs can result in observations and measurements which can be evaluated. During the eclipse of 1896, such an event was photographed with ordinary cameras.

Approximately once every 40 hours there is a "coronal mass ejection" (CME). At sunspot maximum the frequency of ejections is around one every ten hours. At mimimum these are about 0.1–0.3 CME per day. The rate of coronal mass ejections is still quite uncertain. Some scientists question the

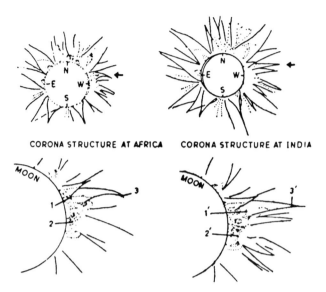

CORONA STRUCTURE AT AFRICA   CORONA STRUCTURE AT INDIA

Fig. C.2.14. *Coronal Mass Ejection Feb. 16, 1980 (Adachi, 1981).*

dependence of the rate of CME on the cycle. During the eclipses of 1973 and 1980, mass ejections were photographed (Fig. C.2.14). An evaluation of earlier eclipses has produced a similar result for the total eclipses of 1860, 1893, and 1896.

Determining coronal movement, principally during maximum sunspot activity, is quite possible with high resolution and large time intervals using two or more cameras. Today satellites can carry out much more detailed observations. The resolution is, however, still one order of magnitude less than with earth-bound photographs.

C.2.7   Relationships between the Corona and Prominences[†]

The close relationship between corona activity and activity centers and prominences can be seen in Fig. C.2.15, which comes from a publication by Lockyer (1931). The upper section shows the variations in sunspot area (see Section B.2.4); the middle section, the extension of the prominence zone (Section B.10.4); and the lower section, an index similar to the $(a+b)$ value of the corona. The causal relationship between prominences, sunspots and corona can be easily seen despite the poor time resolution. Difficulties

---

[†]Written by Dietmar Staps

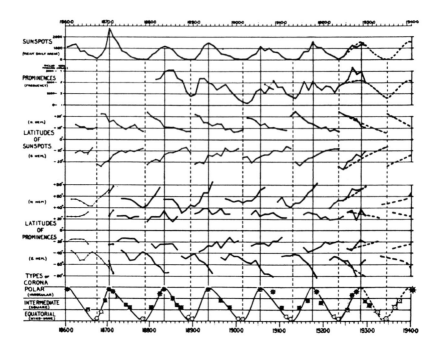

Fig. C.2.15. *Relationship of corona activity to prominences and sunspots.*

occur in better time resolution if chromospheric and photospheric activity
is linked to corona activity. The effects of projection mean that the exact
spatial position of corona structures can be obtained only by polarizing
photographs or by comparative earth-bound coronagraph measurements.
To correlate corona activity with disc activity, the amateur can obtain data
from Solnyechnye Dannye (in Russian) and from the Solar Geophysical Data
(see Section D). Bohlin (1970), who, in addition to solar eclipses and earth-
bound coronagraphs, also used balloon coronagraph measurements over a
period of almost three years, shows the spatial structure of the corona and
its relationship with activity centers (B.2.2). The result is that corona
structures often exhibit considerable extension in heliographic longitude.

The time development of a sunspot group taking into account corona
activity is impressively illustrated by Newkirk (1967) (Fig. C.2.16).

The evaluation of data collected from satellites has already increased
our knowledge in this area. Nevertheless, further evaluation of the material
already obtained over more than ten sunspot cycles at various phases and
with a resolution ten times better than satellite observation, should be
continued (see C.2.8, Newkirk 1967).

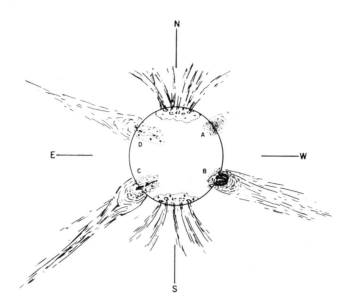

Fig. C.2.16. *Schematic representation of the evolution of a "typical" region in the corona from its early appearance as an enhancement (A) through the active region streamer stage (B) to the long decline as a helmet streamer (C and D). Both the helmet and the accompanying filament are believed to require the presence of extended regions of opposite magnetic polarity (schematically shown) (Newkirk 1967).*

Observations at the solar limb show that prominences have a substantial influence on the structure of the corona. Above the prominences there occur dark cavities (Maunder 1901, Saito and Tandberg-Hanssen 1973) which are accompanied by arch systems and a helmet streamer. If it is possible to take high resolution photographs, it is possible to look for changes in the prominence and corona structure. At the 1981 eclipse definite changes in prominences occurred in only seventy seconds (Stellmacher *et al.* 1986). Eclipses offer the best conditions to study the interaction of corona and prominences. The exposure times to record prominences are relatively short, and an amateur on a suitable site may record very interesting data. Telescopes outside the path of totality equipped with photographic or CCD cameras and Hα filters can deliver additional high-resolution material for comparison over a much longer time-span (Palzer 1992). Motions of arches above prominences have been measured, especially during the 1926 eclipse, but they need very high resolution and sites which are separated by more than one hour on the path of the eclipse (v. Klüber 1932).

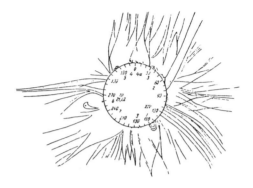

Fig. C.2.17. *Corona illustration July 29, 1927 (Bugoslavskaya 1949).*

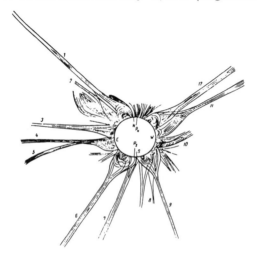

Fig. C.2.18. *Corona illustration June 19, 1936 (Bronshten 1959).*

C.2.8 Historic Eclipses of the Sun[†]

All the observation details in Sections C.2.1–C.2.7 can be considered within a historical context.   Since 1871, high quality photographs of the corona have been available, and a large amount of data has been dispersed among a number of astronomical publications.   A systematic study of this material and an investigation of particular points could be undertaken by the amateur.   Various professional studies have already provided some interesting facts.

[†]Written by Dietmar Staps

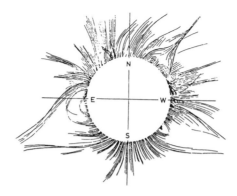

Fig. C.2.19. *Corona illustration Nov. 12, 1966 (Waldmeier 1967).*

Fig. C.2.20. *Corona illustration 8/9 August 1896 (Hansky and Kotinsky 1897).*

For instance, Eddy (1974) and others have succeeded in extracting several coronal mass ejections from earlier observations. From photographs of the 1922 eclipse, Eddy has discovered a "neutral sheet," a phenomenon predicted in theory, which separates different polarities in the corona. Bugoslavskaya (1949) evaluated the results of the Russian eclipse observations between 1887 and 1945 (e.g. Fig. C.2.16 and Fig. C.2.17). This standard work shows the multiplicity of corona shapes and investigates movements and relationships with centers of activity, etc.

   Further extensive collections of several eclipses can be found in Ranyard (1877), Hansky and Kotinsky (1897) (Fig. C.2.20), Dyson (1922), Mitchell and Waldmeier (Fig. C.2.19), Koutchmy (1986). A study of frequency, extent etc., of individual structures depending on the phase of the sunspot cycle could provide much interesting information.

C.2.9   Relativistic Light Bending[†]

In his general theory of relativity, Einstein predicted that light beams are bent by a gravitational field. During a total solar eclipse bright stars can be seen in the vicinity of the sun, the apparent positions of which are radially displaced outwards by the gravitational field of the sun (see Fig. C.2.21). Figure C.2.22 shows an exaggerated view of this effect. The true values of light bending which can be expected, according to Einstein, are given in Fig. C.2.23. If there are no bright stars in the vicinity of the sun, stars will be seen on the photograph only at a distance of 3 solar radii because of the corona.

In eclipses close to a minimum, it can be expected that in the polar areas the corona will not extend as far as during a maximum. Therefore a series of photographs can be taken at one pole to reduce coronal interference. To be able to measure a position change of this magnitude at all, the same star field has to be photographed at night several months after the eclipse. It is certain that during daytime photography, different temperature conditions will prevail from those in night photography. Therefore the length of the telescope and the scale will be different. A displacement in the position of stars will increase linearly outwards from the center of the plate. As can be seen, this effect is essentially the opposite of light bending, and it is difficult to separate them, at least in the area where both effects occur.

In addition to the possibility of changing the scale due to temperature measurements at the telescope, which should serve only as an additional control, several methods have been used to determine the scale of the picture:

a) copying on markings, e.g., grating in identical temperature conditions

b) photographing a comparison star field far from the sun

c) separation on the photograph with a very large field of view

Method a) is time-consuming, and there is no assurance that all the mechanical and thermal conditions during copying of the grating are still the same immediately after the eclipse as during the photograph. Also, each additional instrument makes the possibility of errors more likely.

[†]Written by Bernhard Wedel[†]

Fig. C.2.21. *According to the general theory of relativity, a beam of light is bent by the attraction of a large mass. The position of a star therefore appears displaced to the observer.*

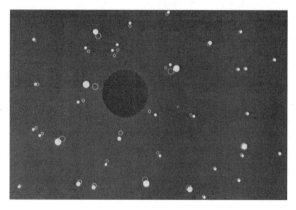

Fig. C.2.22. *In a star field in the vicinity of the sun, the stars appear to be displaced outwards. Displacement is greatest at the edge of the sun and decreases away from it.*

Method b) is also problematic in the experience of several observers, particularly if the comparison field is far from the sun. If only one instrument with a small field, but larger focal length, is available, it is possible to provide for a series of photographs from north to south which overlap slightly. The series should, if possible, also be reversed to obtain identical comparative photographs.

A change in the scale caused by temperature will uniformly affect all plates. Gravitational light bending is away from the sun, hyperbolically decreasing so that at least in the extreme plates the two effects can be

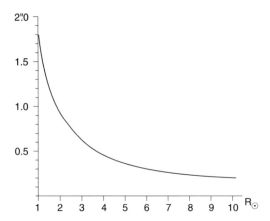

Fig. C.2.23. *The bending of light in arc seconds against the distance from the center of the sun, measured in solar radii (theoretical curve).*

easily separated. A change in the scale caused by temperature during the short period of totality is unlikely, but could possibly be derived from the reverse photographs or the overlaps. Of course, changes in refraction have to be taken into account. Changes in the mechanical conditions because of the movement of the telescope over a few degrees can be ignored.

The orientation of the plate plane is far less problematic in small plates than in large-format plates. The main problem is being able to record sufficient stars.

Hiei (1988) provides a table of observed values of light-deflection at the solar limb along with an extensive discussion.

Part D

A Survey of Solar Astronomy Literature

Chapter D.1

The Survey[†]

D.1.1 Books For Amateur Solar Observers

Astronomical League: *Observe and Understand the Sun,* Washington, D.C., 1991 (available from Astronomical League Sales, 10130 E. King Manor Drive, Tuscon, AZ 85730-4482 [US$9.20]).

Baxter, W.M.: *The Sun and the Amateur Astronomer,* Second rev. ed., David & Charles, Newton Abbot 1973.

Carson Astr. Inst.: *A Professional Guide to Photographing the Sun,* Valencia, 1973.

Littmann, M., Willcox, U.: *Totality—Eclipses of the Sun,* Honolulu, 1991.

Mazereau, P.: *A la Poursuite du Soleil—La Construction du Coronographe d'Amateur,* Paris, 1986.

Pasachoff, J.M., Covington, M.A.: *The Cambridge Eclipse Photography Guide,* Cambridge, 1993.

* Phillips, K.J.H.: *Guide to the Sun,* Cambridge, 1992.

Rao, J.: *Your Guide to the Great Solar Eclipse of 1991,* Cambridge, 1991.

Roth, G.D.: *Astronomy—A Handbook,* New York, 1975, Chapter 9.

Roth, G.D.: *Compendium of Practical Astronomy,* Berlin, 1994, vol. 2, Chapter 13.

Sweetsir, R.A.: *Observe Eclipses,* Washington, 1995 (Rev. (1995) edition in press, available from the Astronomical League).

Tatum, R.: *Monochromatic Handbook,* ALPO Solar Section, Tucson, 1987.

Taylor, P.O.: *Observing the Sun,* Cambridge Univ. Press, 1991.

Trombino, Donald F.: "New Tools for the Solar Observer," *1994 Yearbook of Astronomy,* Part II, Patrick Moore, Ed., Sidgwick & Jackson, Ltd. London, 1994.

[†]Compiled by D. Staps and R. Beck

VdS Solar Section: *Einführung in die Sonnenbeobachtung*, Berlin, 1991 (available from the Vereinigung der Sternfreunde).

Veio, F.N.: *The Sun in H-α Light with a Spectrohelioscope*, Clearlake Park, 1972, 1978, 1991.

Wattenberg, D.: *Die Sonne im Fernrohr*, Berlin, 1954.

D.1.2   Books For the Layman Published Before 1950

Abbott, G.: *The Sun*, New York, 1911, 1929.

Ball, R.S.: *The Story of the Sun*, London, 1906.

Borchardt, B.: *Die Sonne*, Berlin, 1926.

Bosler, B.: *Les Théories Modernes du Soleil*, Paris, 1910.

Carl, P.: *Die Sonne*, Munich, 1864, 1868.

Couderc, P.: *Dans le Champ Solaire*, Paris, 1932.

Deslandres, H.: *Histoire des Idées et des Recherches sur le Soleil*, Paris, 1906.

Gamov, G.: *The Birth and Death of the Sun*, London, 1941.

Gamov, G.: *Geburt und Tod der Sonne*, Basel, 1947.

Guillemin, A.: *Le Soleil*, Paris, 1869.

Henseling, R.: *Sonne und Sternall*, Stuttgart, 1929.

Krause, H.: *Die Sonne*, Leipzig, 1911.

Lalon, E.: *Le Soleil*, Paris, 1858.

Lockyer, N.: *The Sun's Place in Nature*, London, 1897.

Lockyer, N.: *Recent of Coming Eclipses*, London, 1900.

Maunder, E.W.: *The Indian Eclipse*, London, 1899.

Meibauer, R.: *Über die physische Beschaffenheit der Sonne*, Berlin, 1866.

Menzel, D.: *Our Sun*, The Blakiston Company, Philadelphia, 1949.

Meyer, M.W.: *Die Königin des Tages und ihr Reich*, Stuttgart, 1900.

Meyer, M.W.: *Ägyptische Finsternis*, Stuttgart, 1906.

Miczaika, G.: *Die Erforschung der Sonne*, Stuttgart, 1947.

Nicolet, M.: *Le Soleil*, Uccle, 1943.

Pringsheim, G.: *Physik der Sonne*, Leipzig, 1910.

Proctor, R.: *The Sun*, London, 1871.

Rayet: *La Constitution Physique du Soleil*, Paris, 1870.

Reis, P.: *Die Sonne*, Leipzig, 1869.

Scheiner, J.: *Strahlung und Temperatur der Sonne*, Leipzig, 1889.

Secchi, P.A.: *Le Soleil*, Paris, 1870.

Secchi, P.A.: *Die Sonne*, Braunschweig, 1872.

Secchi, P.A.: *Le Soleil*, I and II, Paris, 1875, 1877.

Spörer, G.: *Die Stürme auf der Sonne*, Anclam, 1863.

Stetson, H.T.: *Sunspots in Action*, New York, 1947.

Waldmeier, M.: *Ergebnisse und Probleme der Sonnenforschung*, Leipzig, 1941, 1955.

Woeckel, L.: *Die Sonne und ihre Flecken*, Nürnberg, 1846.

Wussow, R.: *Sonnenflecken und kosmisches Geschehen*, Berlin, 1923.

Young, C.A.: *Le Soleil*, Paris, 1883.

Young, C.A.: *Die Sonne*, Leipzig, 1883.

Young, C.A.: *The Sun*, London, 1895; New York, 1896.

D.1.3   Books For the Layman Published After 1950

(* = available as of 1995)

Abetti, G.: *The Sun*, London, 1962; New York, 1957.

Abetti, G.: *Solar Research*, New York, 1963.

Allen, D. & C.: *Eclipse*, 1987.

Beatty, J.K.: *The New Solar System*, Cambridge/Mass., 1981.

Beatty, J.K.: *Die Sonne und ihre Planeten*, Weinheim, 1983.

* Bellon, G.: *Die Sonne*, Time-Life, Amsterdam, 1990.

* Bertaux, J.L.: *De l'autre Côté du Soleil*, Paris, 1987.

Boischot, A.: *Le Soleil et la Terre*, Paris, 1966.

Brandt, J.C.: *The Sun and Stars*, New York, 1966.

* Brewer, B.: *Eclipse*, Seattle, 1978, 1991.

* Bruzek, A., Durrant, C.J.: *Illustrated Glossary for Solar and Solar-Terrestrial Physics*, Dordrecht, 1977.

Couderc, P.: *Les Eclipses*, Paris, 1971.

Doebel, G.: *Die Sonne*, Stuttgart, 1975.

Duttweiler, G.: *Die Sonne*, Munich, 1962.

* Eddy, J.A.: *A New Sun*, NASA, Washington, 1979.

* Ekrutt, J.W.: *Die Sonne*, Hamburg, 1981.

* Fallow, A.: *The Sun*, Time-Life, Kingsport, 1990.

Foitzik, L.: *Sonnenstrahlung und Lufttrübung*, Leipzig, 1958.

Frazier, K.: *Our Turbulent Sun*, Hemel Hempstead, 1982.

* Frazier, K.: *The Solar System*, Time-Life, Alexandria, 1984.

* Frazier, K.: *Das Sonnensystem*, Time-Life, Amsterdam, 1985.

* Friedman, H.: *Sun and Earth*, New York, 1986.

* Friedman, H.: *Die Sonne*, Heidelberg, 1987.

* Gagnaire, P.: *Cadrans Solaires en Savoie*, Chambery, 1986.

Gamov, G.: *A Star Called the Sun*, Middlesex, 1964.

Gamov, G.: *Sonne—Stern unter Sternen*, Munich, 1967.

Giovanelli, R.G.: *Secrets of the Sun*, Cambridge, 1984.

Giovanelli, R.G.: *Geheimnisvolle Sonne*, Weinheim, 1987.

Gleissberg, W.: *Die Häufigkeit der Sonnenflecken*, Berlin, 1952.

Graff-Lambrecht, *Grundriß der Astrophysik Bd. II: Das Sonnensystem,* Leipzig, 1962.

Gribbin, J.: *The Strangest Star,* Glasgow, 1980.

* Hallwag Map "Die Sonne," Bern, 1981.

Herdeg, W.: *Die Sonne in der Kunst,* Zürich, 1964.

Herder Volume: *Die Sonne—Licht und Leben,* Freiburg, 1975.

Huber, T.: *Die Entstehung unseres Sonnensystems,* Schaffhausen, 1950.

Hufbauer, U.: *Exploring the Sun,* Baltimore, 1991.

Kaiser, P.: *Die Sonne,* Wien, 1981.

Kiepenheuer, K.O.: *Die Sonne,* Berlin, 1957.

Kiepenheuer, K.O.: *The Sun,* Ann Arbor, 1959.

* Kippenhahn, R.: *Der Stern von dem wir leben,* Stuttgart, 1990.

Koltun, M.: *Sonne und Menschheit,* Moscow/Leipzig, 1985.

Malin, M.F.: *The Mystery of the Sun,* Salt Lake City, 1965.

Meadows, A.J.: *Early Solar Physics,* Oxford, 1966.

Menzel, D.H.: *Our Sun,* Cambridge, 1949, 1959.

Michard, R.: *Le Soleil,* Paris, 1966.

Mielke, H.: *Sonnengott und Sternenfeuer,* Berlin, 1975.

Mitton, S.: *Daytime Star,* London, 1981.

Moore, P.: *Sun,* New York, 1968.

Müller, R.: *Sonnenforschung,* Munich, 1958.

Müller, R.: *Sonnen-ABC,* Murnau, 1958.

Newton, H.W.: *The Face of the Sun,* London, 1958.

Nicolson, I.: *The Sun,* London, 1982.

Nicolson, I.: *Die Sonne,* Freiburg, 1982.

* Noyes, R.W.: *The Sun—Our Star,* Cambridge/Mass., 1982.

* Phillips, E.: *The Sun,* Kingsport, 1990.

Porsche, H.: *HELIOS, Bundesministerium für Forschung und Technologie,* Oberpfaffenhofen, 1984.

Ratcliff, J.A.: *Sonne, Erde, Radio,* Munich, 1970.

Rigutti, M.: *Il Sole et la Terre,* Bari, 1960.

Rousseau, P.: *Notre Soleil,* Paris, 1953.

Sigel, F.: *Schuld ist die Sonne,* Thun, 1975.

Singh, M.: *The Sun in Myth and Art,* London, 1993.

Smith, A.G.: *Radio Exploration of the Sun,* Princeton, 1967.

Smithonian Institute: *Fire of Lives,* New York, 1981.

* Smoluchowski, R.: *Das Sonnensystem,* Heidelberg, 1985.

Tandberg-Hanssen, E.: *Solar Activity,* Waltham, 1967.

Vollmer, D.: *Sonnenspiegel,* Rotenburg, 1983.

Waldmeier, M.: *Sonne und Erde,* Zürich, 1959.

Washburn, M.: *In the Light of the Sun,* New York, 1981.

Wawilow, S.I.: *Das Auge und die Sonne,* Berlin, 1953.

* Wentzel, D.G.: *The Restless Sun*, Smithsonian Inst., New York, 1989.
* *Die Sonne in Dichtung und Farbaufnahmen* (Buchers Miniaturen vol. 13), Luzern, 1980.

D.1.4 Monographs for professional astronomers

(* = of special interest for amateurs)

Aarons, J.: *Solar System Radio Astronomy*, New York, 1966.
Adams, W.S.: *Rotation Period of the Sun*, Washington, 1911.
Akasofu, S.I.: *Solar-Terrestrial Physics*, Oxford, 1972.
Akasofu, S.I.: *The Solar Wind and the Earth*, Dordrecht, 1987.
Aller, L.H.: *The Atmosphere of the Sun and Stars*, New York, 1963.
Altrock, R.C.: *Solar and Stellar Coronal Structure and Dynamics*, Sunspot, 1988.
Angström, A.J.: *Recherches sur le Spectre Solaire*, Uppsala, 1868.
Arizona-NASA Atlas of the Infrared Solar Spectrum, Denver, 1980.
Athay, G.: *Radiation Transport in Spectral Lines*, Dordrecht, 1973.
Athay, G.: *Chromospheric Fine Structure*, Dordrecht, 1974.
Athay, G.: *The Solar Chromosphere and Corona*, Dordrecht, 1976.
* Balasubramaniam, K.S., Simon, G.W.: *Solar Active Region Evolution*, San Francisco, 1994.
Ballester, J.L., Priest, E.R.: *Dynamics and Structure of Solar Prominences*, Mallorca, 1988
Bandeen, W.R.: *Possible Relationships between Solar Activity and Meteorological Phenomena*, NASA, Washington, 1975.
Barbera, G.: *Proceedings of the Meeting on Solar Magnetic Fields and High Resolution Spectroscopy*, Florence, 1966.
Baumann, W.: *Das ultrarote Sonnenspektrum*, Leipzig, 1934.
Benz, A.O.: *Radio Continua During Solar Flares*, Dordrecht, 1986.
Berg, H.: *Solar-Terrestrische Beziehungen in Meteorologie und Biologie*, Leipzig, 1957.
Berthomieu, G.: *Inside the Sun*, Dordrecht, 1990.
Beynon, W.J.: *Solar Eclipses and the Ionosphere*, London, 1956.
* Billings, D.E.: *A Guide to the Solar Corona*, New York, 1966.
Birkeland, K.: *Les Taches du Soleil*, Kristiania, 1900.
Bonnet, R.M.: *The Energy Balance and Hydrodynamics of the Solar Chromosphere and Corona*, Clermond-Ferrand, 1977.
Brandt, J.C.: *Solar System Astrophysics*, New York, 1964.
Brandt, J.C.: *Introduction to the Solar Wind*, San Francisco, 1970.
* Bray, R.J.: *The Solar Chromosphere*, London, 1974.
* Bray, R.J.: *Sunspots*, London 1964, New York 1979.

* Bray, R.J.: *The Solar Granulation,* Cambridge, 1984.

Bray, R.J.: *Plasma Loops in the Solar Corona,* Cambridge, 1991.

Brester, A.: *Le Soleil,* La Hague, 1924.

Brizele, K.: *Sonnenaktivität und Biorhythmus des Menschen,* Wien, 1966.

Brückner, G.: *Photometrischer Atlas des nahen UV-Sonnenspektrums 2988Å—3629Å,* Göttingen, 1960.

Bruhar, G.: *Le Soleil,* Paris, 1951.

Bugoslavskaya, N.Y.: *Solar Activity and the Ionosphere,* Oxford, 1962.

Bumba, V.: *Basic Mechanisms of Solar Activity,* Dordrecht, 1976.

Carovillano, R.L.: *Solar-Terrestrial Physics,* Dordrecht, 1983.

* Cram, L.E.: *The Physics of Sunspots,* Sunspot, 1981.

Chambers, G.F.: *The Story of Eclipses,* New York, 1904.

Chapman, S.: *Solar Plasma, Geomagnetism and Aurora,* New York, 1964.

Christensen-Dalsgaard, J.: *Advances in Helio- and Astroseismology,* Dordrecht, 1988.

Coulson, K.L.: *Solar and Terrestrial Radiation,* New York, 1975.

Coutrez, R.: *Radioemission d'Origine Solaire,* Brussels, 1961.

Cox, A.N., Livingston, W.C., Matthews, M.S.: *Solar Interior and Atmosphere,* Tucson, 1991.

Delbouille, L.: *Photometric Atlas of the Solar Spectrum from 3000Å to 10000Å,* Liége, 1973.

Delbouille, L.: *Photometric Atlas of the Solar Spectrum from 1850 to 10000 cm^{-1},* Tucson, 1981.

Dennis, B.R.: *Rapid Fluctuations in Solar Flares,* NASA CP-2449, Washington, 1987.

Domingo, V.: *Physics of Solar Variations,* Dordrecht, 1981.

Dryer, M.: *Solar and Interplanetary Dynamics,* Dordrecht, 1980.

Dumont, S.: *Pleins Feux sur la Physique Solaire,* Paris, 1978.

Duner: *Sur la Rotation du Soleil,* Upsala, 1891.

Dunn, R.B.: *Solar Instrumentation: What's Next?,* Sunspot, 1981.

Durney, B.R.: *The Internal Solar Angular Velocity,* Dordrecht, 1987.

Durrant, C.: *The Atmosphere of the Sun,* Bristol, 1988.

Dyer, F.R.: *Solar-Terrestrial Physics,* Dordrecht, 1972.

Dyson, F.: *Eclipses of the Sun and Moon,* Oxford, 1937.

Eddy, J.A.: *The New Solar Physics,* Boulder, 1978.

Elgaroy, E.O.: *Solar Noise Storms,* Oxford, 1977.

Ellison, M.A.: *The Sun and its Influence,* Boston, 1955.

* Espenak: *Fifty Year Canon of Solar Eclipses,* NASA, Washington, 1987.

European Space Agency: *The Hydromagnetics of the Sun,* Paris, 1984.

Evans, J.: *The Solar Corona,* New York, 1963.

Fomichev, V.V.: *Physics of Solar Flares,* Moskow, 1985 (in Russian).

* Foukal, P.: *Solar Astrophysics,* New York, 1990.

Fricke, W.: *Sun and Planetary System,* Dordrecht, 1982.
Gassmann, G.J.: *The Effect of Disturbance of Solar Origin on Communications,* Oxford, 1963.
Gebbie, K.B.: *The Menzel Symposium on Solar Physics, Atomic Spectra and Gaseous Nebulae,* Washington, 1971.
Giampapa, M.S., Bookbinder, J.A.: *Cool Stars, Stellar Systems, and the Sun,* San Francisco, 1992.
Gibson, E.G.: *The Quiet Sun,* Washington, 1973.
Gough, D.O.: *Seismology of the Sun and the Distant Stars,* Dordrecht, 1986.
Haisch, B.M.: *Solar and Stellar Flares,* Dordrecht, 1989.
Hall, D.B.: *An Atlas of Infrared Spectra of the Solar Photosphere and of Sunspot Umbrae,* Tucson, 1970.
* Harvey, K.: *The Solar Cycle,* San Francisco, 1992.
Hargreaves, J.K.: *The Solar-Terrestrial Environment,* Cambridge, 1992.
* Herman, J.R.: *Sun, Weather and Climate,* Washington, 1978.
Hess, W.N.: *Physics of Solar Flares,* NASA, Washington, 1964.
Houtgast, J.: *Relations entre les Phénomènes Solaires et Géophysiques,* Lyon, 1949.
Howard, R.: *Atlas of the Solar Magnetic Fields 1959–1966,* Washington, 1967.
Howard, R.: *Solar Magnetic Fields,* Dordrecht, 1971.
Hoyle, F.: *Some Recent Researches in Solar Physics,* Cambridge, 1949.
Huber, M.C.: *Solar Physics from Space,* Dordrecht, 1981.
Hundhausen, A.J.: *Coronal Expansion and Solar Wind,* Berlin, 1972.
Ivanov-Rholodnij, G.S.: *The Sun and the Photosphere,* Jerusalem, 1972.
de Jager, C.: *The Solar Spectrum,* Dordrecht, 1965.
de Jager, C.: *The Structure of the Quiet Photosphere and the Low Chromosphere,* Dordrecht, 1968.
de Jager, C.: *Solar Flares and Space Research,* Amsterdam, 1969.
de Jager, C.: *Solar-Terrestrial Physics,* Dordrecht, 1972.
de Jager, C.: *The Physics of Solar Flares,* Dordrecht, 1986.
* de Jager, C.: *Progress in Solar Physics,* Dordrecht, 1986.
Jensen, E.: *Physics of Solar Prominences,* Oslo, 1979.
Johnson, S.J.: *Historical and Future Solar Eclipses,* London, 1896.
Jordan, S.D.: *The Temperature Distribution in the Solar Chromosphere,* NASA, Washington, 1969.
Julius, W.H.: *Zonenphysica,* Groningen, 1928 (in Dutch).
Kane, S.R.: *Solar Gamma-, X- and EUV-Radiation,* Dordrecht, 1975.
Kiepenheuer, K.O.: *The Fine Structure of the Solar Atmosphere,* Wiesbaden, 1966.

Kiepenheuer, K.O.: *Structure and Development of Solar Active Regions*, Dordrecht, 1968.

King, J.W., Newman, W.S.: *Solar-Terrestrial Physics*, London, 1967.

Kirchhoff, G.R.: *Untersuchungen über das Sonnenspektrum*, Berlin, 1866; Osnabrück, 1972.

* von Klüber, H.: *Über Voraussagen zum Sonnenfleckenmaximum*, Berlin, 1947.

Kocharov, G.E.: *Nuclear Astrophysics of the Sun*, Munich, 1980.

Kohl, J.L.: *Center and Limb Solar Spectrum in High Spectral Resolution 225.2 nm to 319.6 nm*, Cambridge, 1978.

Krüger, A.: *Physics of Solar Continuum Radio Bursts*, Berlin, 1972.

Krüger, A.: *Introduction to Solar Radio Astronomy and Radio Physics*, Dordrecht, 1979.

* Kuiper, P.: *The Solar System* vol. I: *The Sun*, Chicago, 1953.

Kundu, M.R.: *Solar Radio Astronomy*, New York, 1965.

Kundu, M.R.: *Radio Physics of the Sun*, Dordrecht, 1980.

Kundu, M.R.: *Energetic Phenomena on the Sun*, NASA CP-2439, Washington, 1986.

Kundu, M.R.: *Solar-Terrestrial Physics*, New Delhi, 1986.

Kundu, M.R.: *Energetic Phenomena on the Sun*, Dordrecht, 1989.

Linsky, J.F., Serio, S.: *Physics of Solar and Stellar Coronae*, Dordrecht, 1993.

Lockyer, N.: *Chemistry of the Sun*, London, 1887.

Lüst, R.: *Stellar and Solar Magnetic Fields*, New York, 1965.

Mackin, R.J.: *The Solar Wind*, Oxford, 1966.

Macris, C.J.: *Physics of the Solar Corona*, Dordrecht, 1971.

Mahler, F.: *Die centralen Sonnenfinsternisse des XX. Jahrhunderts*, Wien, 1885.

Manno, V.: *Intercorrelated Satellite Observations Related to Solar Events*, Dordrecht, 1970.

Marsden, R.G.: *The Sun and the Heliosphere in Three Dimensions*, Dordrecht, 1986.

Mariska, J.T.: *The Solar Transition Region*, Cambridge, 1993.

McAllister, H.C.: *A Preliminary Atlas of the Solar UV Spectrum*, Boulder, 1960.

McCormac, B.M.: *Solar-Terrestrial Influences on Weather and Climate*, Dordrecht, 1979.

McDonald, F.B.: *Solar Proton Manual*, Washington, 1963.

* McIntosh, P.S.: *Solar Activity Oberservations and Predictions*, Boulder, 1972.

* McLean, D.J.: *Solar Radiophysics*, Cambridge, 1985.

* Meeus, J.: *Canon of Solar Eclipses*, Oxford, 1966.

* Meinel, A.: *Sunsets, Twilights, and Evening Skies,* Cambridge, 1983.

Minnaert, M.G.: *De Natuurkunde van de Zon,* The Hague, 1936 (in Dutch).

* Minnaert, M.G.: *Photometric Atlas of the Solar Spectrum from 3612Å to 8771Å,* Amsterdam, 1940.

* Mitchell, S.A.: *Eclipses of the Sun,* Columbia, 1923, 1924, 1932, 1935, 1951.

Mitra, A.P.: *Ionospheric Effects of Solar Flares,* Dordrecht, 1974.

Mohler, O.C.: *Photometric Atlas of the Near Infrared Solar Spectrum,* Ann Arbor, 1950.

Mohler, O.C.: *A Table of Solar Spectrum Wavelengths 11984Å to 25578Å,* Ann Arbor, 1955.

Moore, C.E.: *Atomic Lines in the Sunspot Spectrum,* Princeton, 1933.

* Moore, CE., Minnaert, M.G.J., Houtgast, J.: *The Solar Spectrum 2935Å to 8770Å,* Washington, 1966.

* Muller, R.: *High Resolution in Solar Physics,* Berlin, 1985.

Nakagawa, Y.: *Flare Related Magnetic Field Dynamics,* Boulder, 1974.

* NASA: *Skylab Experiments,* vol. 1: *Solar Astronomy,* Washington, 1973.

* NASA: *Skylab and the Sun,* Washington, 1973.

Neidig, D.F.: *The Lower Atmosphere of Solar Flares,* Sunspot, 1986.

Ness, N.F.: *Solar-Terrestrial Physics,* Dordrecht, 1979.

Newkirk, G.: *Coronal Disturbances,* Dordrecht, 1974.

November, L.: *Solar Polarimetry,* Sunspot, 1991.

Nuppen, W.: *Bibliography on Solar-Weather Relationships,* Washington, 1958.

* O'Connell, D.J.: *The Green Flash,* Vatican, 1958.

Öhman, Y.: *Mass Motions in Solar Flares and Related Phenomena,* Stockholm, 1968.

* von Oppolzer, T.R.: *Canon of Eclipses,* New York, 1962.

Orrall, F.Q.: *Solar Active Regions,* Boulder, 1981.

Ortner, J.: *Introduction to Solar Terrestrial Relations,* Dordrecht, 1965.

Osaki, Y.: *Hydrodynamic and Magnetohydrodynamic Problems in the Sun and Stars,* Tokyo, 1986.

Parker, E.N.: *Interplanetary Dynamical Processes,* New York, 1963.

Pap, J.M., et al.: *The Sun as a Variable Star,* Dordrecht, 1994.

* Pepin, R.O., Eddy, J.A., Merrill, R.B.: *The Ancient Sun,* Elmsford, 1980.

Poland, A.I.: *Coronal and Prominence Plasmas,* NASA CP-2242, Washington, 1986.

* Praderie, F.: *Activity and Outer Atmosphere of the Sun and the Stars,* Saas-Fee, 1981.

Priest, E.R.: *Solar Flare Magnetohydrodynamics,* Oxford, 1980.

Priest, E.R.: *Solar Magnetohydrodynamics,* Dordrecht, 1984.

Priest, E.R.: *Solar System Magnetic Fields,* Dordrecht, 1985.

* Priest, E.R.: *Dynamics and Structure of Quiescent Solar Prominences,* Dordrecht, 1989.

Priest, E.R.: *Basic Plasma Processes on the Sun,* Dordrecht, 1990.

Priest, E.R.: *Advances in Solar System Magnetohydrodynamics,* Cambridge, 1991.

Proctor, M.R.E., et al.: *Solar and Planetary Dynamos,* Cambridge, 1994.

Rabin, D.M., Jefferies, J.T., Lindsey, C.: *Infrared Solar Physics,* Dordrecht, 1994.

Ramaty, R.: *High Energy Phenomena on the Sun,* Washington, 1973.

Robinson, N.: *Solar Radiation,* Amsterdam, 1966.

Rolfe, E.: *Future Missions in Solar, Heliospheric and Space Plasma Physics,* ESA, Noordwijk, 1985.

Rowland, H.A.: *Photographic Map of the Normal Solar Spectrum,* Baltimore, 1887, 1888.

Rozelot, J.P.: *La Couronne Solaire,* Paris, 1973.

Rubashev, B.M.: *Problems of Solar Activity,* Washington, 1964.

Ruediger, G.: *Differential Rotation and Stellar Convection,* New York, 1989.

Rutten, R.J.: *Solar and Stellar Granulation,* Dordrecht, 1989.

Rutten, R.J., Schrijver, C.J.: *Solar Surface Magnetism,* Dordrecht, 1994.

Ruzdjak, V.: *Dynamics of Quiescent Prominences,* Berlin, 1990.

Sacramento Peak Obs.: *Spectrographic Atlas of the Solar Corona,* Sunspot, 1962.

Sakuda, M.: *Workshop on Solar Neutrino Detection,* Tokyo, 1986.

Sakurai, K.: *Physics of Solar Cosmic Rays,* Tokyo, 1974.

Sánchez, F., Collados, M., Vázquez, M.: *Solar Observations: Techniques and Interpretation,* Cambridge, 1992.

Sawyer, C.: *Solar Flare Prediction,* Boulder, 1986.

* Scheffler, H., Elsässer, H.: *Physik der Sterne und der Sonne,* Mannheim, 1974, 1990.

Schellen, H.: *Spectrum Analysis,* London, 1872.

Schmidt, A.: *Die Strahlenbrechung auf der Sonne,* Stuttgart, 1891.

Schmidt, H.U.: *Theoretical Problems in High Resolution Solar Physics,* Munich, 1985.

Schröter, E.H.: *Small Scale Motions on the Sun,* Freiburg, 1979.

Schroeter, J.F.: *Spezieller Kanon der zentralen Sonnen- und Mondfinsternisse,* Kristiania, 1923.

Schüssler, M., Schmidt, W.: *Solar Magnetic Fields,* Cambridge, 1994.

Schwahn, P.: *Mathematische Theorie der astronomischen Finsternisse,* Leipzig, 1910.

Schwenn, R., Marsch, E.: *Physics of the Inner Heliosphere,* vols. 1 and 2, Berlin, 1990, 1991.

Shevnin, A.D.: *Solar Wind and Circumterrestrial Processes,* Moskow, 1986 (in Russian).
Shklovskij, I.S.: *Physics of the Solar Corona,* Oxford, 1965.
* Simon, P.A.: *Solar-Terrestrial Predictions,* Boulder, 1986.
Sivkov, S.I.: *Computation of Solar Radiation Characteristics,* Jerusalem, 1971.
* Slutz, R.J.: *Solar Activity Prediction,* NASA, Washington, 1971.
Smith, H.J.: *Solar Flares,* New York, 1963.
Sonnet, C.P.: *Solar Wind,* Washington, 1972.
Sonnet, C.P., Giampapa, M.S., Matthews, M.S.: *The Sun in Time,* Tucson, 1991.
Spectrographic Atlas of the Solar Corona, Sacramento Peak, Sunspot, 1963.
Spörer, G.: *Beobachtungen von Sonnenflecken,* Anclam, 1862–63
Stenflo, J.O.: *Solar and Stellar Magnetic Fields,* Dordrecht, 1983.
Stenflo, J.O.: *Solar Photosphere: Structure, Convection, and Magnetic Fields,* Dordrecht, 1990.
Stenflo, J.O.: *Solar Magnetic Fields,* Dordrecht, 1994.
Stepanov, V.E.: *Solar Maximum Analysis,* Utrecht, 1987.
Stickland, A.: *Annals of the IQSY,* vols. 1–7, Cambridge, 1970.
* Stix, M.: *The Sun—An Introduction,* Berlin, 1989.
St. John, C.E.: *Revision of Rowland's Table of Solar Spectrum Wavelengths,* Washington, 1928.
Sturrock, P.A.: *Solar Flares,* Denver, 1980.
* Sturrock, P.A.: *Physics of the Sun* (3 volumes), Dordrecht, 1985.
Švestka, Z.: *Catalogue of Solar Particle Events 1955–1969,* Dordrecht, 1975.
Švestka, Z.: *Solar Flares,* Dordrecht, 1976.
Swensson, J.W.: *The Solar Spectrum 7498Å to 12016Å,* Liège, 1970.
* Tandberg-Hanssen, E.: *Solar Prominences,* Dordrecht, 1974.
* Tandberg-Hanssen, E.: *The Physics of Solar Flares,* Cambridge, 1988.
Tandon, J.N.: *Solar Radiations and the Earth,* Delhi, 1973.
Thomas, R.N.: *Physics of the Solar Chromosphere,* New York, 1961.
Todd, D.P.: *Total Eclipses of the Sun,* Boston, 1894.
Uchida, Y.: *Flare Physics in Solar Activity Maximum,* Berlin, 1991.
Ulmschneider, P.H.: *The Chromosphere-Corona Transition Region,* Boulder, 1969.
Ulrich, R.K., et al.: *Gong '94: Helio- and Astro-Seismology from the Earth and Space,* San Francisco, 1995.
Unsöld, A.: *Physik der Sternatmosphären,* Berlin, 1938, 1955.
Utrecht Obs.: *Photometric Atlas of the Solar Spectrum,* Amsterdam, 1940.
Utrecht Obs.: *Preliminary Photometric Catalogue of Fraunhofer Lines,* Utrecht, 1960.

Venkatesan, D.: *Solar Terrestrial Relations*, Calgary, 1973.

Very, F.C.: *The Solar Constant*, Washington, 1901.

* Vitinskij, Y.I.: *Solar Activity Forecasting*, Jerusalem, 1965.

* Waldmeier, M.: *Tabellen zur heliographischen Ortsbestimmung*, Basel, 1950.

* Waldmeier, M.: *Die Sonnenkorona* I und II, Basel, 1951, 1957.

* Waldmeier, M.: *The Sunspot Activity in the Years 1610–1960*, Zürich, 1961.

Walén, C.: *On the Vibratory Rotation of the Sun*, Stockholm, 1949.

Warwick, C.S.: *Physical Processes in the Sun-Earth Environment*, Ottawa, 1959.

* Wilson, P.R.: *Solar and Stellar Activity Cycles*, Cambridge, 1994.

* Wilson, R.M.: *A Comparative Look at Sunspot Cycles*, NASA, Washington, 1984.

White, O.R.: *The Solar Output and its Variation*, Boulder, 1977.

Woolley, R., Stibbs, D.W.N.: *The Outer Layers of a Star*, London, 1953.

* Xanthakis, J.N.: *Solar Physics*, London, 1967.

Xanthakis, J.N.: *Solar Activity and Related Interplanetary and Terrestrial Phenomena*, Berlin, 1973.

Zenger, K.W.: *Die Meteorologie der Sonne*, Wien, 1886.

Zheleznyakov, V.: *Radio Emission of the Sun and Planets*, Oxford, 1970.

* Zirin, H.: *The Solar Atmosphere*, Waltham, 1966.

* Zirin, H.: *Astrophysics of the Sun*, Cambridge, 1988.

Zirin, H., et al.: *The Magnetic and Velocity Fields of Solar Active Regions*, San Francisco, 1993.

Zirker, J.B.: *Coronal Holes and High Speed Wind Streams*, Boulder, 1977.

* Zirker, J.B.: *Total Eclipses of the Sun*, New York, 1995.

Zwaan, C.: *The MHD of Sunspots*, Dordrecht, 1981.

D.1.5 Journals About the Sun

In German:
SONNE—Mitteilungsblatt der Amateursonnenbeobachter,
Contact address: Peter Völker, c/o Wilhelm-Foerster-Sternwarte, Munsterdamm 90, D-12169 Berlin, Germany.

In English:
Solar Physics (Editors: C. de Jager, Z. Švestka and R.F. Howard), Kluwer Academic Publ., Dordrecht, Netherlands.

Solar-Geophysical Data (Editors: National Geophysical and Solar-Terrestrial Data Center), National Oceanic and Atmospheric Administration (NOAA) (includes data of all activity indices, syntoptic charts, daily charts of the emission in white light, Hα, calcium, radio continuum, prominences, corona, magnetograms, sunspot positions and geomagnetic phenomena).

In Russian:

Solnechnye Danye (solar data), St. Petersburg.

Bibliography[†]

The following bibliography is arranged by chapter.

A. Instrumentation

A.1. Choosing a Telescope

Hückel, P.: "Mein Spiegelteleskop für die Sonne," *SONNE* **2,** 105 (1978) no. 7.

Lille, W.: "Sonnenfotos im ultravioletten Licht," *SONNE* **3,** 106 (1979) no. 11.

Mackintosh, Allan: *Advanced Telescope Making Techniques, vol. I Optics,* Willmann-Bell, Inc., Richmond, Virginia, 1986.

Reffke, U.: "Sonnenfotografie im UV-Licht," *SONNE* **5,** 98 (1981) no. 19.

Roth, G.D.: *Astronomy—A Handbook,* New York, 1975, p. 7.

Roth, G.D.: *Compendium of Practical Astronomy,* Berlin, 1994, vol. 1, p. 59.

A.2. Telescope Accessories

A.2.1. Solar Projection Screen

Bendel, U.: "Abbildungsfehler bei der Sonnenprojektion," *SONNE* **2,** 56 (1978) no. 6.

Heidenreich, H.H.: "Bau eines Sonnenprojektionsschirms," *Sterne und Weltraum* **5,** 149 (1966).

Kunz, W.: "Abbildungsgeometrie bei der Sonnenprojektion" *SONNE* **2,** 95 (1978) no. 7.

Roth, G.D.: *Astronomy—A Handbook,* New York, 1975, p. 226.

A.2.2. Spectroscope

Baxter, W.M.: *The Sun and the Amateur Astronomer,* Newton Abbot, 1973.

[†]Compiled by D. Staps and R. Beck

Delvo, P.: "A Spectroscope with a Holographic Grating," *Sky and Telescope* **54**, 65 (1977).

Landolt-Börnstein: *Zahlenwerte und Funktionen,* Neue Serie VI, Berlin, New York, 1965.

Roth, G.D.: *Astronomy—A Handbook,* New York, 1975, p. 99.

Roth, G.D.: *Compendium of Practical Astronomy,* Berlin, 1994, vol. 1, p. 123.

Rowland, H.A.: "Preliminary Table of the Solar Spectrum Wave Lengths," Revised by C.E. St. John, Mount Wilson Obs. Papers, 1928.

Sautter, H.: *Astrophysik I,* Stuttgart, 1972.

Scheffler, H., Elsässer, H.: *Physik der Sterne und der Sonne,* Mannheim, 1974, 1990.

Schmiedeck, W.: "Photograhie des Sonnenspektrums mit einfachsten Hilfsmitteln," *SONNE* **2**, 155 (1978) no. 8.

Schmiedeck, W.: "A Simple Technique for Recording the Sun's Spectrum," *Sky and Telescope* **57**, 395 (1979).

Thackeray, A.D.: *Astronomical Spectroscopy,* New York, 1961.

A.2.3. Micrometers

Bendel, U.: "Bestimmung der Längsausdehnung von Sonnenfleckengruppen mit Hilfe eines Fadenkreuzokulars," *Sirius* (Astr. Obs. Heppenheim) **4**, 20 (1975) no. 1.

Gleissberg, W.: *Die Häufigkeit der Sonnenflecken,* Berlin 1952, p. 20.

Roth, G.D.: *Taschenbuch für Planetenbeobachter,* Düsseldorf, 1966, p. 37.

Roth, G.D.: *Astronomy—A Handbook,* New York, 1975, p. 476.

Roth, G.D.: *Compendium of Practical Astronomy,* Berlin, 1994, vol. 1, p. 121.

Steinbach, M.: "Mikrometer mit fester Meßeinrichtung im Fernrohrbrennpunkt," *Die Sterne* **39**, 11 (1963).

A.3. Filters

Astronomical League: *Observe and Understand the Sun,* R. Hill, Ed., Washington, D.C., 1991.

Chou, B.R.: "Safe Solar Filters," *Sky and Telescope* **62**, 119 (1981).

Chou, B.R.: "Solar Filters," *Astronomie* **19**, no. 7/1991, 66.

Gericke, V.: "Objektivsonnenfilter aus Folie," *SONNE* **2**, 53 (1978) no. 6.

Gericke, V.: "Sonnenfilter aus Folie II," *SONNE* **2**, 104 (1978) no. 7.

Glitsch, I.: "Das 'Gucksonn'," *Orion* **38**, Special Issue 1980, p. 27.

Korte, U.: "Rettungsfolie," *SONNE* **3**, 137 (1979) no. 12.

Lichtenknecker, D.: "Objektivsonnenfilter," *SONNE* **5**, 16 (1981) nos. 17/18.

MacRobert, Alan M.: "Viewing Sunspots with Just a Filter," *Sky and Telescope* **78**, 289 (1989).

Mathers, S.W., Ferris, G.A.J.: "Aluminized Filters for Solar Photography," *J. Brit. Astr. Assoc.* **79**, 376 (1969).

Müller, R.: "The Sun," in G.D. Roth (ed.) *Astronomy—A Handbook,* New York, 1975, p. 221.

Remmert, E.: "Der neue Objektivsonnenfilter," *SONNE* **3**, 4 (1979) no. 9.

Steingrohs, H.: "Erfahrungsbericht über die Sonnenbeobachtung im integralen Licht mit Objektiv-Glasfilter im Vergleich zu Objektiv-Folienfiltern," *SONNE* **2**, 158 (1978) no. 8.

A.4. Special Instruments

A.4.1. Spectrohelioscope

Veio, F.N.: "An Inexpensive Spectrohelioscope by a California Amateur," *Sky and Telescope* **37**, 45 (1969).

Veio, F.N.: *Orion* **29**, 23 (1971) no. 122.

Veio, F.N.: *Orion* **30**, 178 (1972) no. 133.

Veio, F.N.: "Ein extrem kurzgebautes Spektrohelioskop," *Orion* **32**, 62 (1974) no. 141.

Veio, F.N.: *J. Brit. Astron. Assoc.* **85**, 242 (1975).

Veio, F.N.: *The Sun in Hα Light with a Spectrohelioscope,* Clearlake Park, CA 95424, P.O. Box 467, 1972, 1978, 1991.

A.4.2. Prominence Attachment

Gehring, H.: "Über das Loch in der Hilfslinse des Protuberanzenfernrohrs," *SONNE* **5**, 76 (1981), nos. 17/18.

Richter, G.: "Ein vereinfachtes Protuberanzen-Fernrohr," *Die Sterne* **50**, 105–108, 1974.

Trombino, D.F.: "The Baader Prominence Coronograph," *Sky & Telescope,* June, 1994, p. 51.

Trombino, Donald F.: "New Tools for the Solar Observer," *1994 Yearbook of Astronomy,* Part II., Patrick

A.4.4. Birefringent Filters

Behr, A.: "Polarisationsinterferenzfilter," *Die Sterne* **27**, 195, (1951).

A.4.5. Observing the Sun by Radioastronomy

AEG Telefunken: Integrierte Schaltungen, Datenbuch, Ulm 1979/80.

Altenhoff, W.J.: "Fundamentals of Radio Astronomy," in *Compendium of Practical Astronomy,* G.D. Roth (ed.), Berlin, 1994, vol. 1, p. 381.

American Radio Relay League: *The Radio Amateur's Handbook,* Newington, 1991.

Falb, A., Mandel, H., Riese, P.: *Radioastronomie für Amateursternwarten, Sirius* (Publ. Starkenburg Obs. Heppenheim) no. 15, Heppenheim, 1981.

Heisermann, D.: *Radio Astronomy for the Amateur,* TAB Books, Blue Ridge Summit, 1975.

Henne, W.: *Einführung in die Hochfrequenztechnik,* Vordass und Münch Verlag, Munich, 1966.

Hey, J.S.: *The Radio Universe,* Oxford, 1971.

Hey, J.S.: *The Evolution of Radio Astronomy,* Elek Science, London, 1973.

Kraus, J.D.: *Antennas,* McGraw-Hill Book Company, New York, 1950.

Kraus, J.D.: *Radio Astronomy,* Cygnus-Quasar Books, Powell, 1986.

Limann, O.: *Funktechnik ohne Ballast,* Franzis Verlag, Munich, 1978.

Monstein, Chr. A.: "Radioastronomie als Hobby," *Orion* **147**, 127 (1980) no. 179.

Monstein, Chr. A.: "Amateurradioastronomie," *Orion* **148**, 15 (1981) no. 182.

Monstein, Chr. A.: "Höhenmessung mittels Seeinterferometer unter Ausnutzung der solaren Radiostrahlung," *Orion* **149**, 15 (1982) no. 189.

Rohlfs, K.: *Tools of Radio Astronomy,* Springer-Verlag, 1986.

SARA, Society of Amateur Radio Astronomers, President: Chuck Forster (1995), 5661 Vineyard Rd., Oregon, WI 53575, (608) 835-9282.

Smith, J.R.: "A Basic Radio Telescope," *Wireless World,* February, 1978.

Stein, R.S.: "Diode Noise Source for Receiver Noise Measurements," *Ham Radio* 1979, pp. 32–43.

Suzuki, S.: "Multiphase Radio Interferometers for Locating the Sources of the Solar Radio Emission," *Tokyo Astronomical Obs., Astronomical Society of Japan* **11**, no. 4 (1959), Report no. 185.

Swenson, G.W.: "An Amateur Radio Telescope," Tucson, 1980; *Sky and Telescope* **55**, 385, 475 and **56**, 28, 114, 201, 290 (1978).

Urbarz, H.: "Solare Typ III Bursts als nichtstationäre Radioquellen," *Astr. Inst. der Universität Tübingen,* Reprint from "Kleinheubacher Berichte" vol. 12, 1980.

Verschuur, G.L.: *The Invisible Universe—the Story of Radio Astronomy,* Science Library, Heidelberg, 1974.

Verschuur, G.L., Kellermann, K.I.: *Galactic and Extra-Galactic Radio Astronomy,* Springer Verlag, Berlin, 1974.

Wohlllebenr, R., Mattes, H., Krichbaum, T.: *Interferometry in Radioastronomy and Radar Techniques,* Kluwer Academic Publishers, Dordrecht, 1991 (available from the book shop or the author at the Max-Planck-Institut für Radioastronomie, Auf dem Hügel 69, D-53121 Bonn, Germany).

A.5. Photography

A.5.1. The Photographic Emulsion and its Theory

Agfa-Gevaert, AG/1977 Agfapan/Agfaortho Emulsions, Marketing Service.

Angerer, E.v.: *Wissenschaftliche Photographie,* Akademische Verlagsgesellschaft, Leipzig, 1931.

Everhart, E.: "Hypersensitization and Astronomical Use of Kodak Technical Pan Film 2415," *AAS Photo-Bulletin* no. 24/1980, 3.

Granzer, F., Moisar, E.: *Physik in unserer Zeit* **12**, 2 (1981).

Kodak, Data Sheet for Technical Pan 2415 Emulsion.

Merton, G.: "Photography and the Amateur Astronomer," *J. Brit. Astr. Assoc.* **63**, 7 (1952).

Spahni, T.: "Filmkunde für Amateure," *Orion* **36**, 11 (1978) no. 164 and **36**, 58 (1978) no. 165.

A.5.2. Introduction to White Light Photography

Astronomical League: *Observe and Understand the Sun,* R. Hill, Ed., Washington, D.C., 1991.

Jahn, C.H.: "Solar Photography," in *Compendium of Practical Astronomy,* Berlin, 1994, G.D. Roth (ed.), vol. 2, p. 67.

Nemec, G.: "Die Photographie der Sonne," *Publ. Köln Obs.* no. 4/1966.

Remmert, E.: "Die Sonnenphotographie und ihre Probleme," *Sterne und Weltraum* **24**, 158 and 606 (1985).

VdS Solar Section: *Einführung in die Sonnenbeobachtung,* Berlin, 1991.

A.5.4. Photographic Observations of the Chromosphere

Hicks, J., Trombino, D.F.: "Shooting the Sun in H-alpha," *Astronomy,* **11** 7, p. 34 (1983).

A.5.6. Dark Room Techniques

Beck, R., Paech, W., Remmert, E.: "Das Seminar über Sonnenfotografie am 1./2.9.1979," *SONNE* **3**, 138 (1979) no. 12.

Berry, R.: "Setting Up an Astrodarkroom," *Astronomy* **4**, no. 6/1976, 43.

Hudgins, D.: "Printing Your Astrophotographs," *Astronomy* **4**, no. 12/1976, 46 and *Astronomy* **5**, no. 1/1977, 42.

Remmert, E., Beck, R.: "Zweites Sonnenfotografieseminar in Königswinter am 8./9. März 1980," *SONNE* **4**, 93 (1980) no. 15.

A.6. Evaluating Photographs

Beck, R., Pröll, H.J.: "Digitale Auswertung der Sonnenfinsternisaufnahmen vom 30.6.73," *Sterne und Weltraum* **13**, 123 (1974).

Beck, R., Pröll, H.J.: "Neue Auswertungen von Sonnenfinsternisaufnahmen," *Sternzeit* **1**, 50 (1975).

Becker, H.J., Becker, M.: "Untersuchungen über die Leistungsfähigkeit des PDS 1010A Mikrodensitometers in Bonn," *Mitt. Astron. Ges.* **45**, 151 (1979).

Chapman, G.A., Groisman, G.: "A Digital Analysis of Sunspot Areas," *Sol. Phys.* **91**, 45 (1984).

Hilbrecht, H.: "Helle Ringe um Sonnenflecken," *SONNE* **2**, 71 (1979).

Martinez, J.: "A Better Photograph of Coronal Streamers," *Sky and Telescope* **56**, 92 (1978).

Pröll, H.J., Staps, D.: "Die Sonnenfinsternis vom 23.10.1976," *Sterne und Weltraum* **18**, 20 (1979).

Richter, G.M.: "Zur Auswertung astronomischer Aufnahmen mit dem automatischen Flächenphotometer," *Astron. Nachr.* **299**, 283 (1978).

A.7. Digital Image Processing

Berg, R.: Image Processing in Astronomy, *Sky & Telescope*, April 1994, 30 (1994).

Berry, Richard: *Choosing and using a CCD camera. A W-5300 Practical Guide to Getting Maximum Performance from Your CCD Camera*, Willmann-Bell, Richmond, VA, (1992).

Castleman: Digital Image Processing, Prentice Hall (1979). De Jager, Nieuwenhuijzen (eds.): Image processing techniques in astronomy, D. Reidel (1975).

Gonzales; Wintz: *Digital Image Processing*, Addison Wesley (1987).

Howell, S.B. (ed.): *Astronomical CCD observing and reduction techniques*, Astronomical Society of the Pacific conference series vol. 23, San Francisco (1992).

Niblack: *An Introduction to Digital Image Processing*, Prentice Hall (1986)

Philip, A.G.: *CCDs in Astronomy II: New Methods and Applications of CCD Technology*, L. Davis Press (1990).

A.8. Recording Solar Structure Movements

Brägger, H., Moser, E.: "Das Filmen von Sonnenprotuberanzen," *Orion* **32**, 54 (1974) no. 141.

Dürst, J.: "Kinematographie der Chromosphäre," *Astr. Mitt. Eidgen. Sternw. Zürich* no. 289, (1969).

Müller, R.: "Astronomen filmen," *Der Filmkreis* 1/1965, 14.

Völker, P.: "Flarebeobachtungen," *SONNE* **2**, 120 (1978) no. 7.

Völker, P.: "Protuberanzen- und Filamentenbeobachtungen," *SONNE* **4**, 20 (1980) no. 13.

Völker, P.: "Zum Thema astronomischer Trickfilm," *VdS-Nachr.* **15**, 95 (1966) nos. 8–9.

Wattenberg, D.: "Die kinematographische Beobachtung von Sonnenfinsternissen," *Bild und Ton* 12/1954 (= *Mitt. d. Archenhold Stw.*, Berlin-Treptow no. 39 [1954]).

B. Solar Observation

B.1. Observation

B.1.2 Seeing

Kiepenheuer, K.O.: "Solar Site Testing," in J. Rösch: Site Testing, IAU Symposium No. 19, p. 193 (1962).

B.2. Sunspots

B.2.1. The Structure of Sunspots

Beckers, J.M., Schröter, E.H.: "The Intensity, Velocity and Magnetic Structure of a Sunspot Region, II: Some Properties of Umbral Dots," *Sol. Phys.* **4**, 303 (1968).

Beckers, J.M., Schröter, E.H.: "The Intensity, Velocity and Magnetic Structure of a Sunspot Region, IV: Properties of a Unipolar Spot," *Sol. Phys.* **10**, 384 (1969).

Bumba, V.: "Observation of Solar Magnetic and Velocity Fields," *Proc. Enrico Fermi School of Physics* **39**, 77 (1967).

Danielson, R.E.: "The Structure of Sunspot Penumbras," *Astrophys. Journal* **134**, 275 (1961).

Dezsö, L., Gerlei, O.: "Relative Size of the Penumbral and Umbral Areas of Sunspots," *Publ. Debrecen Heliophys. Obs.* **1**, 57 (1964).

Husar, D.: "Klarstellung des Gebrauchs der Bezeichnung 'Pore' bei Sonnenbeobachtungen," *VdS-Nachr.* **16**, 45 (1967) nos. 8–9.

Jäger, F.W.: "Solar Magnetic Fields," *Oss. Astron. di Roma Contributi Scientifici*, Series III, 166 (1966) no. 44.

Jensen, E., Ringnes, T.S.: *Astropysica Norvegia* vol. V, 273 (1957) no. 10.

Kassinskij, W.W.: *Solnechn. Danye* no. 9/1964, 53.

Kassinskij, W.W.: *Solnechn. Danye* no. 11/1964, 42.

Kassinskij, W.W.: *Solnechn. Danye* no. 12/1964, 54.

Kassinskij, W.W.: *Solnechn. Danye* no. 5/1966, 58.

Kneer, F.: "On Some Characteristics of Umbral Fine Structure," *Sol. Phys.* **28**, 361 (1973).

Macris, C.J.: "The Variation of the Mean Diameter of the Photospheric Granules Near Sunspots," *Astron. Astrophys.* **78**, 186 (1979).

Schröter, E.H.: "Einige Beobachtungen und Messungen an Stratoskop I-Negativen," *Zeitschr. f. Astrophys.* **56**, 183 (1962).

Strebel, H.: "Der innere helle Rand der Penumbra von Sonnenflecken," *Zeitschr. f. Astrophys.* **5**, 96 (1932).

Tschistjakov, W.F.: *Solnechn. Danye* no. 2/1964, 56.

Tschistjakov, W.F.: *Solnechn. Danye* no. 3/1964, 56.

Wiehr, E.: "Messung von Magnetfeldern auf der Sonne," *Sterne und Weltraum* **9**, 65 (1970).

Wiehr, E.: "Die Temperatur-Schichtung in Sonnenflecken," *Sterne und Weltraum* **5**, 172 (1980).

Wöhl, H., Wittmann, A., Schröter, E.H.: "A Complete Photoelectric Sunspot Spectrum: An Atlas from 3900–8000Å," *Sol. Phys.* **13**, 104 (1970).

B.2.2. The Development of Sunspots and Sunspot Groups

Abdussamatov, H.I.: "On the Physical Relation between the Magnetic Field and the Brightness in the Sunspot Umbrae," *Bull. Astr. Inst. Czech.* **24**, 118 (1973).

Antalova, A.: "The Motions of the Umbras in Hale Active Regions 16862 and 16863," *Bull. Astron. Inst. Czech.* **34**, 96 (1983).

Bendel, U.: "Die Achsenneigung von bipolaren Sonnenfleckengruppen," *SONNE* **4**, 7 (1980) no. 13.

Bray, R.J., Loughhead, R.E.: *Sunspots,* Chapman and Hall, London, 1964, p. 250.

Bumba, V.: "Development of Spot Group Areas in Dependence on the Local Magnetic Field," *Bull. Astr. Inst. Czech.* **14**, 91 (1963).

Bumba, V.: "Observations of Solar Magnetic and Velocity Fields," *Proc. Enrico Fermi School of Physics* Academic Press, New York, 1967, vol. **39**, 77.

Dezsö, L., Gerlei, O.: "Relative Size of the Penumbral and Umbral Areas of Sunspots," *Publ. Debrecen Heliophys. Obs.* **1**, 57 (1964).

Dezsö, L.: "Sunspot Motions and Magnetic Shears as Precursors of Flares," *Adv. Space Research* **4**, no. 7, 57 (1984).

Gilman, P.A., Howard, R.: "Rotation and Expansion within Sunspot Groups," *Astrophys. Journal* **303**, 480 (1986).

Gnevishev, M.N.: "On the Life-Length of Sun-Spots," *Pulkovo Obs. Circ.* **24**, 37 (1938).

Götz, G.: "Entwicklung von Sonnenfleckengruppen," *SONNE* **1**, 112 (1977) no. 3.

Götz, G.: "Einige Aspekte zur Veränderung der Einzelfleckenzahl während der Gruppenentwicklung," *SONNE* **2**, 112 (1978) no. 7.

Hedewig, R.: "Schnelle Veränderungen in Sonnenflecken," *SONNE* **3**, 17 (1979) no. 9.

Hilbrecht, H.: "Schnelle Veränderungen in Sonnenflecken," *SONNE* **1**, 156 (1977) no. 4.

Kalman, B.: "Magnetic Field Structure Changes in the Vicinity of Solar Flares," *Adv. Space Research* **4**, no. 7, 81 (1984).

Kiepenheuer, K.O.: "Solar Activity," in *The Sun*, G. Kuiper (ed.), Chicago University Press, Chicago, 1953, p. 344.

Kiessig, M.: "Die Verteilung der Flecken auf der Sonnenscheibe," *Himmelswelt* **56**, 181 (1949).

Kopecky, M.: "The Statistics of Spots on the Rotating Sun," *Bull. Astr. Inst. Czech.* **4**, 8 (1953).

Kopecky, M.: "The Periodicity of the Sunspot Groups, " *Adv. Astron. Astrophys.* **7**, 189 (1967).

Künzel, H.: "Statistische Untersuchungen über Häufigkeit, Zonenwanderung und Lebensdauer von Sonnenflecken im 18. Aktivitätszyklus," *Astron. Nachr.* **285**, 169 (1960).

Künzel, H., Mattig, W., Schröter, E.H.: "Beobachtungen einer eigentümlichen Verschmelzung zweier Sonnenfleckengruppen," *Die Sterne* **37**, 198 (1961).

McIntosh, P.S.: in *The Physics of Sunspots,* L.E. Cram and J.H. Thomas (eds.), Sunspot, 1981, p. 7.

Mehltretter, J.P.: "On the Proper Motion of Small Pores in Sunspot Groups," *Sol. Phys.* **63**, 61 (1979).

Newton, H.W.: *The Face of the Sun,* Penguin Books no. A422, Harmondsworth, 1958.

Pfister, H.: "Spezielle Eigenbewegungen in Sonnenfleckengruppen," *Astr. Mitt. Eidgen. Sternw. Zürich* no. 342, (1975).

Remmert, E.: "Kurzzeitige Veränderungen in großen Sonnenfleckengruppen," *Sterne und Weltraum* **18**, 356 (1979).

Roggenhausen, M.: "Die Sichtbarkeitsfunktion der Sonnenflecken," *Zeitschr. f. Astrophys.* **30**, 249 (1952).

Schüssler, M.: "Neues zur Theorie der Sonnenaktivität," *Sterne und Weltraum* **19**, 331 (1980).

Waldmeier, M.: "Heliographische Karten der Photosphäre für das Jahr 1946," *Publ. Eidgen. Sternw. Zürich* no. 9, 2 (1947).

Waldmeier, M.: "Ergebnisse und Probleme der Sonnenforschung," *Akademische Verlagsgesellschaft,* Leipzig, 1955.

Waldmeier, M.: "Anomale Teilung eines Sonnenflecks," *Zeitschr. f. Astrophys.* **57**, 207 (1963).

Waldmeier, M.: "Der Sonnenfleck mit der größten Lebensdauer," *SONNE* **8**, 60 (1984) no. 30.

Wilson, P.R.: "The Structure of a Sunspot," *Sol. Phys.* **3**, 243 (1968).

Yilmaz, F.: "Some Properties of Bipolar Sunspot Groups," *Publ. Istanbul Univ. Obs.* no. 79 (1964).

B.2.3. Classification of Sunspots and Sunspot Groups

Beck, R.: "Eine neue Definition der Sonnenfleckenrelativzahl," *SONNE* **1**, 56 (1977) no. 2.

Beck, R.: "Die Häufigkeit der Fleckenklassen nach Waldmeier im 21. Zyklus der Sonnenaktivität," *SONNE* **6**, 10 (1982) no. 21.

Bray, R.J., Loughhead, R.E.: *Sunspots,* Chapman and Hall, London, 1964, p. 234.

Brunner,W.: "Heliographische Übersichtskarten," *Publ. Eidgen. Sternw. Zürich* no. 7, 6 (1939).

Gericke, V.: "Fleckenklassifikation 1974–1982," *SONNE* **7**, 128 (1983) no. 27.

Kleczek, J.: "Relations between Flares and Sunspots," *Bull. Astr. Inst. Czech.* **4**, 9 (1953).

Künzel, H.: "Statistische Untersuchungen über die Häufigkeit, Zonenwanderung und Lebensdauer von Sonnenflecken," *Astron. Nachr.* **285**, 169 (1960).

Künzel, H.: "Zur Klassifikation von Sonnenfleckengruppen," *Astron. Nachr.* **288**, 177 (1964).

McIntosh, P.S.: "The Classification of Sunspot Groups," *Sol. Phys.* **125**, 251 (1990).

NOAA: "Solar-Geophysical Data, Explanations of Data Reports" (Appendix to each February issue).

Sandner, W.: "Zur Charakterisierung der Sonnenflecken," *Die Sterne* **13**, 101 (1933).

Sandner, W.: "Größe und Gestalt der Sonnenflecken," *Astron. Nachr.* **251**, 219 (1934).

Schambeck, C.: "Die Sonnenaktivität 1977," *SONNE* **3**, 29 (1979) no. 9.

Schulze, W.: "Untersuchungen über die Größe der Sonnenflecke," *Die Sterne* **54**, 154 (1978).

Ventura, F.J., Tanti, T.: "Analyzing Sunspot Activity," *J. Brit. Astron. Assoc.* **98**, 282 (1988).

Waldmeier, M.: "Chromosphärische Eruptionen," *Zeitschr. f. Astrophys.* **16**, 286 (1938).

B.2.4. Measurements of Solar Activity

Archenhold, G.H.A.: "Some Problems Concerning the Distribution of Sunspots over the Sun's Disc," *Monthly Not. Roy. Astr. Soc.* **100**, 645 (1940).

Beck, R.: "Eine neue Definition der Sonnenfleckenrelativzahl," *SONNE* **1**, 56 (1977) no. 2.

Beck, R.: "Die Abhängigkeit des k-Faktors von der Luftgüte," *SONNE* **2**, 79 (1978a) no. 6.

Beck, R.: "Probleme der Relativzahl und Relativzahlstatistik," *SONNE* **2**, 142 (1978b) no. 8.

Beck, R.: "Bemerkungen zum Artikel 'Erfahrungen mit der neuen Sonnenfleckenrelativzahl von Beck,'" *Korona* (Astr. Assoc. Kassel) no. 17, 43 (1978c).

Beck, R.: "Untergang der Züricher Sonnenfleckenrelativzahl?," *SONNE* **4**, 90 (1980) no. 15.

Bendel, U.: "Das R-k-Diagramm," *Sternzeit* **2**, 95 (1976).

Bendel, U.: "Ergänzungen zum R-k-Diagramm," *Sternzeit* **4**, 4 (1978a).

Bendel, U.: "Abbildungsfehler bei der Sonnenprojektion," *SONNE* **2**, 56 (1978b) no. 6.

Bendel, U.: "Neues vom k-Faktor," *SONNE* **3**, 16 (1979) no. 9.

Bruzek, A., Durrant, C.J.: *Illustrated Glossay for Solar and Solar-Terrestrial Physics,* Dordrecht 1977, p. 74.

Bumba, V.: in *Stellar and Solar Magnetic Fields,* R.Lüst (ed.), New York, 1965, p. 192.

Dougherty, L.M.: "Measurement of Areas on the Solar Disk," *J. Brit. Astr. Assoc.* **91**, 75 (1980).

Dreyhsig, J.: "Lohnt sich eine Reduktion der k-Faktoren des Relativzahlnetzes SONNE durch Seeing-Abgaben nach der Kiepenheuer-Skala?," *SONNE* **9**, 24 (1985) no. 33.

Fracastoro, M.G., Marocchi, D.: "A Sunspot Analysis 1943–1977," *Sol. Phys.* **60**, 171 (1978).

Gerland, L.: "Erste Ergebnisse einer Untersuchung zur Korrelation der Neuen Flächenzahl und der klassischen Relativzahl," *SONNE* **2**, 110 (1978) no. 7.

Gerland, L.: "AG-Bericht Sonne," *Korona* (Astr. Assoc. Kassel) no. 27, 16 (1981).

Giovanelli, R.G.: "Sunspot Minima," *The Observatory* **84**, 57 (1964).

Gleissberg, W.: *Die Häufigkeit der Sonnenflecken,* Berlin, 1952, p. 10.

Götz, M.: "Jahresbericht des Pettiszahlnetzes," *SONNE* **8**, 44 (1984) no. 29; *SONNE* **9**, 84 (1985) no. 34 (and following years).

Hedewig, R.: "Erfahrungen mit der neuen Sonnenfleckenrelativzahl von Beck," *Korona* (Astr. Assoc. Kassel) no. 16, 25 (1978a).

Hedewig, R.: "Fläche und Relativzahl von Sonnenflecken," *SONNE* **2**, 23 (1978b) no. 5.

Hotinli, M.: "On the Foreshortening Law of Sunspots," *Publ. Istanbul Obs.* Nr. 42 (1951).

Houtgast, J., van Sluiters, A.: "Statistical Investigations Concerning the Magnetic Fields of Sunspots," *Bull. Astr. Inst. Netherlands* **10**, 325 (1948).

Husar, D.: "Klarstellung des Gebrauchs der Bezeichnung 'Pore' bei Sonnenbeobachtungen," *VdS-Nachr.* 8/1967, 45 (1967).

Karkoschka, E.: "Auswertung der Netz-Relativzahl," *SONNE* **6**, 35 (1982) no. 21.

Karkoschka, E., Reinsch, K.: "Neues Auswertungsverfahren für die Netz-Relativzahlen," *SONNE* **6**, 144 (1982) no. 23.

Keller, H.U.: "'A'-Sonnenfleckenbeobachtungen von bloßem Auge," *Orion* **38**, 180 (1980) no. 181.

Krüger, M.: "Zur Klassifizierung randnaher Fleckengruppen," *SONNE* **4**, 159 (1980) no. 16.

Künzel, H.: "Hinweise für die heute übliche Zählweise von Sonnenflecken zur Bestimmung der Relativzahl," *Astronomie und Raumfahrt* 4/1976, 121.

McIntosh, P.S.: in *The Physics of Sunspots,* L.E. Cram and J.H. Thomas (eds.): Sunspot, 1981, p. 7.

Newton, H.W.: "The Lineage of the Great Sunspots," *Vistas in Astronomy* **1**, 666 (1955).

Newton, H.W.: *The Face of the Sun,* Harmondsworth, 1958.

Pettis, H.S.: "Eine systematische Studie von Sonnenflecken," *Saturn* (Astr. Assoc. Paderborn) 11/1978, 11.

Reil, A.: "Monatsmittel der Neuen Relativzahl nach Beck," *SONNE* **4**, 48 (1980) no. 14.

Reinsch, K.: "Das Relativzahlnetz der Amateursonnenbeobachter," *SONNE* **4**, 34 and 168 (1980) nos. 13 and 16.

Schindler, R.D.: "Bemerkungen über Reduktionsfaktoren II," *SONNE* **5**, 62 (1981) nos. 17–18.

Schulze, W.: "Sonnenbeobachtungen des Amateurastronomen," *Astronomie und Raumfahrt* 5/1978, 145.

Schulze, W.: "Zur Anwendung der Kiepenheuer-Skala," *SONNE* **4**, 13 (1980) no. 13.

Seeck, A., Hinrichs, A.: "Untersuchung der k-Faktoren der Sonnenfleckenrelativzahl," *SONNE* **1**, 101 (1977) no. 3.

Tang, F., Howard, R., Adkins, J.M.: "A Statistical Study of Active Regions 1967–1981," *Sol. Phys.* **91**, 75 (1984).

Taylor, P.O.: *Observing the Sun,* Cambridge Univ. Press, 1991, p. 15.

Wagner, S.: "Solar Observations of the Planetary System Working Group," Report of the IAYC 1979, p. 56.

Waldmeier, M.: *Ergebnisse und Probleme der Sonnenforschung*, 1st ed., Leipzig, 1941, p. 116, or 2nd ed. 1955, p. 140.

Waldmeier, M.: *The Sunspot Activity in the Years 1610–1960*, Zürich, 1961.

Waldmeier, M.: "Die Beziehung zwischen der Sonnenfleckenrelativzahl und der Gruppenzahl," *Astr. Mitt. Eidgen. Sternw. Zürich* no. 285, (1968).

Waldmeier, M.: "Sunspot Numbers and Sunspot Areas," *Astr. Mitt. Eidgen. Sternw. Zürich* no. 358 (1978a).

Waldmeier, M.: "How close to the Limb can Sunspots be seen?," *Astr. Mitt. Eidgen. Sternw. Zürich* no. 359 (1978b).

Wiechoczek, R.: "Beobachtungsprogramm Sonne," *SONNE* **1**, 30 (1977) no. 1.

Wolf, R.: *Mittheilungen über die Sonnenflecken* no. 1, Zürich, 1856, p. 12.

B.2.5. Temporal Changes in Sunspot Activity

Ahnert, P.: "Die nächsten Extreme der Sonnenfleckenkurve," *Kalender für Sternfreunde 1974*, J.A. Barth, Leipzig, 1973, p. 141.

Ahnert, P.: "Die Zahl der fleckenfreien Tage pro Monat als Kriterium für die Sonnenfleckenminima," *Kalender für Sternfreunde 1979*, J.A. Barth, Leipzig, 1978, p. 173.

Bendel, U., Staps, D.: "Kurz- und mittelfristige Sonnenfleckenprognose mit der P17-Mittelung," *Sterne und Weltraum* **19**, 180 (1980).

Cullen, Ch.: "Was There a Maunder Minimum?," *Nature* **283**, 427 (1980).

Eddy, J.A.: "The Maunder Minimum," *Science* **192**, 1189 (1976).

Eddy, J.A.: "The Maunder Minimum: A Reappraisal," *Sol. Phys.* **89**, 195 (1983).

Gleissberg, W.: *Die Häufigkeit der Sonnenflecken*, Akademie-Verlag, Berlin, 1952.

Gleissberg, W.: "Eine unerwartete Anomalie in der jährlichen Verteilung der Sonnenfleckenmaxima," *Mitt. Astr. Ges.* **36**, 139 (1975).

Gleissberg, W., Damboldt, Th.: "Reflections on the Maunder Minimum of Sunspots," *J. Brit. Astron. Assoc.* **89**, 440 (1979).

Hartmann, R.: "A New Representation of the 80-Year-Cycle in Sunspot Frequency," *Sol. Phys.* **21**, 246 (1971).

Henkel, R.: "Evidence for an Ultra-Long Cycle of Solar Activity," *Sol. Phys.* **25**, 498 (1972).

Junker, E.: "Nord-Süd-Asymmetrie der Sonnenaktivität 1980–1991," *SONNE* **15**, 127 (1991) no. 60.

Karkoschka, E.: "Neue Relativzahl-Mittelung," *SONNE* **3**, 33 (1979) no. 9.

Keller, H.U.: " 'A'-Sonnenfleckenbeobachtungen von bloßem Auge," *Orion* **38**, 180 (1980) no. 181.

Kiepenheuer, K.O.: "Solar Activity," in *The Sun,* G. Kuiper (ed.), Chicago, 1953, p. 324.

Kopecky, M.: "The Periodicity of the Sunspot Groups," *Adv. Astr. Astrophys.* **7**, 189 (1967).

Kopecky, M.: "When Did the Latest Minimum of the 80-Year Sunspot Period Occur?", *Bull. Astr. Inst. Czech.* **42**, 158 (1991).

Kuklin, G.V.: "Cyclical and Secular Variations of Solar Activity," in *Basic Mechanisms of Solar Activity,* Bumba and Kleczek (eds.), Dordrecht, 1976, p. 147.

Letfus, V.: "Prediction of the Height of Solar Cycle 23," *Sol. Phys.* **149**, 405 (1994).

Meeus, J.: "Une Fourmule d'Adoucissement pour l'Activité Solaire," *Ciel et Terre* **74**, 445 (1958).

Meeus, J.: "Sunspot Activity 1749–1976," *Vereniging voor Sterrenkunde Memoirs no. 4,* Brussels, 1977.

Müller, R.: "Die Sonnenfleckentätigkeit im ersten Halbjahr 1965," *Die Sterne* **42**, 10 (1966).

Reinsch, K.: "Getrennte Erfassung der Aktivität von Nord- und Südhalbkugel," *SONNE* **7**, 138 (1983) no. 27.

Reinsch, K.: "Die Sonnenaktivität 1984," *SONNE* **9**, 44 (1985) no. 33.

Reinsch, K.: "The SONNE Network—Amateur Solar Astronomy in Germany," in: *Research Amateur Astronomy,* ASP Conference Series **33** (ed. S.J. Edberg), p. 22 (1992).

Ruf, K.: "American und Zürich Sunspot Relative Numbers," *Journal Interdiscipl. Cycle Res.* **8**, 215 (1977).

Schroeter, K.H.: "Bemerkungen zur jahreszeitlichen Verteilung der Sonnenfleckenmaxima," *Mitt. Astr. Ges.* **38**, 140 (1976).

Schulze, W.: "Der 20. Sonnenfleckenzyklus," *Die Sterne* **54**, 96 (1978a).

Schulze, W.: "Sonnenbeobachtungen des Amateurastronomen," *Astronomie und Raumfahrt* 5/1978, 145 (1978b).

Schulze, W.: "Die Sonnenfleckenhäufigkeit im elfjährigen Zyklus," *Die Sterne* **57**, 203 (1981).

Schulze, W.: "Der achtzigjährige Zyklus der Sonnenfleckenhäufigkeit," *Die Sterne* **60**, 163 (1984).

Schulze, W.: "Der 21. Sonnenfleckenzyklus," *Die Sterne* **64**, 293 (1988).

Schwabe, H.: "Sonnen-Beobachtungen im Jahre 1843," *Astron. Nachr.* **21**, 233 (1844) (reprinted in *SONNE* **5**, 190 (1981) no. 20).

Tarnutzer, A.: "Sunspot Observations with the Unaided Eye, in: *Research Amateur Astronomy,* ASP Conference Series **33** (ed. S.F. Edberg), p. 32 (1992).

Taylor, P.O.: *Observing the Sun,* Cambridge University Press, 1991.

Vitinskii, Y.I.: "Solar-Activity Forecasting," Israel Program for Scientific Translations, Jerusalem, 1965.

Waldmeier, M.: "Neue Eigenschaften der Sonnenfleckenkurve," *Astr. Mitt. Eidgen. Sternw. Zürich* **133**, 105 (1935).

Waldmeier, M.: *Ergebnisse und Probleme der Sonnenforschung*, 2nd ed., Akademische Verlagsges., Leipzig, 1955.

Waldmeier, M.: "Der lange Sonnenzyklus," *Zeitschr. f. Astrophys.* **43**, 149 (1957).

Waldmeier, M.: "Statistics and Evolution of Sunspots," *Astr. Mitt. Eidgen. Sternw. Zürich* no. 274, (1966).

Waldmeier, M.: "Sonnenfleckenkurven und die Methode der Sonnenaktivitätsprognose," *Astr. Mitt. Sternw. Zürich* no. 286 (1968).

Waldmeier, M.: "Das letzte Sonnenfleckenmaximum und seine Prognose," *Sterne und Weltraum* **20**, 105 (1981).

Wallenhorst, S.G.: "Sunspot Numbers and Solar Cycles," *Sky and Telescope*, 9/1982, p. 234.

White, O.R., Trotter, D.E.: "Note on the Distributions of Sunspots between the North and South Solar Hemispheres," *Astrophys. Journal Suppl.* **33**, 391 (1977).

Wilson, R.M.: "An Early Estimate for the Size of Cycle 23," *Sol. Phys.* **140**, 181 (1992).

Wittmann, A.D.: "The Sunspot Cycle Before the Maunder Minimum," *Astron. Astrophys.* **66**, 93 (1978).

Wittmann, A.D., Xu, Z.T.: "A Catalogue of Sunspot Observations from 165 BC to AD 1684," *Astron. Astrophys. Suppl. Ser.* **70**, 83 (1987).

Wolf, R.: "Bericht über neue Untersuchungen über die Periode der Sonnenflecken und ihre Bedeutung," *Astron. Nachr.* **35**, 369 (1853).

Xanthakis, J.: "The Different Indices of Solar Activity and the Time of Rise," in *Solar Physics* (Herausg. J. Xanthakis), Wiley and Sons, London, 1967, p. 157.

Yixin, Z., Chuanle, C.: "Did the 11-year Solar Cycle Exist in Antiquity?," *Vistas in Astronomy* **31**, 123 (1988).

B.2.6. Naked-Eye Sunspot Observations

Heath, A.W.: "Naked Eye Sunspots and the Solar Cycle," *Journal of the BAA* vol. 104, 86–87 (1994).

Keller, H.U.: " 'A'-Sonnenfleckenbeobachtungen von blossem Auge," *Orion* Nr. **181**, 180 (1980).

Keller, H.U.: "Eine Sammelstelle für Sonnenfleckenbeobachtungen von blossem Auge," *SONNE* **31**, 123 (1984).

Keller, H.U.: "Skizzen von Sonnenfleckenbeobachtungen mit dem blossen Auge," *SONNE* **58**, 45 (1991).

Keller H.U.: "A*: Eine neue Zahl des A-Netzes," *SONNE* **64**, 128 (1992).
Wade, P: "Naked-eye Sunspots 1980–1992," *Journal of the BAA* vol. 104, 86-87 (1994).
Wittmann, A.D. et al.: "A catalogue of sunspot observations from 165 BC to AD 1684," *Astron. Astrophys. Suppl. Ser.* **70**, 83 (1987).

B.3. Position Determination

B.3.2. Observation Methods

Ahnert, P.: *Kalender für Sternfreunde,* p. 141, Leipzig, 1953.
Ahnert, P.: "Die Messung der heliographischen Koordinaten der Sonnenflecken," *Astronomie und Raumfahrt* 4/1978, p. 103.
Balthasar, H., Stark, D., Wöhl, H.: "The Solar Rotation Elements i and ω Derived from Recurrent Single Sunspots," *Astron. Astrophys.* **174**, 359 (1987).
Bendel, U.: "Ausgewählte Methoden zur Positionsbestimmung von Sonnenflecken für den Amateursonnenbeobachter," p. 11, *Special Publ. Darmstadt Obs.* (1975).
Bendel, U.: "Abbildungsfehler bei der Sonnenprojektion," *Publ. Darmstadt Obs.* **9**, 65 (1977) and *SONNE* **2**, 56 (1978) no. 6.
Bendel, U.: "Positionsbestimmung von Sonnenflecken mit kleinen Fernrohren," *Publ. Darmstadt Obs.* **9**, 121 (1977).
Bendel, U.: "Gradnetzschablonen zur Heliographischen Ortsbestimmung," *Publ. Darmstadt Obs.* **11**, 75 (1979).
Bendel, U.: "Rechner-Programm zur heliographischen Ortsbestimmung," *SONNE* **3**, 77 and *SONNE* **3**, 116 (1979) nos. 10 and 11.
Brandt, R.: *Das Fernrohr des Sternfreundes,* Stuttgart, 1967, p. 32.
Fritz, U., Treutner, H., Vogt, O.: "Positionsbestimmung von Sonnenflecken," *Orion* **33**, 38 (1975) no. 147.
Fritz, U.: "Methoden zur Positionsbestimmung von Sonnenflecken," *SONNE* **1**, 66 (1977) no. 2.
Kiepenheuer: *The Sun,* Ann Arbor, 1959.
Litt, M.: "Heliographische Ortsbestimmung," *Publ. Bonn Univ. Obs.* no. 44 (1956).
Meyerdierks, H.: "Reduktion von Positionsbestimmungen durch Koordinatentransformation," *SONNE* **6**, 130 (1982) no. 23.
Peter, K., Bendel, U.: "Durchsichtige Koordinatennetze zur heliographischen Ortsbestimmung," *Sterne und Weltraum* **14**, 371 (1975).
Peter, K., Bendel, U.: "Durchsichtiges Gradnetz zur heliographischen Ortsbestimmung," *Sterne und Weltraum* **16**, 60 (1977).
Roth, G.D.: *Astronomy—A Handbook,* New York 1975, p. 245.

Stark, D., Wöhl, H.: "On the Solar Rotation Elements as Determined from Sunspot Observations," *Astron. Astrophys.* **93**, 241 (1981).

Treutner, H.: "Sonnenpositionsphotographie," *SONNE* **1**, 141 (1977) no. 4.

Vogt, O.: "Zur Genauigkeit von Sonnenfleckenpositionen," *SONNE* **1**, 68 (1977) no. 2.

Vogt, O.: "Positionsbestimmung von Sonnenflecken," *Sterne und Weltraum* **16**, 58 (1977).

Waldmeier, M.: *Tabellen zur heliographischen Ortsbestimmung,* Basel, 1950.

B.3.3. Suggestions for Evaluation

B.3.3.1. Mapping the Sun

Dahmen, N., Grunert, A., Wolf, C.: "Synoptische Karten der Sonnenphotosphäre der synodischen Carringtonrotationen 1837 bis 1840," *SONNE* **15**, 51 (1991) no. 58.

Dahmen, N., Junker, E., Hoell, J., Schwaab, G., Wolf, C., Grunert, A., Schwab, M.: "Jahresauswertung 1988 der synoptischen Karten," *SONNE* **13**, 66 (1989) no. 50.

Hammerschmidt, S.: Endgültiges Schmetterlingsdiagramm des 21. Syklus," *SONNE* **11**, 11 (1987) no. 41.

Fritz, U.: "Fleckenübersichts-Diagramme," *SONNE* **1**, 119 (1977) no. 3 and following issues until *SONNE* **3**, 87 (1979) no. 10.

Junker, E.: "Synoptische Karten der Photosphäre der Sonne," *SONNE* **4**, 100 (1980) no. 15 and following issues.

B.3.3.2. Sunspot Distribution

Åkeson, D.A.: "The Motion and Distribution of the Sun-Spots," Lunds Universitets Årsskrift, N.F. Afd. 2, Bd. 10, Nr. 10 (1914).

Becker, U.: "Untersuchungen über die Herdbildung der Sonnenflecken," Mitt. Fraunhofer Inst., Freiburg, no. 24 (1955) and *Zeitschr. f. Astrophys.* **37** (1955) no. 1.

Bruzek, A.: "Die hypothetische Neigung der Sonnenfleckenachsen," *Zeitschr. f. Astrophys.* **33**, 267 (1954).

Carrington, R.C.: "On the Distribution of the Solar Spots in Latitude Since the Beginning of the Year 1854," *Mon. Not. Roy. Astr. Soc.* **19**, 1 (1858).

Gleissberg, W.: *Die Häufigkeit der Sonnenflecken,* Berlin, 1952, p. 52.

Kopecky, M., Künzel, H.: "Die heliographische Verteilung von Sonnenfleckengruppen verschiedener Klassen im 18. Aktivitätszyklus," *Astron. Nachr.* **286**, 193 (1962).

Künzel, H.: "Statistische Untersuchung über die Häufigkeit, Zonenwanderung und Lebensdauer von Sonnenflecken im 18. Aktivitätszyklus," *Astron. Nachr.* **285**, 169 (1960).

Losh, H.M.: "Distribution of Sun-spots in Longitude," *Publ. Michigan Univ. Obs.* **7**, 127 (1939).

Maunder, A.S.D.: "An Apparent Influence of the Earth on the Numbers and Areas of Sun-spots in the Cycle 1889–1901," *Mon. Not. Roy. Astr. Soc.* **67**, 451 (1907).

Reinsch, K.: "Methoden und Ergebnisse der 'Heliographischen Ortsbestimmung' und der statistischen Untersuchung der Verteilung der Aktivitätsgebiete auf der Sonne," *SONNE* **1**, 62 (1977) no. 2.

Reinsch, K., Delfs, M., Götz, M., Schwab, M., Wolf, C.: "Die Sonnenaktivität auf dem Weg zum Rekordmaximum," *Sterne und Weltraum* **29**, 52 (1990) no. 1.

Schulze, W.: "Der 20. Sonnenfleckenzykus—ein zusammenfassender Bericht," *Die Sterne* **54**, 96 (1978) no. 2.

Stemmler, G.: "Die Häufigkeit von Sonnenflecken in heliographischen Breiten >40d und <1d," *Die Sterne* **59**, 33 (1983).

Waldmeier, M.: "Die Zonenwanderung der Sonnenflecken," *Astr. Mitt. Eidgen. Sternw. Zürich* **14**, 470 (1939).

Waldmeier, M.: *Ergebnisse und Probleme der Sonnenforschung*, Leipzig, 1941, p. 132.

Waldmeier, M.: *Experientia* **5**, 44 (1949).

B.3.3.3. Extension Measurement of Sunspot Groups

Beck, R.: "Eine neue Definition der Sonnenfleckenrelativzahl," *SONNE* **1**, 56 (1977) no. 2.

Bendel, U.: "Abbildungsfehler bei der Sonnenprojektion," *SONNE* **2**, 56 (1978) no. 6.

Kroupa, P.: "Bestimmung der Längenausdehnung von Sonnenfleckengruppen," *SONNE* **6**, 133 (1982) no. 23.

Thiele, S.: "Koordinatenbestimmung von Sonnenflecken und differentielle Rotation der Sonne," *SONNE* **4**, 66 (1980) no. 14.

Zerm, R.: "Die Messungen der orthodromen Länge von Sonnenfleckengruppen," *Astronomie und Raumfahrt* **20**, 136 (1982) no. 5.

B.3.3.4. Axis Inclination of Bipolar Sunspot Groups

Babcock, H.W.: "The Topology of the Sun's Magnetic Field and the 22-Year Cycle," *Astrophys. Journal* **133**, 572 (1961).

Brunner, W.: "Gesetzmäßigkeiten in der Anordnung der Sonnenflecken zu Gruppen," *Astr. Mitt. Eidgen. Sternw. Zürich* **13**, 67 (1930).

Hale, G.E. et al.: "The Magnetic Polarity of Sunspots," *Astrophys. Journal* **49**, 153 (1919).

Pfister, H.: "Spezielle Eigenbewegungen in Sonnenfleckengruppen," *Astr. Mitt. Eidgen. Sternw. Zürich* no. 342 (1975).

B.3.3.5. Inherent Motion in Sunspot Groups

Bendel, U.: "Merkwürdige Eigenbewegung eines Sonnenflecks," *Sterne und Weltraum* **15**, 290 (1976).

Dezsö, L.: "Sunspot Motions and Magnetic Shears as Precursors of Flares," *Adv. Space Research* **4**, no. 7, 57 (1984).

Fritz, U., Treutner, H., Vogt, O.: "Ein Sonnenfleck mit ungewöhnlicher Eigenbewegung," *Sterne und Weltraum* **15**, 326 (1976).

Gesztelyi, L.: "Consecutive Homologous Flares and Their Relation to Sunspot Motion," *Adv. Space Research* **4**, no. 7, 19 (1984).

Gilman, P.A., Howard, R.: "On the Correlation of Longitudinal and Latitudinal Motions of Sunspots," *Sol. Phys.* **93**, 171 (1984).

Kalman, B.: "Magnetic Field Structure Changes in the Vicinity of Solar Flares," *Adv. Space Research* **4**, no. 7, 81 (1984).

Mehltretter, J.P.: "On the Proper Motion of Small Pores in Sunspot Groups," *Sol. Phys.* **63**, 61 (1979).

Pfister, H.J.: "Proper Motion in the Large Sunspot from July 30 to August 10, 1972," World Data Center A—Report VA6-28I (1973).

Pfister, H.J.: "Spezielle Eigenbewegungen in Sonnenfleckengruppen," *Astr. Mitt. Eidgen. Sternw. Zürich* no. 342 (1975).

Pfister, H.J.: "Klassifikationsschema für Eigenbewegungen," *Sterne und Weltraum* **28**, 598 (1989).

Spörer, G.: "Beobachtungen von Sonnenflecken in den Jahren 1885 bis 1893," *Publ. Astrophys. Obs. Potsdam* **10**, 143 (1895) no. 32.

Waldmeier, M.: *Ergebnisse und Probleme der Sonnenforschung*, Leipzig, 1955, p. 169.

B.3.3.6. Differential Rotation

Balthasar, H., Wöhl, H.: "Differential Rotation and Meridional Motions of Sunspots in the Years 1940–1968," *Astron. Astrophys.* **92**, 111 (1980).

Balthasar, H., Lustig, G., Wöhl, H.: "On the Determination of Heliographic Positions and Rotation Velocities of Sunspots," *Sol. Phys.* **91**, 53 (1984).

Balthasar, H., Vazquez, M., Wöhl, H.: "Differential Rotation of Sunspot Groups in the Period 1874–1976," *Astron. Astrophys.* **155**, 87 (1986).

Clark, D.H.: "Differential Solar Rotation Depends on Solar Activity," *Nature* **280**, 299 (1979).

Howard, R.: "Solar Rotation Results at Mount Wilson," *Sol. Phys.* **83**, 321 (1983).

Joppich, H.: "Die Sonnenrotation gemessen an p- und f-Flecken bipolarer Gruppen," *SONNE* **15**, 83 (1991) no. 59.

Lustig, G.: "Solar Rotation 1947–1981—Determined from Sunspot Data," *Astron. Astrophys.* **125**, 355 (1983).

Lustig, G.: "Untersuchungen der differentiellen Rotation der Sonne von 1960 bis 1979," *Die Sterne* **59**, 29 (1983).

Scheiner, C.: "ROSA URSINA sine SOL ex admirando facularum et macularum suarum phänomeno varius," Bracciani, 1626–1630.

Tuominen, J.: On the Latitude Drift of Sunspot Groups and Solar Rotation," *Sol. Phys.* **79**, 161 (1982).

Vogt, O.: "Zur Beobachtung der differentiellen Sonnenrotation," *SONNE* **1**, 147 (1977) no. 4.

Waldmeier, M.: "Ergebnisse und Probleme der Sonnenforschung," Leipzig, 1955, p. 50.

Wöhl, H.: "Großräumige Plasmabewegungen auf Sternen," *Sterne und Weltraum* **16**, 363 (1977).

Wöhl, H.: "On the Determination of Heliographic Positions and Rotation Velocities of Sunspots," *Sol. Phys.* **88**, 65 (1983).

B.4. Wilson Effect

Abetti, G.: *The Sun,* London, 1963.

Bray, R.J., Loughhead, R.E.: *Sunspots,* London, 1964, p. 94.

Chistyakov, V.F.: "A Study of the Wilson Effect in Sunspots," *Soviet Astronomy* **5**, 471 (1961).

Chistyakov, V.F.: "On the Observed Depths of Sunspots," *Soviet Astronomy* **6**, 363 (1962).

Jaedicke, H.: "Der Wilson-Effekt—Geschichtliches," Report of the *Olbers-Gesellschaft Bremen,* 1975, no. 1.

Jaedicke, H., Seeck, A.: "Der Wilson-Effekt aus heutiger Sicht," Report of the Olbers-Gesellschaft Bremen, 1975, no. 1.

Jensen, E., Brahde, R., Ofstad,P.: "The Wilson-Effect and the Transparency of Sunspot Models," *Sol. Phys.* **9**, 397 (1969).

Mattig, W.: "Über die Physik der Sonnenflecken," *Sterne und Weltraum* **4**, 152 (1965).

Mattig, W.: "The Geometrical High-Scale and the Pressure Equilibrium in the Sunspot Umbra," *Sol. Phys.* **8**, 291 (1969).

Prokakis, T.: "The Depth of Sunspots," *Sol. Phys.* **35**, 105 (1974).

Seeck, A.: "Untersuchung des Wilson-Effekts," *SONNE* **1**, 70 (1977) no. 2.

Secchi, A.: *Die Sonne,* Braunschweig, 1872.

Waldmeier, M.: "How Close to the Limb Can Sunspots Be Seen?," *Astr. Mitt. Eidgen. Sternw. Zürich* no. 359 (1978).

Wilson, P.R., Cannon, C.J.: "The Structure of a Sunspot, III: Observations of the Wilson Effect," *Sol. Phys.* **4**, 3 (1968).

Wilson, P.R., McIntosh, P.S.: "The Structure of a Sunspot, V: What is the Wilson Effect?," *Sol. Phys.* **10**, 370 (1969).

Wittmann, A.: "Der Wilson-Effekt in Sonnenflecken," *Sterne und Weltraum* **7**, 268 (1968).

B.5. Light Bridges

Abdussamatov, H.I.: "Preliminary results of a study of magnetic field strength in a sunspot with a photospheric bridge," *Solnechn. Danye* 12/1967, 78.

Abdussamatov, H.I.: "The Structure of the Magnetic Field in a Sunspot with a Photospheric Light-bridge at Two Levels in the Solar Atmosphere," *Soviet Astronomy-AJ* **14**, 64 (1970).

Abdussamatov, H.I.: "On the Physical Relation Between the Magnetic Field and the Brightness in the Sunspot-umbrae," *Bull. Astr. Soc. Czech.* **24**, 118 (1973).

Abdussamatov, H.I.: "The Problem of Classification of Light-bridges in Sunspots," *Solnechn. Danye* 1/1974, 91.

Beckers, J.M., Schröter, E.H.: "The Intensity, Velocity and Magnetic Structure of a Sunspot Region, II: Some Properties of Umbral Dots," *Sol. Phys.* **4**, 303 (1968).

Beckers, J.M., Schröter, E.H.: "The Intensity, Velocity and Magnetic Structure of a Sunspot Region, IV: Properties of a Unipolar Sunspot," *Sol. Phys.* **10**, 384 (1969).

Bray, R.J., Loughhead, R.E.: *Sunspots,* Chapman and Hall, London, 1964, p. 90; New York, 1979, p. 89.

Bumba, V.: "Short Note on the Connections Between the Facular Network and Sunspots," *IAU Symp.* no. 22, 192 (1965).

Bumba, V.: "Some Notes on Sunspot Fine Structure," *IAU Symp.* no. 22, 305 (1965).

Bumba, V.: "Observation of Solar Magnetic and Velocity Fields," *Proc. Enrico Fermi School of Physics* **39**, 77 (1967).

Danielson, R.E.: "The Structure of Sunspot Penumbras," *Astrophys. Journal* **134**, 275 (1961).

Hilbrecht, H.: "Lichtbrücken—ein wiederentdecktes Beobachtungsgebiet für den Amateur," *SONNE* **1**, 72 (1977) no. 2.

Hilbrecht, H.: "Verteilungsstatistik von Lichtbrücken," *SONNE* **1**, 145 (1977) no. 4.

Hilbrecht, H.: "Lichtbrücken-Beobachtungsprogramm," *Sterne und Weltraum* **17**, 385 (1978).

Hilbrecht, H.: "Neues Formblatt 'Lichtbrücken' für Beobachtungen erhältlich," *SONNE* **2**, 154 (1978) no. 8.

Hilbrecht, H.: "Lichtbrücken—eine Einführung," *Sterne und Weltraum* **18**, 228 (1979).

Hilbrecht, H.: "Beobachtungsgruppe Lichtbrücken—Zwischenauswertung," *SONNE* **6**, 6 (1982) no. 21.

Kneer, F.: "On Some Characteristics of Umbra Fine Structure," *Sol. Phys.* **28**, 361 (1973).

Korobova, Z.B.: "Photospheric Structure Above a Sunspot," *Soviet Astronomy-AJ* **10**, 380 (1966).

Korobova, Z.B.: "The Ionized Calcium Lines in Spectra of Light Bridges of Sunspots," *Izv. AN Uz. SSR Ser. fiz-matem. n.* 43 (1968) no. 4.

Korobova, Z.B.: "Evolution of Light Bridges," *Solnechn. Danye* 3/1968, pp. 77 and 96.

Macris, C.J.: "The Variations of the Mean Diameter of the Photospheric Granules Near the Sunspots," *Astron. Astrophys.* **78**, 186 (1979).

Mamadasimov, M.M.: "The Evershed Effect in a Spot with a Weak Light Bridge," *Solnechn. Danye* 10/1968, 96.

Minasjants, G.S., Obashev, S.O., Minasjants, T.M.: "Orientation of Light Bridges in Sunspots," *Solnechn. Danye* 9/1971, 72.

Muller, R.: "The Fine Structure of Light Bridges in Sunspots," *Sol. Phys.* **61**, 297 (1979).

Schambeck, C.M.: "Der Teilungsprozeß der Sonnenflecken auf der magnetischen Neutrallinie," *Sterne und Weltraum* **21**, 168 (1982).

Secchi, P.A.: *Die Sonne,* Braunschweig, 1872.

Strebel, H.: "Studium über Sonnenfleckenbrücken," *Astron. Nachr.* **246**, 14 (1932).

Tschistjakov, W.F.: "The Morphologic Peculiarities of Sunspot Fragmentation," *Solnechn. Danye* 3/1968, 70.

Tschistjakov, W.F.: "Kinematic Pecularities of Sunspot Fragmentation," *Solnechn. Danye* 4/1968, 84.

Vazquez, M.: "A Morphologic Study of the Light Bridges in Sunspots," *Sol. Phys.* **31**, 377 (1973).

L'Astronomie 4/1957, 129.

B.6. Photospheric Faculae

Appelt, G., Treutner, H.: "Fotografisches Fackelbeobachtungsprogramm," *SONNE* **6**, 24 (1982) no. 21.

Bispham, K., Hill, H.: "Observations of polar faculae," *J. Brit. Astron. Assoc.* **79** (3), 200 (1969).

Brauckhoff, D.: "Sonnenfackelpositionen – ein Erfahrungsbericht," *SONNE* **10**, 77 (1986) no. 39.

Brauckhoff, D., Delfs, M., Stetter,H.: "Polfackeln – Neuland für den Amateursonnenbeobachter I–V," *SONNE* **10**, 114 (1986) no. 40; *SONNE* **11**, 42 (1987) no. 42; *SONNE* **11**, 79 (1987) no. 43; *SONNE* **12**, 120 (1988) no. 48; *SONNE* **13**, 74 (1989) no. 50.

Bray, R.J.: "High resolution photography of the solar chromosphere II. The relationship between chromospheric and photospheric faculae," *Sol. Phys.* **4**, 318 (1968).

Brown, G.M., Evans, D.P.: "The Use of Solar Faculae in Studies of the Sunspot Cycle," *Sol. Phys.* **66**, 233 (1980).

Brown, G.M., Evans, D.P.: "Latitude Variations of Photospheric Activity Areas with Particular Reference to Solar Faculae," *Sol. Phys.* **68**, 141 (1980).

Bumba, V.: "Do polar faculae terminate or commence an extended cycle of solar activity?," *Bull. Astr. Inst. Czech.* **41**, no. 5, 325 (1990).

Chapman, G.A.: "New models of solar faculae," *Astrophys. Journal* **232**, 923 (1979).

Chapman, G.A.: "Active regions from the photosphere to the chromosphere," *Solar active regions*, 43 (1981), Monograph from Skylab Sol. Workshop III 1978/1979.

Chiang, W.-H., Foukal, P.: "The influence of faculae on sunspot heat blocking," *Sol. Phys.* **97**, no.1, 9 (1985).

Cortesi, S.: "Facules Polaires," *Astr. Mitt. Eidgen. Sternw. Zürich* no. 362 (1978).

Dicke, R.H.: "Why are sunspots dark and faculae bright?," *Astrophys. Journal* **159**, 25 (1970).

Dreyhsig, J.: "Fackeln, Fackelgruppen und Fackelrelativzahl als Maßzahl der Fackelaktivität I–IV," *SONNE* **12**, 46 (1988) no. 46; *SONNE* **12**, 74 (1988) no. 47; *SONNE* **12**, 118 (1988) no. 48; *SONNE* **13**, 76 (1989) no. 50.

Fitton, A.: "Markings at the solar poles near sunspot minimum," *J. Brit. Astron. Assoc.* **75** (4), 236 (1965).

Foukal, P.V.: "The case of the missing faculae," *Bull. American. Astronom. Society* **24**, no. 2, 738 (1992).

Hersé, M.: "Facular Model," *Sol. Phys.* **63**, 35 (1979).

Hirayama, T.: "A Model of Solar Faculae and Their Lifetime," *Publ. Astr. Soc. Japan* **30**, 337 (1978).

Hirayama, T., Mariyama, F.: "Center to Limb Variation of the Intensity of the Photospheric Faculae," *Sol. Phys.* **63**, 251 (1979).

Ivanov, E.V.: "On space-time distribution of faculae and sunspots," *Solnechn. Danye.* 7/1986, 61.

Jahn, J.: "Breitenverteilung von Fackelherden," *SONNE* **6**, 22 (1982) no. 39.

Knŏska, Š.: "The initial phase of development of chromospheric faculae," *Bull. Astr. Inst. Czech.* **28**, 114 (1977).

Kononovich, E.V.: "On the geometry of facular granules," *Astr. Tsirk.* no. 670, 5 (1972), in Russian.

Kononovich, E.V., Shakura, N.N.: "On possible sources of solar radio emission connected with polar faculae," *Astr. Tsirk.* no. 872, 2 (1975), in Russian.

Kramynin, A.P.: "Morphological pecularities of photospheric faculae," *Sol. phenomena research*, Vladivostok, 111 (1975), in Russian.

Kramynin, A.P.: "Longitude distribution of photospheric faculae and the sector structure of the interplanetary magnetic field," *Solnechn. Danye.* 9/1978, 95.

Krat, V.A., Stojawa, M.N.: "On the Structure of Solar Faculae," *Sol. Phys.* **20**, 57 (1971).

Kusminych, W.D.: "A model of an average facula," *Astrophys. Journal USSR* **41**, 692 (1964), in Russian.

Makarov, V.I., Makarova, V.V.: "On the structure of polar faculae," *Solnechn. Danye.* 12/1984, 89.

Makarov, V.I., Makarova, V.V.: "On the latitude migration of polar faculae in the solar activity cycle," *Journ. Astrophys. Astron.* **7**, no. 2, 113 (1986).

Makarov, V.I., Makarova V.V., Sivaraman, K.R.: "Butterfly diagram for polar faculae and sunspots during 1940–1985," *Solnechn. Danye.* 4/1987, 70.

Makarov, V.I., Makarova, V.V., Sivaraman, K.R.: "Do polar faculae predict a sunspot cycle?," *Sol. Phys.* **119**, no.1, 45 (1989).

Makarova,V.V.: "On polar faculae in the 20th solar cycle," *Solnechn. Danye.* 5/1978, 99.

Makarova, V.V., Solonskij, Yu.A.: "Differential rotation of polar regions of the solar atmospheres," *Solnechn. Danye.* 12/1986, 56.

Mehltretter, J.P.: "Die Feinstruktur von photosphärischen Fackeln," *Mitteil. Astronom. Gesellschaft* no. 36, 138 (1975).

Muller, R.: "The dynamical behavior of facular points in the quiet photosphere," *Sol. Phys.* **85**, no. 1, 113 (1983).

Nagovitsyn, Yu. A.: "North–south asymetry of solar activity in the equatorial and polar zones," *Solnechn. Danye.* 7/1989, 71.

Nagovitsyn, Yu.A., Nagovitsyna, E.Yu.: "A study of the velocity field of polar faculae," *Solnechn. Danye.* 12/1986, 52.

Ni, X.-b., Jiang, Y.-t., Chen, Z.-z., Fang, C.: "A possible mechanism for the formation of faculae," *Chin. Astronom. Astrophys.* **9**, no. 4, 273 (1985).

Reinsch, K.: "Anmerkungen zur Auswertung von Beobachtungen polarer Fackeln," *SONNE* **13**, 22 (1989) no. 49.

Saito, K., Tanaka,Y.: "Polar faculae of the sun," *Publ. Astr. Soc. Japan* **9**, 106 (1957).

Saito, K., Tanaka,Y.: "Addition to Polar faculae of the sun," *Publ. Astr. Soc. Japan* **9**, 210 (1957).

Saito, K., Tanaka,Y.: "Polar faculae of the sun III," *Publ. Astr. Soc. Japan* **12**, 556 (1960).

Schatten, K.H.: "A hillock and cloud model for faculae," *Astrophys. Journal* **311**, 460 (1986).

Schatten, K.H., Mayr, H.G., Orosz, J.: "Do faculae blanket sunspots?," *Bull. American. Astr. Soc.* **20**, no. 4, 988 (1988).

Sheeley, N.R. Jr.: "Polar faculae: 1906–1990," *Astrophys. Journal* **374**, 306 (1991).

Stahl, M.: "Simulation von Fackelstrukturen mit TRS-80," *SONNE* **4**, 64 (1980) no. 14.

Stetter, H.: "Häufigkeitsverteilungen photosphärischer Fackeln, getrennt nach heliografischen Breiten und Fackeltypen mit zugehörigen Sichtbarkeitsfunktionen," *SONNE* **10**, 78 (1986) no. 39.

Stetter, H.: "Änderungen in der Breitenverteilung der Polfackeln," *SONNE* **14**, 11 (1990) no. 56.

Stojanowa, M.N.: "Structure peculiarities of facula fields," *Solnechn. Danye.* 7/1989, 86.

Stojanowa, M.N.: "On the contrast dependence of polar faculae," *Solnechn. Danye.* 3/1990, 81.

Szymanski, W.: "Photospheric faculae 1966–1970," *Acta Geophys. Polonia* **23**, no.1, 105 (1975).

Tanaka, Y.: "Polar faculae of the sun IV," *Publ. Astr. Soc. Japan* **16**, 336 (1964).

Waldmeier, M.: "Breitenverteilung und Sichtbarkeitsfunktion der polaren Fackeln," *Astronomische Mitteilungen Zürich* no. 251 (1962).

Waldmeier, M.: "Polare Fackeln," *Zeitschr. f. Astrophys.* **38**, 37 (1955).

Wiehr, E., Stellmacher, G.: "Ein Modell für solare Filigrees und Fackeln," *Mitt. Astron. Ges.* **45**, 149 (1979).

Wilson, P.R.: "Faculae, Filigree and Calcium Bright Points," *Sol. Phys.* **69**, 9 (1981).

Willis, D.M., Tulunag, Y.N.: "Statistics of the Largest Sunspot and Faculae Areas Per Solar Cycle," *Sol. Phys.* **64**, 234 (1979).

Yimaz, F.:   "Über die Veränderung der Fackelflächen in Sonnenak-
tivitätszentren," *Publ. Istanbul Univ. Obs.* **78**, 63 (1964).

Zachariadis, T.G.: "Bright faculae points (filigree) in active regions," *Publ.
Astr. Inst. Czechoslovakia Acad. Sci.* no. 66, 37 (1987).

B.7. Granulation

Birkle, K.:   "Über das Verhalten der photosphärischen Granulation im
Fleckenzyklus," *Zeitschr. f. Astrophys.* **66**, 252 (1967).

Bray, R.J., Loughhead, R.E.:   "Observation of Changes in the Photospheric
Granules," *Austr. J. Phys.* **11**, 507 (1958).

Bray, R.J., Loughhead, R.E., Durrant, C.J.: *The Solar Granulation,* Cambridge University Press, p. 256 (1984).

Macris, C.J.:   "The Variation of the Mean Diameters of the Photospheric
Granules Near the Sunspots," *Astron. Astrophys.* **78**, 186 (1979).

Mehltretter, J.P.:   "Was wissen wir von der Granulation?," *Sterne und Weltraum* **17**, 207 (1978).

Schröter, E.H.:   "Die Sonnengranulation I," *Sterne und Weltraum* **2**, 100
(1963).

Schröter, E.H.:   "Die Sonnengranulation II," *Sterne und Weltraum* **2**, 127
(1963).

Tschistjakov, W.F.: *Solnechn. Danye* 3/1964, 56.

Wittmann, A.:   "Small Scale Motions on the Sun," Colloquium held on the
occasion of change of the name of the former Fraunhofer-Institut into
Kiepenheuer-Institut für Sonnenphysik, Freiburg, 1–3 Nov. 1978, p. 29.

B.8. Amateur Magnetic Field Observation

Beckers, J.M., Schröter, E.H.:   "The Intensity, Velocity and Magnetic Structure of a Sunspot Region," *Sol. Phys.* **10**, 384 (1969).

Bumba, V.:   "Results of the Investigation of the Single Sunspot Magnetic
Field," *J. Astron. Obs. Krim* no. 23, 213 (1960).

Jäger, F.W.:   "Solar Magnetic Fields," *Oss. Astron. di Roma Contributi
Scientifici,* Series III, 166 (1966) no. 44.

Klüber, H.v.:   "Über den Nachweis und die Messung lokaler Magnetfelder
auf der Sonnenoberfläche," *Zeitschr. f. Astrophys.* **24**, 121 (1948).

Künzel, H.:   "Über den Zusammenhang zwischen Penumbraformen und
magnetischer Polaritätsverteilung in Sonnenfleckengruppen," *Astron.
Nachr.* **291**, 265 (1969).

Veeder, G.J., Zirin, H.:   "The Chromospheric Magnetograph," *Sol. Phys.*
12, 391 (1970).

Veio, F.N.:   "Polaritätsbestimmungen an Sonnenflecken mit dem Spektrohelioskop," *Orion* **33**, 48 (1975) no. 147.

Wiehr, E.: "Messung von Magnetfeldern auf der Sonne," *Sterne und Weltraum* **9**, 65 (1970).

B.9. Solar Observation in Hα Light

B.9.3. Chromosphere

Athay, R.G.: *Chromospheric Fine Structure,* Dordrecht, 1974.

Athay, R.G.: *The Solar Chromosphere and Corona,* Dordrecht, 1976.

Athay, R.G., Thomas, R.N.: "The Chromosphere Near Active Regions, The Number and Motions of Solar Spicules," *Astrophys. Journal* **125**, 1957.

Böhm-Vitense, E.: "Die Sonnenchromosphäre," *Zeitschr. f. Astrophys.* **36**, 145 (1955).

Beckers, J.M.: in *Illustrated Glossary for Solar and Solar-terrestrial Physics,* Bruzek, A. und C.J. Durrant, Dordrecht, 1977, p. 26.

Bray, R.J.: "High-Resolution Photography of the Solar Chromosphere," *Sol. Phys.* **4**, 318 (1968).

Bray, R.J., Loughhead, R.E.: *The Solar Chromosphere,* London, 1974.

Bruzek, A.: "Über die Spikulen auf der Sonnenscheibe," *Zeitschr. f. Astrophys.* **47**, 191 (1959).

Hale, G.E.: "The Spectrohelioscope and its Work," *Astrophys. Journal* **70**, 285 (1929).

Hale, G.E., Ellerman, F.: "The Rumford Spectroheliograph of the Yerkes Observatory," *Publ. of the Yerkes Obs.* **3**, Part I, 1 (1903).

Hale, G.E., Ellerman, F.: "Calcium and Hydrogen Flocculi," *Astrophys. Journal* **19**, 41 (1904).

Kiepenheuer, K.O.: "Erfahrungen mit einem Lyotschen Hα-Filter sowie vorläufige Ergebnisse über die Struktur der Chromosphäre," *Zeitschr. f. Astrophys.* **42**, 209 (1957).

Kiepenheuer, K.O.: "The Fine Structure of the Solar Atmosphere (Colloquium at Anacapri 1966)," *Research Report no. 12 of the Deutsche Forschungsgemeinschaft,* Franz Steiner Verlag, Wiesbaden, 1966.

Kiepenheuer, K.O.: *Structure and Development of Solar Active Regions,* Dordrecht, 1968.

Kuiper, G.P.: *The Sun,* Chicago, 1962.

Lippincott, S.: "Chromosph. Spicules," *Smithonian Contr. Astrophys.* **2**, 15, 1957.

Macris, C.: "Recherches Sur Les Spicules en Projection Sur la Disque Solaire," *Ann. d'Astrophysique* **20**, 179 (1957).

Martres, M.J., Bruzek, A.: in *Illustrated Glossary for Solar and Solar-Terrestrial Physics,* A. Bruzek, Dordrecht, 1977, p. 65.

Mitchell, S.A.: *Eclipses of the Sun,* Columbia, 1935.

Rush, J.H., Roberts, W.O.: "Recent Studies of Chromospheric Spicules," *Austr. J. Phys.* **7**, 230 (1954).

Secchi, A.: *Die Sonne,* Braunschweig, 1872.

Tandberg-Hanssen, E.: *Solar Prominences,* Dordrecht, 1974.

Trombino, D.F.: "Solar Observing Through Rose Coloured Glasses," *Astronomy Now,* vol. V, no. 2, **22** (1991).

Trombino, D.F.: "Observing the Sun With the Solaris H Telescope System," *Sky & Telescope,* vol. 84, no. 2, p. 145 (1992).

Trombino, D.F.: "The Sun: Our Amazing Daytime Star," *Journal of Arts & Sciences,* Museum of Arts & Sciences, Daytona Beach, Florida, Spring 1992.

Woltjer, L.: "A Photometric Investigation of the Spicules and the Structure of the Chromosphere," *Bull. Astr. Netherlands* **12**, 165 (1954).

B.9.4. Prominences/Filaments

Athay, R.G.: "Velocity Effects on the Profiles of Hα and Two FeI Lines," *Sol. Phys.* **12**, 175 (1970).

d' Azambuja: "Ann. de l'Observatoire de Paris" (Meudon) **6**, no. 7 (1948).

Becker, U.: "Über Protuberanzen und Filamente," *Die Sterne* **27**, 76 (1951).

Beckers, J.M.: *Thesis,* Utrecht, 1964.

Beckers, J.M.: "Solar Spicules," *Sol. Phys.* **3**, 367 (1968).

Bendel, U.: "Bestimmung der Ausdehnung von Sonnenflecken mit Hilfe eines Mikrometer-Plättchens," *Special Publ. Darmstadt Obs.,* Darmstadt, 1975.

Bendel, U., Kunz, W.: "Flecken-Fackeln-Filamente," *Special Publ. Darmstadt Obs.,* Darmstadt, 1975, p. 10.

Bruzek, A.: "Motions in Arch Filament Systems," *Sol. Phys.* **8**, 29 (1969).

Bulczynski, G.: "Detailbeobachtungen auf der Sonne," Philips Contest, 1973, p. 18.

Catanina Solar Observations (yearly).

Dara, H.C., Macris, C.J.: *Study on the Motion of Three Solar Prominences,* Athens, 1978.

Desző, L.: "Beispiele von Bewegungen in Protuberanzen auf Grund von Aufnahmen mit dem Koronographen," *Publ. Eidgen. Sternw. Zürich* **7**, p. 37 (1940) nos. 2/3.

Engvold, O.: "The Fine Structure of Prominences," *Sol. Phys.* **49**, 283 (1976).

Fritz, U.: "Methoden zur Positionsbestimmung von Sonnenflecken," *SONNE* **1**, 66 (1977) no. 2.

Fritz, U., Treutner, H., Vogt, O.: "Positionsbestimmung von Sonnenflecken," *Orion* **33**, 38 (1975) no. 147.

Giovanelli, R.G.: "The Motion of Eruptive Prominences," *Astrophys. Journal* **91**, 83 (1940).

Grossmann-Doerth, U., Uexküll, M.v.: "Spectral Investigation of Chromospheric Fine Structure," *Sol. Phys.* **20**, 31 (1971).

Grotrian, W. et al.: "Klassifikation der Protuberanzen," in: *Zur Erforschung des Weltalls*, Berlin, 1934, p. 152.

Haupt, H., Ellerbrock, W.: "Die aufsteigende Protuberanz vom 11. April 1959, I. Beschreibung des Aufstiegs," *Zeitschr. f. Astrophys.* **49**, 192 (1960).

Haupt, K.-P.: "Aktivitätserscheinungen auf der Sonne," *Korona* (Astr. Soc. Kassel) 4/1977, 21, no. 14.

Izsák, I.: "Bewegungen in Sonnenprotuberanzen, II. Beschreibung des Protuberanzenaufstieges vom 18. Juli 1956," *Zeitschr. f. Astrophys.* **45**, 91 (1958) = *Astr. Mitt. Eidgen. Sternw. Zürich* no. 213.

Jones, F.S.: "Classification of Solar Prominences," *J. Astr. Soc. Canada* **52**, 149 (1958).

Keenan, P.C.: "Observations of Radial Movements of Prominences," *Astrophys. Journal* **83**, 55 (1936).

Klaus, G.: "Der Protuberanzenaufstieg vom 25. März 1967," *Orion* **32**, 52 (1974) no. 141.

Klaus, G; Moser, E., Schaedler, H.J.: "Protuberanzen 1969," *Orion* **28**, 69 (1970).

Klepešta, J.: "Eine bemerkenswerte Erscheinung in der Sonnenchromosphäre," *Orion* **25**, 105 (1967) no. 102.

Krause, A.: *Die Sonne*, B.G. Teubner Verlag, Leipzig, 1911, p. 84.

Larmore, L.: "A Study of the Motions of Solar Prominences," *Astrophys. Journal* **118**, 436 (1953).

Leitmeier, E.: "Protuberanzenbeobachtungen an 100 Tagen," *VdS-Nachr.* 8/1967, p. 43.

Lille, W.: "Protuberanzenbeobachtungen," *SONNE* **2**, 134 (1978) no. 8.

Maiwald, D., Paech, W., Völker, P.: "Große Protuberanz am 30.7.1977 —Manila—NOAA—-WFS," *SONNE* **2**, 27 (1978) no. 5.

Mangis, S.J.: NOAA Technical Report ERL 315-SEL 32: "Introduction to Solar Terrestrial Phenomena and the Space Environment Services Center," pp. 14 and 30 (1975).

Mattig, W.: "Die Häufigkeit der Sonnenflecken," *Sterne und Weltraum* **2**, 196 (1963).

McMath, R.R.: "The Structure of the Nearest Star," *Journal of the Society of Motion Picture Engineers*, 3/1939, p. 264.

McMath, R.R., Pettit, E.: "Prominence Studies," *Astrophys. Journal* **88**, 244 (1938).

Menzel, D.H.: "Classification of Solar Prominences," *Astron. Journal* **56**, 135 (1951).

Newton, H.W.: "The Distribution of Radial Velocities of Dark Hα Markings near Sunspots," *Mon. Not. Roy. Astron. Soc.* **94**, 472 (1934).

Newton, H.W.: "Note on Two Alied Types of Chromospheric Eruptions," *Mon. Not. Roy. Astron. Soc.* **95**, 650 (1935).

Paech, W.: "Kodak SO-115," *SONNE* **2**, 61 (1978) no. 6.

Paech, W.: "Eine außergewöhnlich aktive Protuberanzen-Erscheinung," *Sterne und Weltraum* **17**, 266 (1978).

Paech, W.: "Beobachtung einer eruptiven Protuberanz," *SONNE* **3**, 98 (1979) no. 11.

Paech, W., Völker, P.: "Große Protuberanz am 30.7.1977," *SONNE* **2**, 64 (1978) no. 6.

Pettit, E.: "The Forms and Motions of the Solar Prominences," *Publ. Yerkes Obs.* **3**, 205 (1925).

Pettit, E.: "Characteristic Features of Solar Prominences," *Astrophys. Journal* **76**, 9 (1932).

Pettit, E.: "The Motions of Prominences of the Eruptive and Sun-spot Types," *Astrophys. Journal* **84**, 319. (1936)

Pettit, E.: "The Properties of Solar Prominences as Related to Type," *Astrophys. Journal* **98**, 6 (1943).

Pettit, E.: "The Evidence for Tornado Prominences," *Publ. Astr. Soc. of the Pacific* **62**, 144 (1950).

Pettit, E.: "The Motion of Eruptive Prominences," *Publ. Astr. Soc. of the Pacific* **63**, 237 (1951).

Pettit, E.: "Prominence Studies" in Ingall's *ATM III,* p. 427 (1961).

Rustad, B.M.: "Protuberanser," *Astronomisk Tidskrift* **6**, 6 (1973).

Saul, A.: "Astronomie bei Tageslicht," Astron. Soc. Hamburg, 1975, p. 34.

Saupe, H.: "Beobachtungen am Protuberanzenfernrohr der Feriensternwarte Calina in Carona/Schweiz," *Publ. Darmstadt Obs.* **4**, 109 (1972).

Scheffler, H., Elsässer, H.: "Physik der Sterne und der Sonne," *Bibl. Inst.,* Mannheim, 1974.

Secchi, P.A.: "Die verschiedenen Formen der Chromosphäre und der Protuberanzen," in: *Die Sonne,* Braunschweig, 1872, p. 425.

Severny, A.: *Solar Physics,* Foreign Languages Publishing House, Moskow, 1959, p. 120.

Shapley, A.H. et al.: *International Ursigram and World Days Service I.U.W.D.S., Synoptic Codes for Solar and Geophysical Data,* 3rd revised edition, pp. 181 and 185 (1973).

Smith, H.J., Smith, E.V.P.: *Solar Flares,* The Macmillan Co., New York, 1963, p. 26.

Tandberg-Hanssen, E.: *Solar Prominences,* Dordrecht, 1974.

Unsöld, A.: *Physik der Sternatmosphären,* Berlin, 1955.

Völker, P.: "Visuelle Beobachtung einer eruptiven Sonnenprotuberanz," *Sterne und Weltraum* **8**, 111 (1969).

Völker, P.: "Die Protuberanzenbeobachtung des Amateurs," *Sterne und Weltraum* **9**, 14 (1970).

Waldmeier, M.: "Aufsteigende Protuberanzen," *Zeitschr. f. Astrophys.* **15**, 299 (1938).

Waldmeier, M.: "Bewegungen in aufsteigenden Protuberanzen," *Zeitschr. f. Astrophys.* **18**, 241 (1939).

Waldmeier, M.: *Ergebnisse und Probleme der Sonnenforschung,* Akademische Verlagsgesellschaft, Leipzig, 1941, pp. 207, 209, 211.

Waldmeier, M.: "Strömungen in Sonnenprotuberanzen I, ein neues Gesetz für Protuberanzenbewegungen," *Zeitschr. f. Astrophys.* **21**, 130 (1942).

Waldmeier, M.: "Bewegungen in Sonnenprotuberanzen, I. Aufsteigendes polares Filament," *Zeitschr. f. Astrophys.* **44**, 213 (1958) = *Astr. Mitt. Eidgen. Sternw. Zürich* no. 212.

Waldmeier, M.: "Bewegungen in Sonnenprotuberanzen, V. Eine direkte Beobachtung des Solar Wind," *Zeitschr. f. Astrophys.* **53**, 198 (1961).

Waldmeier, M.: *Astr. Mitt. Eidgen. Sternw. Zürich* no. 343 (1976).

Waldmeier, M.: "The Ascending Prominence of June 23, 1942," *Astr. Mitt. Eidgen. Sternw. Zürich* no. 348 (1976).

Waldmeier, M., Beck, B.: "Strömungen in Sonnenprotuberanzen II, Aufwärtsbewegungen," *Zeitschr. f. Astrophys.* **21**, 286 (1942).

Wattenberg, D.: "Die Statistik und Periodizität der Protuberanzen," *Die Sterne* **16**, 95 (1936).

Westin, H., Liszka, L.: "Motions of Ascending Prominences," *Sol. Phys.* **11**, 409 (1970).

Wöhl, H.: "Bewegungen in solaren Loop-Protuberanzen," *Sterne und Weltraum* **8**, 237 (1969).

Wöss, W.: "Amateur-Beobachtung der Sonne im Hα-Licht," *Der Sternenbote* (Wien) 5/1977, p. 83.

B.9.5. Flares

Abetti, G.: *The Sun,* London, 1962, pp. 107 and 329.

Avignon, Y., Martres, M.J., Pick, M.: "Identification de Classes d'Éruptions Chromosphériques Associées aux Émissions de Rayons Cosmiques et à l'Activité Radioélectrique," *Ann. Astrophys.* **27**, 23 (1964).

Behr, A., Siedentopf, H.: "Zur Statistik von Sonneneruptionen," *Zeitschr. f. Astrophys.* **30**, 177 (1952).

Bendel, U.: "Der große Sonnenfleck vom Juli 1978," *Publ. Darmstadt Obs.* **10**, 86 (1978).

Bray, R.J., Loughhead, R.E.: *The Solar Chromosphere,* London, 1974, p. 227.

Bruzek, A.: *Mitt. Sonnenobs. Kanzelhöhe* 4/1951.

Bruzek, A.: "Die Filamente und Eruptionen eines Aktivtätszentrums," *Zeitschr. f. Astrophys.* **44**, 183 (1958).

Bruzek, A.: "Beobachtungen über das Verhalten von Filamenten während chromosphärischer Eruptionen," *Zeitschr. f. Astrophys.* **28**, 277 (1951).

Bruzek, A.: "Anzeiger d.Österr." *Akad. d. Wiss.* **12**, no. 6 (1951).

Bruzek, A.: "Sonneneruptionen I," *Sterne und Weltraum* **5**, 228 (1966).

Bruzek, A.: "Sonneneruptionen II," *Sterne und Weltraum* **5**, 260 (1966).

Bruzek, A.: "Hα-Strukturen in Fleckengruppen," *Sterne und Weltraum* **7**, 88 (1968).

Bruzek, A., Durrant, C.J.: *Illustrated Glossary for Solar and Solar-Terrestrial Physics,* Dordrecht, 1977, p. 81.

Bumba, V., Krivsky, L., Martres, M.J., Soru-Iscovici, I.: "Flare Activity and Sunspot Groups Development" in Kiepenheuer, K.O. (ed.): *IAU Symposium* no. 35, p. 311, Dordrecht, 1968.

Catania Solar Observations, Catania (yearly).

Dezsö, L.: "Sunspot Motions and Magnetic Shears as Precursors of Flares," *Adv. Space Research* **4**, 57 (1984) no. 7.

Dodson, H.W., Hedeman, E.R.: "Major Hα Flares in Centers of Activity with Very Small or No Spots," *Sol. Phys.* **13**, 401 (1970).

Ellerman, F.: "Solar Hydrogen 'Bombs,' "*Astrophys. Journal* **46**, 298 (1917).

Ellison, M.A.: "Characteristic Properties of Chromospheric Flares," *Mon. Not. Roy. Astron. Soc.* **109**, 3 (1949).

Ellison, M.A., McKenna, S.M.P., Reid, J.H.: "Light-Curves of 30 Solar Flares," *Dunsink Obs. Publ.* **1**, 3 (1960).

Elwert, G.: "Die Röntgenabbildung der Sonne und ihr Beitrag zur Koronaforschung I.," *Sterne und Weltraum* **17**, 193 (1978).

Elwert, G.: "Die Röntgenabbildung der Sonne und ihr Beitrag zur Koronaforschung II.," *Sterne und Weltraum* **17**, 236 (1978).

Fokker, A.D.: "Homology of Solar Flare-Associated Radio Events," *Sol. Phys.* **2**, 316 (1967).

Gesztelyi, L.: "Consecutive Homologous Flares and Their Relation to Sunspot Motion," *Adv. Space Research* **4**, 19 (1984) no. 7.

Giovanelli, R.G.: "The Relations Between Eruptions and Sunspots," *Astrophys. Journal* **89**, 555 (1939).

Gopasiuk, S.I., Ogir, M.B., Severny, A.B., Shapshnikova, E.F.: "The Structure of Magnetic Fields and Its Variations in Flare Regions," *Izv. Krym. Astrofiz. Obs.* **29**, 15 (1963).

Hale, G.E.: "The Spectrohelioscope and Its Work III: Solar Eruptions and Their Apparent Terrestrial Effects," *Astrophys. Journal* **73**, 379 (1931).

Haupt, K.-P.: "Aktivitätserscheinungen auf der Sonne," *Korona* (Astr. Assoc. Kassel) **14**, 22 (1977).

Hess, W.N. (ed.): "The Physics of Solar Flares," *Proc. AAS—NASA-Symposium,* Goddard Space Flight Center 1963, NASA, Washington, 1964.

Hunter, A.: "Short-Lived Hα Prominences Observed on the Sun's Disk," *The Observatory* **64**, 201 (1942).

Hyder, C.: "A Phenomenological Model for Disparitions Brusques," *Sol. Phys.* **2**, 49 and 267 (1967).

Kalman, B.: "Magnetic Field Structure Changes in the Vicinity of Solar Flares," *Adv. Space Research* **4**, 81 (1984) no. 7.

Kiepenheuer, K.O.: *The Sun,* Ann Arbor, 1959.

Kiepenheuer, K.O.: in *The Sun,* Kuiper, G.P., Chicago, 1962, pp. 376 and 696.

Kiepenheuer, K.O.: "Die magnetischen Erscheinungen auf der Sonne," *Sterne und Weltraum* **3**, 178 (1964).

Kundu, M.R.: *Solar Radio Astronomy,* Interscience Publishers, Div. of John Wiley and Sons, New York, 1965.

Künzel, H.: "Die Flare-Häufigkeit in Fleckengruppen unterschiedlicher Klasse und magnetischer Struktur," *Astron. Nachr.* **285**, 271 (1960) = *Mitt. d. Astrophys. Obs. Potsdam* no. 87.

Loughhead, R.E.: "High Resolution Photography of the Solar Chromosphere, III.: The Fine Structure of A Class I Flare," *Sol. Phys.* **4**, 422 (1968).

Maag, R., Hancock, D.: "Observe and Understand the Sun," Astronomical League, 1976, p. 41.

Mangis, S.J.: NOAA Technical Report ERL 315-SEL 32: "Introduction to Solar Terrestrial Phenomena and the Space Environment Services Center," Boulder, 1975, p. 26.

Mattig, W.: "Erscheinungen der Sonnenoberfläche," *Sterne und Weltraum* **1**, 165 (1962).

McIntosh, P.S., Donnelly, R.F.: "Properties of White Light Flares," *Sol. Phys.* **23**, 444 (1972).

McKenna-Lawlor, S.M.P.: "An Identification of Three Different Varieties of Solar Flare," *Astrophys. Journal* **153**, 367 (1968).

McMath, R.R., Mohler, O.C., Dodson, H.W.: "Solar Features Associated with Ellerman's Solar Hydrogen Bombs," *Proc. Nat. Acad. Sci.* **46**, 165 (1960).

Menzel, D.H.: *Our Sun,* Cambridge, 1959.

Müller, R.: "Im integralen Licht sichtbare Sonneneruptionen," *Die Natur-wissenschaften* **38**, 545 (1951).

Müller, R.: "Sonnenüberwachung wofür?," *Sterne und Weltraum* **7**, 38 (1968).

Newton, H.W.: "Solar Flares at the Sun's Limb," *J. Brit. Astron. Assoc.* **57**, 54 (1947).

Paech, W.: "Kodak SO-115," *SONNE* **2**, 61 (1978) no. 6.

Petri, W.: "Eruptionen auf der Sonne," *Die Sterne* **28**, 181 (1952).

Pike, R.C., Kunz, W.: "Flare-Beobachtung im weißen Sonnenlicht," *Mitt. Darmstadt Obs.* **6**, 120 (1974).

Rust, D.M., Hegwer, F.: "Analysis of the Aug. 7, 1972 White Light Flare," *Sol. Phys.* **40**, 141 (1975).

Seiler, M.: "Die Sonnenaktivität im Juli und August 1975," *Sterne und Weltraum* **14**, 373 (1975).

Shapley, A.H.: *International Ursigram and World Days Service IUWDS, Synoptic Codes for Solar and Geophysical Data*, 3rd rev. ed., 1973, pp. 11 and 134.

Smith, H.J., Smith, E.v.P.: *Solar Flares*, New York, 1963.

Smith, S.F., Harvey, K.L.: in *Physics of the Solar Corona*, Macris, C. (ed.) Dordrecht, 1971, p. 156.

Smith, S.F., Ramsey, H.E.: "Flare Positions Relative to Photospheric Magnetic Fields," *Sol. Phys.* **2**, 158 (1967).

Solar Section of the B.A.A.: "The Observation of Solar Flares and the Work of the Solar Section," *J. Brit. Astron. Assoc.* **86**, 232 (1976).

Švestka, Z.: "Motions in Chromospheric Flares," *Bull. Astr. Inst. Czech.* **13**, 190 (1962).

Švestka, Z.: "Mass Motions in Flares Indicated by Line Profiles and Filter-grams," in Öhman, Y. (ed.): "Mass Motions in Solar Flares and Related Phenomena," *Proc. Ninth Nobel Symposium*, p. 17, Almqvist och Wiksell, Stockholm, 1968.

Švestka, Z.: "The Phase of Particle Acceleration in the Flare Development," *Sol. Phys.* **13**, 471 (1970).

Švestka, Z.: *Solar Flares*, Dordrecht, 1976.

Tandberg-Hanssen, E.: Earth Extraterrest. Sci. **2**, 89 (1973).

Uchida, Y., Altschuler, M.D., Newkirk, G.J.: "Flare-Produced Coronal MHD-fast-mode Wavefronts and Moreton's Wave Phenomenon," *Sol. Phys.* **28**, 495 (1973).

Uchida, Y., Hudson, H.: "Search for Weak White-Light Flares by Time-Wise Photographic Cancellation," *Sol. Phys.* **26**, 414 (1972).

Veio, F.N.: *The Sun in H-α Light with a Spectrohelioscope*, Clearlake Park, 1972, p. 10.

Vorpahl, J.A.: "X-Radiation, Hα and Microwave Emission During the Impulsive Phase of Solar Flares," *Sol. Phys.* **26**, 397 (1972).

Waldmeier, M.: "Chromosphärische Eruptionen I," *Zeitschr. f. Astrophys.* **16**, 276 (1938).

Waldmeier, M.: "Chromosphärische Eruptionen II," *Zeitschr. f. Astrophys.* **20**, 46 (1940).

Waldmeier, M.: *Ergebnisse und Probleme der Sonnenforschung,* Leipzig, 1941, p. 192.

Waldmeier, M.: *Astr. Mitt. Eidgen. Sternw. Zürich* no. 153 (1948).

Waldmeier, M., Bachmann, H.: "Statistik der Sonneneruptionen 1945–1954," *Zeitschr. f. Astrophys.* **47**, 81 (1959).

Waldmeier, M.: *Sonne und Erde,* Zürich, 1959, p. 106.

Zirin, H.: "Solar Flares," *Vistas Astron.* **16**, 1 (1974).

B.9.6. Chromospheric Faculae (Plages)

Kiepenheuer, K.O.: *The Sun,* Ann Arbor 1959.

Mangis, S.J.: NOAA Technical Report ERL 315-SEL 32: "Introduction to Solar Terrestrial Phenomena and the Space Environment Services Center," Boulder, 1975, p. 20.

Rothe, R.: "Beziehungen zwischen chromosphärischen und photosphärischen Fackeln," *SONNE* **3**, 154 (1979) no. 12.

Tandberg-Hanssen, E.: *Solar Prominences,* Dordrecht, 1974.

Waldmeier, M.: *Ergebnisse und Probleme der Sonnenforschung,* Leipzig, 1941, p. 233.

B.10. The Aurora

Akasofu, S.I.: *Polar and Magnetospheric Substorms,* Reidel, 1969.

Akasofu, S.I., Kamide, Y., (Eds.) *The Solar Wind and The Earth,* Reidel, Dordrecht, 1987.

Bartels, J., *Geomagnetism,* Oxford, 1970.

Bone, N., *The Aurora,* Ellis Horwood, London, 1991.

Brekke, A., Egeland, A.: *The Northern Lights from Mythology to Space Research,* Springer, Berlin, 1983.

Eather, R.H.: "The Majestic Light, the Aurora in Science, History and the Arts," American Geophysical Union, Washington D.C., 1980.

Eather, R.H., Mende, S.B.: *Auroral Precipation Patterns, The Radiating Atmosphere,* Reidel, 1971.

Ellison, M.A.: *The Sun and its Influence,* Routledge Kegan, Paul, London, 1968.

Evans, D.S., Jessop, G.R.: *VHF–UHF Manual,* Radio Society of Great Britain, London, 1978.

Fritz, H.: *Das Polarlicht,* F.A. Brockhaus, Leipzig, 1881.

Harang, L.: *The Aurora,* International Astrophysical Series, Chapman & Hall, 1981.

Hargreaves, J.K.: *The Upper Atmosphere and Solar–Terrestrial Relations,* Van Norstrand, London, 1979.

International Geodesic and Geophysical Union: "Photographic Atlas of Auroral Forms and Scheme for Visual Observations of Aurorae," Broggers, Oslo, 1930.

International Geodesic and Geophysical Union: "Supplements to the Photographic Atlas of Auroral Forms," Broggers, Boktrygger, A/S Oslo, 1932.

International Union of Geodesy and Geophysics: *The International Aurora Atlas,* Edinburgh University Press, 1963.

I.T.T.: *Reference Data for Radio Engineers,* Indianapolis, 1977.

Legrand, J.P.: "Introduction Elementaire à la Physique Cosmique et à la Physique des Relations Soleil–Terre," CNRS–INAG, France, 1984.

Meng, C.I., Rycroft, M.J., Frank, L.A., (Eds.): *Auroral Physics,* Cambridge U.P., Cambridge, 1991.

Newton, C., *Radio Auroras,* Radio Society of Great Britain, Potters Bar, 1991.

Newton, H.W.: *The Face of the Sun,* Pelican, 1958.

Omholt, A.: *The Optical Aurora,* Springer, Berlin, 1971.

Ratcliffe, J.A.: *Physics of the Upper Atmosphere,* Academic Press, 1980.

C. Solar Eclipses

C.1. An Introduction to Solar Eclipses

C.1.1. Preparing an Expedition to Observe a Solar Eclipse

Beck, R.: "Die Beobachtung totaler Sonnenfinsternisse," *SONNE* **3**, 102 (1979) no. 11.

Brewer, B.: *Eclipse,* Seattle, 1978, 1991.

Dyer, A.: "When Worlds Align," *Astronomy* **19** no. 7/1991, 62.

Espenak, F.: "The Total Solar Eclipse of 1981," *Star & Sky,* vol. II, no. 10, p. 32, (1980).

Fiala, A.D., De Young, J.A., Lukac, M.R.: "Solar Eclipses, 1991–2000," *U.S. Naval Circular* **170**, Washington, 1986.

Littmann, M., Willcox, K.: *Totality—Eclipses of the Sun,* Honolulu, 1991.

Meeus, J.: *Canon of Solar Eclipses,* Oxford, 1966.

Mucke, H., Meeus, J.: *Canon der Sonnenfinsternisse, −2003 bis +2526,* Vienna, Astronomisches Büro, 1983.

Oppholzer, T.R. von: *Canon of Eclipses,* New York, 1962.

Pasachoff, J.M., Covington, M.A., Espenak, F.: *The Cambridge Eclipse Photography Guide*, Cambridge, 1994.

Pröll, H.J., Staps, D.: "Die Sonnenfinsternis vom 23.10.76," *Sterne und Weltraum* **18**, 20 (1979).

Schmeidler, F.: "Über Sonnenfinsternisexpeditionen," *Sterne und Weltraum* **2**, 53–56 (1962).

StarGuides 1994; A directory of astronomy, space sciences and related organizations of the world 1994, CDS SP no. 23, Observatoire Astronomique, Strasbourg, 1994.

Sweetsir, R.A., Reynolds, M.A.: *Observe Eclipses*, Washington, 1995.

Trombino, D.F.: "Annular Eclipse—Bogota, Columbia SA," *Modern Astronomy*, vol. V, no. 5 (1994).

Trombino, D.F.: "Eclipse '81: Report from Siberia," *Star & Sky*, vol. II, no. 10, (1980).

Waldmeier, M., Arber, H., Bachmann, H.: "Die totale Sonnenfinsternis und die Korona vom 20.06.55," *Zeitschr. f. Astrophys.* **42**, 156 (1957).

Zirker, J.B.: "Total Eclipses of the Sun," *Science* **210**, 1313 (1980).

* Various authors: "Solar Eclipse of March 7th, 1970," *Nature* **226**, 1097 (1970).

C.1.2. Visual Observations of Total Solar Eclipses

Brewer, B.: *Eclipse*, Seattle, 1978, 1991.

Burnham, R.: "How to Watch an Eclipse," *Astronomy* **6** no. 11/1978, 39.

Littmann, M., Willcox, K.: *Totality—Eclipses of the Sun*, Honolulu, 1991.

Lockyer, Sir N.: *Recent and coming eclipses*, London, 1900.

Mädler, J.H.: *Über Sonnenfinsternisse*, Jena, 1861.

Pringsheim, G.: *Physik der Sonne*, Leipzig, 1910.

Rao, J.: *Your Guide to the Great Solar Eclipse of 1991*, Cambridge, 1991.

Reports on the Total Solar Eclipses of July 29, 1878 and January 11, 1880, Washington Observations for 1876. Appendix III, Washington, 1880.

Secchi, P.A.: *Die Sonne*, Braunschweig, 1872.

Stratton, F.J.M.: *Modern Eclipse Problems*, Oxford, 1927.

Sweetsir, R.A., Reynolds, M.A.: *Observe Eclipses*, Washington, revised 1995.

Waldmeier, M.: *Sonne und Erde*, Zürich, 1959.

Zirker, J.B.: *Total Eclipses of the Sun*, New York, 1984, p. 183–189.

C.1.3. Photographic Observations

"The Future of Photography," *American Photo*, May/June 1994, p. 11–18, 54–100.

Beck, R.: "Die Beobachtung totaler Sonnenfinsternisse," *SONNE* **3**, 102 (1979).

Beck, R., Hünecke, W.: "A Film for Obtaining Isophotic Contours," *Sky and Telescope* **47**, 270 (1974).

Berry, R.: "Film the Eclipse," *Astronomy* **6** no. 11/1978, 44.

Burckhalter, C.: "Apparatus for Photographing the Solar Corona," *Popular Astronomy* **8**, p. 494–496 (1900).

Codona, J.L.: "The Scintillation Theory of Eclipse Shadow Bands," *Astron. Astrophys.* **164**, 415 (1986).

Codona, J.L.: "The Enigma of Shadow Bands," *Sky and Telescope* **81**, 482 (1991).

Dürst, J., Zelenka, A.: "A Corona to Remember," *Sky and Telescope* **60**, 8 (1980).

Dürst, J.: "Two Colour Photometry and Polarimetry of the Solar Corona of 16 February 1980," *Astron. Astrophys.* **112**, 241 (1982).

Dyer, A.: "How to Photograph the Eclipse," *Astronomy* **19** no. 4/1991, 68.

East, G.: "Some Hints for Photographers of Total Solar Eclipses," *Sky and Telescope* **45**, 322 (1973).

Ekrutt, J.W.: *Die Sonne,* Hamburg, 1981, p. 164.

Ganser, H.: "Die Bestimmung der Belichtungszeit von Aufnahmen der Sonnenkorona," *Sterne und Weltraum* **2**, 186 (1963).

Gibson, E.G.: *The Quiet Sun,* Washington, 1973.

Hicks, J., Trombino, D.F.: "Shooting the Sun in H-alpha," *Astronomy,* **11** 7, p. 34 (1983).

Koutchmy, S.: in "Modern Techniques of Astronomical Photography" (eds. R.W. West and J.L. Heudier), ESO, Geneva 1978, p. 225.

Koutchmy, S.: "Small Scale Coronal Structure," in Altrock, R.C. (ed.): *Solar and Stellar Coronal Structure and Dynamics*, Sunspot, 1988, p. 208–235.

Koutchmy, S. et al.: "Image Processing of Coronal Pictures," in Altrock, R.C. (ed.): *Solar and Stellar Coronal Structure and Dynamics*, Sunspot, 1988, p. 256–266.

Leavens, P.A.: "Hints on Photographing the Eclipse," *Sky and Telescope* **43**, 358 (1972).

Littmann, M., Willcox, K.: *Totality, Eclipses of the Sun,* Honolulu, 1991, p. 125–126.

Mädlow, E.: "Hinweise für die Beobachtung der ringförmigen Sonnenfinsternis am 20.5.1966," *VdS-Nachr.* 12/1965, p. 157.

Marschall, L.A.: "Shadow-Bands, Solar Eclipse Phantoms," *Sky and Telescope* **67**, p. 116–118 (1984).

Maunder, M.: "Eclipse Chasing," in Moore, P. (ed.): *1990 Yearbook of Astronomy*, p. 139–157 (1989).

Menzel, D.H., Pasachoff, J.M.: "Eclipse Instrumentation for the Solar Corona," *Applied Optics* **9**, 2626 (1970) no. 12.

Mullar, D.: "Rapporto dei Signori Ing. Muller e Capitano Serra," *Rapporti della Commissione Italiana*, p. 165–189 (1870).

Newkirk, G. et al.: "Magnetic Fields and the Structure of the Solar Corona," *Solar Physics* **15**, p. 15–39 (1970).

Nye, D.D.: "Some Tips on Video Recording Solar Eclipses," in Edberg (ed.), *J. Research Amateur Astronomy*, San Francisco, 1992, p. 18–21.

Paech, W.: "Einige Hinweise zur Fotografie von Sonnenfinsternissen," *SONNE* **3**, 99 (1979) no. 11.

Pasachoff, J.M; Covington, M.A.,: *The Cambridge Eclipse Photography Guide*, Cambridge, 1993, p. 102–110.

Seltzer, A.: "How to Observe and Photograph the Annular Solar Eclipse," *Astronomy* **12** no. 5/1984, 50.

Seykora, E.J.: "A Search for Optical Modulation of the Solar Corona During The 16 February 1980 Total Solar Eclipse," *Proc. Indian Nat.Science Acad.* **3**, no. 3, 64 (1982).

Shklovskij, I.S.: *Physics of the Solar Corona,* Oxford, 1965, p. 3.

Todd, D.P.: "On a modified form of Revolving Occulter," *Monthly Notices of the Royal Society* **61**, p. 531–533 (1901).

van de Hulst, H.C.: "The Chromoshere and Corona," in Kuiper, G.P. (ed.): *The Sun*, Chicago, 1953.

Vial, J.-C., Koutchmy, S. and the CFH Team: "Evidence of Plasmoid Ejection in the Corona from 1991 Eclipse Oberservations," *Solar Physics and Astrophysics at Interferometric Resolution*, Paris, 1992, p. 87–90.

Young, A.T.: "The Problem of Shadow Band Observations," *Sky and Telescope* **43**, p. 291–292 (1972).

Waldmeier, M.: "Ergebnisse der Zürcher Sonnenfinsternisexpedition 1954. VIII. Helligkeitsverteilung und Komponentenzerlegung," *Zeitschrift für Astrophysik* **53**, p. 81–94 (1961).

Wedel, B.: "Beobachtung der totalen Sonnenfinsternis am 16.Februar 1980 in Kenia," *Sterne und Weltraum* **19**, 197 (1980).

Wolf, M.: "Die fliegenden Schatten," *Himmelswelt* **39**, 193 (1929).

Young, A.T.: "Shadow Band and the March Solar Eclipse," *Sky and Telescope* **39**, 176 (1970).

Young, A.T.: "The Problem of Shadow Band Observation," *Sky and Telescope* **43**, 291 (1972).

"Hellseher, Infrarotfilme von Konica und Kodak," *Foto und Labor* **14**, p. 30–33 (1993).

Kodak Publication no. M–28, *Applied Infrared Photography*, Rochester, 1981.

Zirker, J.B.: *Total Eclipses of the Sun*, New York, 1984, p. 129–132.

"More about October's Solar Eclipse," *Sky and Telescope* **55**, 181 (1978).
"Solar Eclipse Photography for the Amateur," Kodak Publ. no. AM-10.
Infrared and polarization photography

Beck, R., Pröll, H.J.: "Digitale Auswertung der Sonnenfinsternisaufnahmen
vom 30.6.73," *Sterne und Weltraum* **13**, 123 (1974).
Beck, R., Pröll, H.J.: "Digitale Auswertung von Sonnenfinsternisaufnah-
men," *Sternzeit* 3/1975, 50.
Lilliequist, C., Schmahl, E.: "More March 7th Eclipse Results," *Sky and
Telescope* **40**, 77 (1970).
Pröll, H.J., Staps, D.: "Die Sonnenfinsternis vom 23.10.1976," *Sterne und
Weltraum* **18**, 20 (1979).
Scholz, G.: "Untersuchungen über die Struktur der Sonnenkorona," *Astron.
Nachr.* **291**, 188 (1969).

C.1.5. Meteorological Observations

Brooks, C.F., et al.: "Eclipse Meteorology," *Harvard Meteorological Studies
No. 5,* Milton, 1941.
di Cicco, Dennis: "Photographing the Moon's Shadow," *Sky and Telescope*
53, 323 (1977).
Mims, F.M.: "How to monitor ultraviolet radiation from the sun," *Scientific
American,* p. 86–89 (Aug. 1990).
Mims, F.M.: "Amateur Observations of the 1991 Solar Eclipse," *Science
Probe,* p. 83–90 (Jan. 1992).
Zirker, J.B.: *Total Eclipses of the Sun,* New York, 1984, p. 129–165.

C.2. Observable Phenomena

C.2.1. Flash Spectrum

Beck, R.: "Das Flash-Spektrum der Sonne vom 16.2.1980," *SONNE* **4**, 81
(1980) no. 14.
Bray, R.J., Loughhead, R.E.: in *The Solar Chromosphere,* London, 1974,
p. 159.
Dunn, R.B. et al.: "The Chromospheric Spectrum at the 1962 Eclipse,"
Astrophys. Journal Suppl. **15**, 1167 (1968).
East, G. et al.: "The Maximum Eclipse" *Sky and Telescope* **59**, 386 (1980).
Hiei, E., Fukatsu, M.: "Photometric atlas of emission lines of the solar
chromosphere between 3599Å and 4017Å," *Annals Tokyo Astronomical
Observatory II. Ser.* **14**, no. 2, p. 37–84 (1974).
Kanno, M.: "Joint Japanese Expedition to Mauretania," *Sky and Telescope*
46, 220 (1973).
Mitchell, S.A.: *Eclipses of the Sun,* Columbia, 1951, p. 250.

Pierce, A.K.: "The Chromospheric Spectrum Outside of Eclipses," *Astrophys. Journal Suppl.* **17**, 1 (1968).

Qi-de et al.: "The chromospheric spectrum of the June 11, 1983 solar eclipse," *Publ. of the Purple Mountain Observatory* **5**, p. 279–377 (1986).

Redman, R.O.: "Spectrographic Observations at the Total Solar Eclipse of 1940 October 1," *Mon. Not. Roy. Astr. Soc.* **102**, 140 and **103**, 173 (1942).

C.2.2. Corona Shapes and Parameters

Dürst, J.: "Helligkeit, Polarisationsgrad und Elektronendichte der Sonnenkorona," *Astr. Mitt. Eidgen. Sternw. Zürich* no. 320 (1973).

Gulyaev R.A.: "The Solar Corona: Flat Formation," *Solar Physics* **142**, p. 213–216 (1992a).

Gulyaev R.A.: "Eclipse Observations of the outer solar corona and the Soho Mission," in Mariska, J., Domingo, V., Poland, A. (eds.): *Coronal Streamers, Coronal Loops, and Coronal and Solar Wind Composition*, p. 133–136, Noordwijk, 1992b.

Guhathakurta, M.: "The large and small scale density structure in the solar corona," Thesis University of Denver, Aug. 1989.

Koutchmy, S. et al.: "Photometrical Analysis of the June 30, 1973 Solar Corona," *Astron. Astrophys.* **69**, 35 (1978).

Layden et al.: "Dynamo-based scheme for forecasting the magnitude of solar activity cycles," *Solar Physics* **132**, p. 1-40 (1991).

Löchel, K., Högner,W.: "Isophotendarstellung der Sonnenkorona vom 15. Februar 1961 mit Hilfe photographischer Äquidensiten," *Zeitschr. f. Astrophys.* **62**, 121 (1965).

Ludendorff, H.: "Über die Abhäugigkeit der Form der Sonnenkorona von der Sonnenfleckenhäufigkeit," *Sitzungsber. Preuss. Akad. d. Wiss.,* vol. 16, p. 185-214 (1928).

Pröll, H.J., Staps, D.: "Die Sonnenfinsternis vom 23.10.1976," *Sterne und Weltraum* **18**, 20 (1979).

Ramberg, J.M.: "Results from Observations of the Total Solar Eclipse of 1945 July 9," *Stockholm Obs. Annaler* **16**, 3 (1951) p. 1–43.

Rušin, V., Rybanský, M., Minarovjech, M.: "The white-light, far-red (600–700 nm) and emission coronae at the July 11, 1991 eclipse," in Rabin, D.M. et al. (eds.): *Infrared Solar Physics*, p. 211–215, Dordrecht, 1994.

Suess, S.T., McComas, D.J., Hoeksema, J.T.: "Prediction of the Heliospheric Current Sheet Tilt: 1992-1996," *Geophysical Research Letters* **20**, no. 3, p. 161–164 (1993).

Waldmeier, M.: "Form und Struktur der Korona bei der Sonnenfinsternis vom 7. März 1970," *Astron. Mitt. Sternwarte Zürich*, no. 299, 1970.

C.2.3. Polarization of the Corona

Beck, R., Pröll, H.J.: "Digitale Auswertung der Sonnenfinsternis-Aufnahmen vom 30.6.73," *Sterne und Weltraum* **13**, 123 (1974).

Beck, R., Pröll, H.J.: "Digitale Auswertung von Sonnenfinsternisaufnahmen," *Sternzeit* 3/1975, 50.

Billings, D.E.: *A Guide to the Solar Corona,* New York, 1966.

Clette, F., Cugnon, P., Koeckelenbergh, A.: "Observations of the Solar Corona in Polarized White Light during the Total Solar Eclipse of February 16, 1980: Preliminary results," *Solar Physics* **98**, p. 163–171 (1985).

Clette, F., Gabryl, J.R.: "The July 11, 1991 Solar Corona observed in Polarized White Light," in Mariska, J., Domingo, V., Poland, A. (eds.): *Coronal Streamers, Coronal Loops, and Coronal and Solar Wind Composition,* p. 351–353, Noordwijk, 1992.

Newkirk, G.: "Structure of the Solar Corona," *Annual Review of Astronomy and Astrophysics* **5**, p. 213–266 (1967).

Rabin, D.M; Jefferies, J.T; Lindsey,C.: *Infrared Solar Physics,* p. 139–221, Dordrecht, 1994.

Scholz, G.: "Untersuchungen über die Struktur der Sonnenkorona," *Astron. Nachr.* **291**, 188 (1969).

C.2.4. Infrared Corona and Coronal Lines

Beck, R.: "Wellenlängen der stärksten Korona-Linien," *SONNE* **3**, 141 (1979) no. 12.

Billings, D.E.: *A Guide to the Solar Corona,* New York, 1966.

Dollfus, A.: in *Physics of the Solar Corona,* Macris, C.J. (ed.) Dordrecht, 1971, p. 97-113.

Gibson, E.G.: *The Quiet Sun,* NASA SP 303, Washington, 1973.

Lillequist, C., Schmahl, E.: "More March 7th Eclipse Results," *Sky and Telescope* **40**, 77 (1970).

Noens, J.-C.: "Observations of coronal material associated with prominences," in Altrock, R.C. (ed.): *Solar and Stellar Coronal Structure and Dynamics,* Sunspot, 1988, p. 182-190.

Rozelot, J.P.: *La Couronne Solaire,* Paris, 1973.

Waldmeier, M.: in *Physics of the Solar Corona,* Macris, C.J. (ed.) Dordrecht, 1971, p. 130.

Zirin, H.: *The Solar Atmosphere,* Waltham, 1966, p. 111-154.

Literature used for the table of coronal lines

Billings, D.E.: *A Guide to the Solar Corona,* New York, 1966.

Graff-Lambrecht: *Grundriß der Astrophysik* vol. II, Leipzig, 1962.

Rozelot, J.: *La Coronne Solaire,* Paris, 1973.

Shklovskij, I.S.: *Physics of the Solar Corona,* Oxford, 1965.
Svensson, L.A. et al.: "The Identification of Fe IX and Ni XI in the Solar Corona," *Sol. Phys.* **34**, 173 (1974).
van der Hulst, H.C.: in *The Sun,* Kuiper, G.P. (ed.), Chicago, 1953.

C.2.5. Phenomena in the Solar Corona

Billings, D.: *A Guide to the Solar Corona,* New York, 1966.
Bohlin, J.D.: "Solar Coronal Streamers," *Sol. Phys.* **12**, 240 and **13**, 153 (1970).
Bugoslavskaja, E.: "Structure of the Solar Corona," *Publ. Astron. Sternberg Inst. Moskow,* vol. XIX (1949) (in Russian).
Burkepile, J.T., St. Cyr, O.C.: "A Revisted and Expanded Catalogue of Mass Ejections Observed by the Solar Maximum Mission Coronagraph," *NCAR Technical Note* 369+STR, 1993.
de Mastus, H.L. et al.: "Coronal Disturbances," *Sol. Phys.* **31**, 449 (1973).
Dunn, R.B.: in *Physics of the Solar Corona,* Macris, C.J. (ed.), Dordrecht, 1971, p. 128.
Koutchmy, S.: in *Illustrated Glossary,* Bruzek, A., Dordrecht, 1977, p. 39–52.
Koutchmy, S.: "Small Scale Coronal Structure," in Altrock, R.C. (ed.): *Solar and Stellar Coronal Structure and Dynamics,* Sunspot, 1988, p. 208–235.
Koutchmy, S.: "Streamer Eclipse Observations," in Mariska, J., Domingo, V., Poland, A. (eds.): *Coronal Streamers, Coronal Loops, and Coronal and Solar Wind Composition,* p. 133–136, 1992.
Newkirk, G.: "Structure of the Solar Corona," *Ann. Rev. Astron. Astrophys.* **5**, 213 (1967).
Orrall, F.Q.: "The Corona," in: *IAU—Transactions* de Jager, C. (ed.) **15A**, Dordrecht, 1973, p. 142.
Teske, R.G. et al.: "Association of Coronal Structures with Chromospheric Structure," *Nature* **226**, 1145 (1970).
Treutner, H.: "Richtlinien für die fotografische Sonnenbeobachtung," *SONNE* **2**, 10 (1978) no. 5.
Vsessvijatsky, S., Bougoslavsky, E.: "The Solar Eclipse of 1936 June 19," *Mon. Not. Roy. Astron. Soc.* **104**, 140 (1944).
Vsekhsvyatskii, S.K. et al.: "Joint Soviet-French investigations of the solar corona. 3. Structure and some dynamic features of the solar corona of June 30, 1973," *Sov. Astron.* **25** (4), p. 463–470 (1981).

C.2.6. Movements in the Corona

Adachi, K.: "Temporal changes in coronal fine structures," in *Observations of Solar Eclipse of 16 February 1980* (Prelimary Results), New Dehli, 1981, p. 1–2.

Bugoslavskaja, E.: "Structure of the Solar Corona," *Publ. Astron. Sternberg Inst. Moskow,* vol. XIX (1950) (in Russian).

Koutchmy, S. et al.: "CHFT eclipse observations of the very fine-scale solar corona," *Astron. Astrophys.* **281**, p. 249–257 (1994).

Matsuura, O.T., Picazzio, E., Campos, R.P.: "Image Analysis of the solar corona from the July 11, 1991 Eclipse," *Solar Physics* **144**, p. 89–99, (1993).

Mitchell, S.A.: "Eclipses of the Sun," in Eberhard, G. et al. (eds.): *Handbuch der Astrophysik,* vol. IV, p. 231 (1929).

Wagner, W.J.: "Coronal Mass Ejections," *Ann. Rev. Astron. Astrophys.* **22**, 267 (1984).

Zirker, J.B.: "Structural changes in the corona during the July 1991 eclipse," *Astron. Astrophys.* **258**, p. L1–L4 (1992).

C.2.7. Relationships between the Corona and Prominences

Bohlin, J.D.: "Solar Coronal Streamers," *Sol. Phys.* **12**, 240 and **13**, 153 (1970).

Bugoslavskaja, E.: *Publ. Sternberg Inst.* **19** (1949) (in Russian).

Lockyer, W.J.S.: "On the Relationship Between Solar Prominences and the Forms of the Corona," *Mon. Not. Roy. Astron. Soc.* **91**, 797 (1931).

Newkirk, E.: "Structure of the Solar Corona," *Ann. Rev. Astron. Astrophys.* **5**, 213 (1967).

Palzer, W.: "Sonnenprotuberanzen: Wiesbaden kontra Mexiko," *Sterne und Weltraum* **31**, p. 185, (1992).

Saito, K., Tandberg-Hanssen, E.: "The Arch systems, Cavities and Prominences in the Helmet Streamer observed at the solar eclipse, November 12, 1966," *Solar Physics 31,* p. 105–121, 1973.

Stellmacher, G., Koutchmy, S., Lebecq, C.: "The 1981 total solar eclipse. III. Photometric study of the prominence remnant in the reversing south polar field," *Astron. Astrophys.* **162**, p. 307–311 (1986).

Tandberg-Hanssen, E.: *Solar Prominences,* Dordrecht, pp. 1 and 131, 1974.

C.2.8. Historic Eclipses of the Sun

Bronshten, V.A.: "The structure of the far outer corona of June 19, 1936," *Astronomical Journal* **36**, p. 845–850, (1959).

Bugoslavskaja, E.: "Structure of the Solar Corona," *Publ. Astron. Sternberg Inst. Moskow,* vol. XIX (1949) (in Russian).

Dyson, F.: "Drawings of the Corona from Photographs at Total Eclipses from 1896 to 1922," *Mem. Roy. Astron. Soc.* **64**, 363 (1927).

Eddy, J.A.: "A Nineteenth-century Coronal Transient," *Astron. Astrophys.* **34**, 235 (1974).

Eddy, J.A.: "Observation of a Possible Neutral Sheet in the Corona," *Sol. Phys.* **30**, 385 (1973).

Hansky, A.: *Eclipse totale du 8/9 Aout 1896,* St. Petersburg, 1897.

Mitchell, S.A.: *Eclipses of the Sun,* 1st–5th eds., Columbia, 1923, 1924, 1932, 1935, 1951.

Ranyard, A.C.: "Observations Made During Total Solar Eclipses," *Mem. Roy. Astron. Soc.* **41** (1879).

Waldmeier, M.: Various Astron. Mitt. Sternwarte Zürich, 1952–1981.

Waldmeier, M.: "Die Expedition zur Beobachtung der totalen Sonnenfinsternis vom 12. November 1966," *Astron. Mitt. Sternwarte Zürich,* no. 276, 1967.

C.2.9. Relativistic Light Bending

Dewitt, B.S. et al.: "Relativity Eclipse Experiment Refurbished," *Sky and Telescope* **47**, 301 (1974).

Freundlich, E., v. Klüber, H., v. Brunn, A.: "Über die Ablenkung des Lichtes im Schwerefeld der Sonne," *Abh. der preuss. Akad. der Wiss.,* p. 1–46, 1931.

Hiei, E., Soma, M., Fukushima, H.: "Passage of the Venus and the Mercury behind the Sun," in Altrock, R.C. (ed.): *Solar and Stellar Coronal Structure and Dynamics,* Sunspot, 1988, p. 267–281.

Schmeidler, F.: "Messung der Lichtablenkung während der Sonnenfinsternis am 15. Februar 1961," *Astron. Nachr.* **306**, 71 (1985).

Wedel, B., Paech, W.: "Die totale Sonnenfinsternis vom 30.6.1973," *Publ. Wilhelm Foerster Obs.* no. 35, Berlin, 1974.

Zirker, J.B.: *Total Eclipses of the Sun,* New York, 1984, p. 166–182.

Appendix A

Supplier Sources

A.1 Sources

This list contains only names and addresses of North American and European manufacturers and dealers and is not intended to be comprehensive.

Baader Planetarium GmbH, Zur Sternwarte, D-82291 Mammendorf, Germany, Fax: (0049) 8145-8805.

- Eyepiece Filters (glass), objective filters, foils, Herschel optical wedges, coronagraphs, and DayStar filters.

- Objective filters (high precision surfaces from $\lambda/4$ up to $\lambda/10$ wavelength plane-parallelity). Unmounted and mounted for lens cells from 110 up to 205 mm diameter, one side coated with chrome, other side antireflection optical coating, transmission = 0.03.

- 12 micron objective foil, custom made for safe solar observations, both sides of the substrate are aluminum coated (therefore one sheet provides sufficient filtration). Sheets of 100 by 60 cm. Available with transmissions of 0.001 or 0.03 for visual and photographic use, respectively.

- 2-inch Herschel optical wedge (Carl Zeiss wedge prism) for visual use with 2-inch and $1\,1/4$-inch eyepieces and photographic adapters T2, Hasselblad (6 cm by 6 cm), and Pentax (6 cm by 7 cm).

- High resolution solar spectrum on 35 mm color positive film (over one meter long!), after an original by the University Observatory in Göttingen, Germany.

503

- Energy rejection filters (ERF) with diameters from 110 to 205 mm, plane-parallelity $\lambda/4$ and higher on special order.

- Objective filters (white light and ERF), on special order with infrared blocking dielectric coating, diameter 110 mm to 205 mm.

- DayStar H-alpha filters.

- Individual 2Å or 10Å H-alpha filter for do-it-yourself coronographs

- H-alpha coronagraphs with 2Å or 10Å H-alpha filter, fully blocked (with manual in English).

Celestron International, 2835 Columbia Street, Torrance, CA 90503 (310) 328-328-9560, FAX (310) 212-5835.

- Manufactures a wide range of telescopes, eyepieces and filters.

Meade Instruments Corporation, 1654 Millikan Ave., Irvine CA 92714 (714) 756-2291, FAX (714) 756-2291.

- Manufactures a wide range of telescopes, eyepieces and filters.

Dr. J. Heidenhain, Postfach 1260, D-83301 Traunreut, Germany.

- Micrometer lamellae

Thousand Oaks Optical, Box 4813, Thousand Oaks, CA 91359 (805) 491-3642, FAX (805) 491-2393.

- Wide range of glass and Mylar solar filters.

Tele Vue Optics, 100 S Route 59, Suffern, NY 10901 (914) 357-9522.

- Manufacturer of the Tele Vue Genesis Solar Kit which attaches to any Tele Vue Genesis or Genesis-sdf telescope to provide full field Hα observing with the DayStar T-scanner.

Astro-Physics, Inc., 11250 Forest Hills Road, Rockford, IL 61115, (815) 282-1513.

- Manufacture of high quality telescopes and accessories.

Orion Telescope Center, 2450 17th Ave. P.O. Box 1158, Santa Cruz, CA 95061, (800) 447-1001.

- Dealer in telescopes and accessories.

University Optics, P.O. Box 1205, Ann Arbor, MI 48106, (313) 665-3575.

- Manufacture of high quality telescope components, eyepieces and other accessories.

J.M.B. Inc., 20762 Richard, Trenton, MI 48183, (313) 675-3490, Fax: (313) 285-3015.

- Dealer in solar filters, wide range of glass amd Mylar solar filters.

Lichtenknecker Optics AG, Grote Breemstraat, B-3500 Hasselt, Belgium, Fax: 011-250090.

- Eyepiece filters (glass), objective filters, solar penta prisms.

- Unmounted and mounted glass filters for Lichtenknecker lens cells from 70 up to 250 mm diameter, coated with chrome, transmission = 0.1%.

- Special solar penta prism, usable with 1.25″ and 2″ eyepieces (together with neutral density filters) and photographic use up to middle format cameras.

Schott & Gen, Post Box 2401, D-55014 Mainz, Germany.

- Unmounted color and neutral density filters, standard diameter 50 mm and squared 50 x 50 mm). Single filters are very cheap, but there is a mimimum order of DM 250. Bulk orders are recommended.

Carl Zeiss Jena GmbH, Astronomical Instruments, D-07740 Jena, Germany, Fax: (0049) 3641-642023.

- Objective filters (high precision surfaces from $\lambda/4$ up to $\lambda/10$ wavelength planparallelity). Only mounted for Carl Zeiss lens cells from 100–150 mm diameter, transmission = 0.001% and 0.03%.

Roger W. Tuthill, 11 Tanglewood Lane, Mountainside, NJ 07092, USA.

- Manufacturer of Solar Skreen Mylar objective solar filters, telescopes and accessories.

Göttinger Farbfilter GmbH, Brauweg 36a, D-37073 Göttingen, Germany

- Radial gradient filters.

Lumicon, 2111 Research Drive, Livermore, CA 94550, (510) 447-9570.

- Manufacturer of filters and telescope accessories.

LRTF Photographic Enhancement, 13 Burke Avenue, Newport News, VA 23601, U.S.A.

- Radial gradient filters

DayStar Filter Corp., Diamond Bar, CA 91765, FAX (909) 591-6886.

- Birefringent filters for H-α and Calcium from 1.5Å to 0.5Å .

F.M.B. Inc., 20762 Richard, Trenton, MI 48183. Voice (313) 675-3490, FAX (313) 285-3015.

- Wide range of glass and Mylar solar filters.

A.2 NASA Solar Eclipse Bulletins

Circulars containing detailed predictions, maps, and meteorological data for future central solar eclipses are available in printed form or by electronic mail. Eclipse bulletin requests may be send to Jay Anderson, Prairie Weather Centre, 900-266 Graham Avenue, Winnipeg, MB, Canada R3C 3V4 and must be accompanied by a 9 x 12 inch SASE (self addressed stamped envelope) with sufficient postage for each bulletin (11 oz. or 310 g.). Use stamps only; cash or checks are not accepted. Print the eclipse date (year & month) of the bulletin ordered in the lower left corner of the SASE. Requests from outside U.S and Canada may use international postal coupons sufficient to cover postage. The eclipse bulletins are also available electronically over the Internet. They can be read or downloaded via the World-Wide Web server with a mosaic client from SDAC (Solar Data Analysis Center) home page:
http://umbra.gsfc.nasa.gov/sdac.html
The top-level URL for the eclipse bulletins themselves are:
http://umbra.gsfc.nasa.gov/eclipse/yymmdd/rp.html
jjmmtt := eclipse-year,-month,-day
BinHex-encoded, StuffItLite-compressed version of the original Word and PICT files are available via anonymous ftp at:
file://umbra.gsfc.nasa.gov/pub/eclipse
as are directories of GIF figures, ASCII tables, and JPEG maps accessible through the Web.

A.3 Daily Coronal Images

Coronalerts and daily Fe XIV and Ca XV pseudo full disk maps (NOAO Newsletter) are available on the Internet and can be downloaded as follows:
ftp ftp.sunspot.noao.edu (or ftp 146.5.2.1)
when connected, respond with login as:
anonymous

use as a password:
`your e-mail address`
change the directory:
`cd pub/corona.maps`
copy the readme file:
`get readme`
enter a data directory:
`cd fexiv, caxv, idl or coronalert`
to get a directory listing (Caution: there are many files!):
`dir`
or copy the data using:
`get filename`
`bye`

A.4 National and International Associations of Amateur Solar Observers

Argentina: Asociación Argentina, Amigos de la Astronomía, Avda. Patricias Argentinas 550, 1405 Buenos Aires

Australia: British Astronomical Association (BAA), c/o Ralph Buttigieg, Sydney Observatory, Observatory Hill, Sydney, NSW 2000

Belgium: Vereniging voor Sterrenkunde (V.V.S.), Werkgroep Zon, c/o Jan Janssens, Oxdonkstraat 52, 1880 Kapelle-op-den-Bos

Bolivia: Astronomía Sigma Octante, Departamento Solar, Casilla 2299, Cochabamba

Asociación Boliviana de Astronomía, Calle México 1771, Casilla 7707, La Paz

Brasil: Clube Estudantil de Astronomia (CEA), c/o Lupercio Braga Bezerra, Caixa Postal No. 736, 50001 Recife-Pe

Observatório do Capricórnio, Departamento Solar, c/o Roberto Maçon, Caixa Postal No. 657, 13001 Campinas/SP

Bulgaria: Bulgarian Federation of Amateur Astronomers, c/o B. Bonev, 6000 Stara Zagora

Colombia: Asociación de Astrónomos Autodidactos de Colombia, Carrera 32 No. 71-A-31, Distrito Especial, Zona 2, Apartado Aéreo No. 59534, Bogotá

Denmark: Astronomisk Forening for Sydsjælland, c/o Per T. Aldrich, Næsbyholmvej 6, 2700 Brønshøj

Finland: SIRIUS, c/o Jalo Ojanperää, Emännäntie 12 as 1, 40740 Jyväskylä

URSA Astronomical Association, Solar Section, c/o Tuomo Roine, Rantakiventie 11G, 00960 Helsinki

France: Association Francaise d'Astronomie, c/o Alain Cirou, 17, Rue Emile Deutsch de la Me, 75014
GFOES, c/o Jacques Cazeneuve, 46 Rue Marechal Leclerc, 69800 Saint Priest
Societé d'Astronomie Populaire, 1, Avenue Camille-Flammarion, 31500 Toulouse
Germany: Vereinigung der Sternfreunde e.V. (VdS), Fachgruppe SONNE, c/o Peter Völker, Wilhelm-Foerster-Sternwarte, Munsterdamm 90, 12169 Berlin
Hong Kong: Astronomer's Club, 120 Causeway Road, Causeway Bay
Hungary: Board of the AAAS, c/o Tibor Juhasz, Nemzetör u. 8., 8900 Zalaegerszeg
Hungarian Astronomical Association (METEOR), Solar Section, c/o Joszef Iskum, Rosza u. 48 3/18, 1041 Budapest
Italy: Unione Astrofili Italiani (UAI), Solar Section, c/o Michele Ferrara, Via A. Gosa 168, 25085 Gavardo-BS
Japan: The Oriental Astronomical Association (O.A.A.), Solar Division, c/o Miyoshi Suzuki, 1-17 Mikkaichi 1 Chome, Suzuka-Shi, Mie-Ken, 513
Malta: URANIA, Solar Section, c/o Frank Ventura, 4 Triq it-Trincetta, Ta'Mlit, Mosta, Naxxar XXR03
Mexico: Sociedad Astronómica Orion, Oficina: Calle Rosario 745, Apartado Postal 384, Nogales, Sonora 84000
Namibia: Astronomical Work Group of the Scientific Society, c/o Mrs. S. Encke, Box 5198, Windhoek
Netherlands: Ned ver voor Weer-en Sterrekunde (NVWS), Werkgroep Zon, c/o Benno Houweling, Veenenburg 36, 2804 WZ Gouda
Norway: Norsk Astronomisk Selskap, Avd. Solgruppen, P.O. Box 677, 4001 Stavanger
Norwegian Astronomical Society, c/o Snorre Winger Steen, Flaskebekkveien 72, 1450 Nesoddtangen
Peru: Asociación Peruana de Astronomía (APA), c/o M. Casaverde, Enrique Palacios 374, Chorillos, Lima 9
Poland: Towarzystwo Obserwatorów Słońca, c/o Piotr Urbański, ul. Sawickiej 1/9, 99-320 Zychlin
Portugal: Associacão Portuguesa de Astronomos Amadores, Rua Alexandre Herculano 57-4, 1200 Lisboa
Romania: Cercul Astronomic Victor Anestin, Str. Grigore Alexandrescu 25, Sc. II Etajul IV, Ap. 24, 3400 Cluj-Napoca
Slowakia: The Slovak Centre of Amateur Astronomy, Solar Section, c/o Dr. Ivan Dorotovic, Post Box 42, 94701 Hurbanovo
Astronomical Observatory, Solar Section, P.O. Box 23, 97980 Rimavska Sobota

South Africa: ASSA, Solar Section, c/o Jim Knight, 17 Mars Street, Atlasville, Bocksburg, 1459

Spain: Agrupació Astronómica de Barcelona, Grup Solar, c/o Ricard Martinez, Passeig de Gracia, 71, Atic, Barcelona-8

Agrupacion Astronomica de Sabadell, Secretaria, Apartat de Cordeus No. 50, 08200 Sabadell (Barcelona)

Asociación Valenciana de Astronomía, Apdo. Correos 2069, 46080 Valencia

Sweden: Svensk Amatör Astronomisk Förening (SAAF), c/o Jan Persson, Skogsgatan 93, 582 57 Linköping

Switzerland: Sonnenbeobachtergruppe der Schweizerischen Astronomischen Gesellschaft (SOGSAG), c/o Thomas K. Friedli, Plattenweg 32, 3098 Schliern b. Köniz

Taiwan: Taipei Amateur Astronomers Association (TAAA), Solar Section, No. 5 Sec. 4 Chung Shan N. Road, Yuan-Shan 10452, Taipei

United Kingdom: British Astronomical Association (B.A.A.), Solar Section, c/o Bruce Hardie, 13 Glencree Park, Jordanstown, Co. Antrim, Northern Ireland BT37 0QS

U.S.A.: American Association of Variable Star Observers (AAVSO), Solar Division, c/o Peter O. Taylor, 4523 Thurston Lane #5, Madison, WI 53711-4738

Society of Amateur Radio Astronomers (SARA), President: Chuck Forster (1995), 5661 Vineyard Rd., Oregon, WI 53575, (608) 835-9282.

Association of Lunar and Planetary Observers (ALPO), Solar Section, c/o Richard E. Hill, Lunar and Plaetary Laboratory, University of Arizona, Tucson, AZ 85721

Venezuela: Liga Ibero-Americana de Astronomía (Universo), c/o Dr. Ignazio Ferrin, Apartado 700, Merida 5101-A

Index